INTRODUCTION TO LINEAR PROGRAMMING, WITH APPLICATIONS

PRENTICE-HALL INTERNATIONAL, INC., *London*
PRENTICE-HALL OF AUSTRALIA, PTY. LTD., *Sydney*
PRENTICE-HALL OF CANADA, LTD., *Toronto*
PRENTICE-HALL OF INDIA (PRIVATE) LTD., *New Delhi*
PRENTICE-HALL OF JAPAN, INC., *Tokyo*

INTRODUCTION TO LINEAR PROGRAMMING, WITH APPLICATIONS

WILLIAM R. SMYTHE, JR.

Associate Professor of Mathematics
Georgia Institute of Technology

LYNWOOD A. JOHNSON

Associate Professor of Industrial Engineering
Georgia Institute of Technology

Prentice-Hall, Inc., *Englewood Cliffs, N.J.*

Current Printing (last digit):
10 9 8 7 6 5 4 3 2 1

Library of Congress Catalog Card Number 66-23373
Printed in the United States of America
48618C

PREFACE

Linear programming, briefly described, deals with the optimization of linear functions subject to linear constraints. The basic tool for solving such optimization problems is an iterative process known as the simplex algorithm. The principal aims of this book are to develop carefully, yet at an elementary level, the mathematical theory of the simplex algorithm and to describe some of the applications of linear programming to industrial operations. The presentation is elementary in the sense that the formal prerequisites for studying the book are few. Basic algebra and the simplest elements of analytic geometry suffice for everything except two or three exercises and the proof of one theorem, where some calculus is needed. On the other hand, the presentation is not, it is hoped, elementary in the sense of being oversimplified. A fair amount of mathematical maturity is needed to follow the logical development.

In Chapter 1, linear programming is introduced via the geometrical solution of two-variable problems. Chapter 2 presents the mathematical background essential for the development of the simplex process. This chapter is actually a short course in linear algebra covering basic matrix algebra, systems of linear equations, vector spaces, and the associated concepts of linear independence and dependence, bases, and basic solutions of linear systems. The computational procedure for making changes of basis, using the tableau format, is also included in Chapter 2. In Chapter 3 the simplex algorithm is developed in easy stages, computational procedures being explained and illustrated along with the theoretical development. The two-phase process is used for problems requiring artificial variables. Proofs are given that both the standard simplex and the two-phase processes can be terminated in a finite number of steps. Chapter 4 is devoted to some special types of *integer programming* problems, i.e., linear programming problems in which the variables are required to be integers. The problems treated all involve flows in networks: the maximal flow, transshipment, and transportation problems. The concluding chapter deals with those applications of linear programming relating to the operation of an industrial organization. The emphasis in this chapter is on formulation of problems rather than on computational procedures. Several specific problems are formulated in the text and many others appear in the exercises.

It is intended that the chapters be read in the order presented. However, it is possible to study Chapter 5 at any point after Chapter 1.

Throughout the book illustrative examples and exercises are provided to assist the reader in following the logical development, to test his understanding of principles, and to give him practice in applying computational procedures. Answers are given to all exercises requiring specific numerical answers or other short responses.

The first three chapters have been class-tested several times by one of the authors and some of his colleagues in the School of Mathematics at Georgia Tech in a one-quarter, three-hour course. The students were mostly juniors who had had a year of calculus but little or no linear algebra. Our experience indicates that this material, if covered carefully, is ample for such a course. By omitting Sections 3-5, 3-7, and 3-9 and some of the proofs, one should be able to cover Chapter 4 or Chapter 5 or parts of both as well. In a semester course it should be possible to cover all five chapters fairly carefully.

The authors would like to thank their colleagues who used this material in the classroom for their suggestions and for pointing out errors in the manuscript. Most of these errors have, we believe, been corrected. We should also like to thank the School of Mathematics of Georgia Tech for providing secretarial assistance to help with the typing. Finally, we wish to express our appreciation to Prentice-Hall, Inc. for their fine editorial work and their patience and cooperation in seeing this work through.

WILLIAM R. SMYTHE, JR.
LYNWOOD A. JOHNSON

CONTENTS

INTRODUCTION TO LINEAR PROGRAMMING, WITH APPLICATIONS

CHAPTER ONE

INTRODUCTION

We frequently hear of practical, "real-life" problems being solved by use of mathematics. Actually, however, the techniques of mathematics can only be used to solve mathematical problems, i.e., problems stated in terms of mathematical concepts such as numbers, points, lines, functions, and so on. What, then, does it mean to say that mathematics is used to calculate the orbits of planets or to determine the maximum load a bridge can safely support or to estimate the number of claims an insurance company is likely to pay in the next year? What is meant by each such statement is that a mathematical problem has been formulated which in some sense fits the given problem, that mathematical techniques have been employed to solve this mathematical problem, and that the solution of the mathematical problem has been interpreted in terms of the original problem.

Many practical problems have been solved, in the above sense, by use of the methods of linear programming. Two such problems are discussed in this chapter (Section 1–2) for the purpose of giving the student an idea of the type of problem to which linear programming may be applied. However, discussing applications is not our main objective. It is our opinion that the student should first concentrate on understanding the mathematics involved in linear programming. Assuming that he gains such understanding, he will then be in an excellent position to consider applications of the subject to the solution of practical problems, some of which appear in Chapter 5.

In this first chapter, in addition to discussing the two applications mentioned above, we formally state the linear programming problem (Section

1–1) and give a detailed explanation of graphical methods which can be used to solve problems involving only two variables and which give us some geometrical insight into the nature of linear programming problems in general (Section 1–3).

1–1. *STATEMENT OF THE PROBLEM.*

Linear programming deals with the solution of the following type of problem: We are given a function f of n real variables defined by a rule of the form

$$f(x_1, x_2, \ldots, x_n) = c_1x_1 + c_2x_2 + \cdots + c_nx_n, \tag{1}$$

where $c_1, c_2, \ldots, c_n$ are real constants, and a set of inequalities and/or equations (referred to as *constraints*) in $x_1, x_2, \ldots, x_n$ of the form

$$\left\{\begin{array}{l} a_{11}x_1 + a_{12}x_2 + \cdots + a_{1n}x_n \ (\leqq, =, \geqq)\ b_1, \\ a_{21}x_1 + a_{22}x_2 + \cdots + a_{2n}x_n \ (\leqq, =, \geqq)\ b_2, \\ \quad \cdots \qquad \cdots \qquad \cdots \\ a_{m1}x_1 + a_{m2}x_2 + \cdots + a_{mn}x_n \ (\leqq, =, \geqq)\ b_m, \end{array}\right. \tag{2}$$

where in each line of (2) exactly one of the three symbols $\leqq, =, \geqq$ appears. The coefficients a_{ij} and b_i in (2) are real constants. A function f of the form (1) is called a *linear* function. We are required to find either the minimum or the maximum value of f, subject to the constraints (2). As examples, consider the following two problems:

Example 1. Minimize the function f, where

$$f(x_1, x_2) = -4x_1 + 3x_2,$$

subject to the conditions

$$\left\{\begin{array}{l} x_1 - 2x_2 \geqq -4, \\ 2x_1 + 3x_2 \leqq 13, \\ x_1 - x_2 \leqq 4, \\ x_1 \geqq 0, \quad x_2 \geqq 0. \end{array}\right.$$

Example 2. Find the maximum value of the function f, where

$$f(x_1, x_2, x_3) = 2x_1 + 2x_2 + 3x_3,$$

subject to the conditions

$$\left\{\begin{array}{l} 3x_1 + 5x_2 + 5x_3 \leqq 60, \\ 12x_1 - 2x_2 + 9x_3 \geqq 108, \\ 3x_1 + 5x_2 + 15x_3 \leqq 120, \\ x_1 \geqq 0, \quad x_2 \geqq 0, \quad x_3 \geqq 0. \end{array}\right.$$

These are examples of mathematical problems of the linear programming type. For the present we are not concerned with solving these problems, although the student may find it interesting and instructive to attempt their solution before reading Section 1–3.

1–2. *PRACTICAL PROBLEMS TO WHICH LINEAR PROGRAMMING MAY BE APPLIED.*

Example 3. Consider a manufacturer who makes several different products and utilizes several different resources in their manufacture. He wishes to know how much of each product to produce in order to obtain the greatest over-all profit. Let the different products that he makes be numbered 1, 2, . . . , n, and let the resources required (such as labor, capital, steel, and other raw materials) be numbered 1, 2, . . . , m. Suppose that systems of units are chosen in terms of which the amount of each product made and each resource used can be measured. For example, the amount of steel used might be measured in tons; labor, in man hours; and so on. Now we make some assumptions about the nature of the manufacturing process, which may or may not be valid in a particular situation. If they are not, then the linear programming problem which we are about to formulate may not fit that situation very well. Assume first that, for each product, a fixed amount of each resource is required to make a unit of that product. Let a_{ij} be the number of units of resource number i required to produce one unit of product number $j\,(1 \leqq i \leqq m,\ 1 \leqq j \leqq n)$. Referring to a_{ij} as "fixed" means that it is a number determined by i and j only and does not vary with the amount of product j produced. Next, suppose that we consider some fixed period of time during which a fixed known amount of each resource is available for use and that this amount cannot be exceeded during that time. Let b_i be the number of units of resource number i available during the fixed time period $(1 \leqq i \leqq m)$. Finally, suppose that all products made during the time interval we are considering will be sold and that there is a known profit per unit of each product, which is independent of the number of units produced. Let c_j be the number of units of money which is the profit from the sale of one unit of product number $j\,(1 \leqq j \leqq n)$. Then, if x_j units of product $j\,(1 \leqq j \leqq n)$ are produced in the given time interval, the profit will be $c_1x_1 + c_2x_2 + \cdots + c_nx_n$ and the amount of resource $i\,(1 \leqq i \leqq m)$ used will be $a_{i1}x_1 + a_{i2}x_2 + \cdots + a_{in}x_n$. Since we wish to maximize the total profit subject to the above conditions, we are led to formulate the following linear programming problem:

Maximize $c_1x_1 + c_2x_2 + \cdots + c_nx_n$ subject to the constraints

$$\begin{cases} a_{11}x_1 + a_{12}x_2 + \cdots + a_{1n}x_n \leqq b_1, \\ a_{21}x_1 + a_{22}x_2 + \cdots + a_{2n}x_n \leqq b_2, \\ \quad\cdots \qquad \cdots \qquad \cdots \\ a_{m1}x_1 + a_{m2}x_2 + \cdots + a_{mn}x_n \leqq b_m, \\ x_j \geqq 0 \qquad (j = 1, 2, \ldots, n). \end{cases}$$

The restrictions $x_j \geqq 0$ $(j = 1, 2, \ldots, n)$ are present because it is meaningless to talk about producing a negative amount of a product. In certain applications it may be meaningless to consider nonintegral values of the unknowns x_j. If the restriction that some or all of $x_1, x_2, \ldots, x_n$ must be integers is added to the problem, it may become much more difficult to solve and, strictly speaking, is no longer a linear programming problem. For an example, see Exercise 4 following Section 1–3.

Example 4. Suppose varying amounts of a certain product are stored in m warehouses $W_1, W_2, \ldots, W_m$ and it is desired to transport the product from the warehouses to n retail outlets $R_1, R_2, \ldots, R_n$. Some convenient system of units is chosen in terms of which there is a known supply of s_i units of the product at W_i and a known demand of d_j units at R_j. Also, it is assumed that the cost of shipping the product from W_i to R_j is proportional to the amount shipped and that each of the costs c_{ij} per unit shipped from W_i to R_j is known. The problem is to determine how much of the product should be sent from each warehouse to each retail outlet so that all demands are satisfied and the transportation cost is minimized. If we denote by x_{ij} $(i = 1, \ldots, m;\ j = 1, \ldots, n)$ the number of units of the product to be shipped from W_i to R_j, then the total transportation cost will be

$$c(x_{11}, x_{12}, \ldots, x_{mn}) = \sum_{i=1}^{m} \sum_{j=1}^{n} c_{ij} x_{ij}. \tag{3}$$

Since the amount shipped from a given warehouse cannot exceed the supply at that warehouse, we must have

$$\sum_{j=1}^{n} x_{ij} \leqq s_i \qquad (i = 1, \ldots, m). \tag{4}$$

The requirement that the demand of each retail outlet be met is expressed by

$$\sum_{i=1}^{m} x_{ij} \geqq d_j \qquad (j = 1, \ldots, n), \tag{5}$$

Finally, it is clear that we must have $x_{ij} \geqq 0$ for each i and j. Hence, the mathematical problem here is to minimize the function c given by (3), subject to the constraints (4) and (5) and subject to $x_{ij} \geqq 0$ $(i = 1, \ldots, m;$ $j = 1, \ldots, n)$. This problem is known as the *transportation problem* and will be discussed further in Chapter 4.

It was convenient to use double subscripts in formulating this problem, and, at first glance, it may appear that this is not the same type of problem as that described in Section 1–1. However, a little thought should convince the student that, although the notation is different, the form of the problem is the same as that of Section 1–1, so that the transportation problem is indeed a linear programming problem.

1–3. *GRAPHICAL SOLUTION OF TWO-VARIABLE PROBLEMS.*

In this section we shall explain graphical methods which can be used to solve linear programming problems involving only two variables. These methods are of little importance as far as direct application to practical problems is concerned, because significant practical problems usually involve more than two variables. Our purpose here, however, is to give the student some geometrical insight into the nature of the problem, which will be of value to him later on when we consider the more abstract, algebraic approach to the problem. As we shall see, several different situations may occur in connection with two-variable problems, and each has its analogue for n-variable problems, $n > 2$. We now give a series of four examples, illustrating four different possibilities that may arise.

Example 5. As a first illustration, let us consider Example 1 of Section 1–1. We interpret each ordered pair of real numbers (x_1, x_2) as a point in the x_1x_2 plane, and we think of the x_1 axis as horizontal and the x_2 axis as vertical. First we must describe geometrically the collection of all points (x_1, x_2) whose coordinates satisfy the constraints of the problem. To do this we make use of the following facts: If m and b are real constants, the equation $x_2 = mx_1 + b$ represents a straight line with slope m and x_2 intercept b. The inequality $x_2 \leqq mx_1 + b$ represents the *closed half-plane* consisting of all points lying on or below the line $x_2 = mx_1 + b$. The inequality $x_2 \geqq mx_1 + b$ represents the closed half-plane consisting of all points lying on or above the line $x_2 = mx_1 + b$. The equation $x_1 = a$, where a is constant, represents a straight line parallel to the x_2 axis. The inequality $x_1 \leqq a$ represents the closed half-plane consisting of all points lying on or to the left of the line $x_1 = a$. The inequality $x_1 \geqq a$ represents the closed half-plane consisting of all points lying on or to the right of the line $x_1 = a$. The above statements about equations should be familiar to the reader from analytic geometry; he should be able to convince himself of the truth of the ones concerning inequalities with a little thought.

In the example we are considering, each constraint can be written as an inequality of one of the above types; hence, for each constraint, the set of all points whose coordinates satisfy that constraint is a closed half-plane. For instance, the first inequality in Example 1 can be written as $x_2 \leqq \frac{1}{2}x_1 + 2$. This represents, then, the closed half-plane consisting of all points on or below the line $x_2 = \frac{1}{2}x_1 + 2$. To picture this graphically, we draw the line and indicate with arrows pointing downward the fact that the line forms the *upper* boundary of the set (see Fig. 1). Proceeding in a similar way with the other constraints, we obtain the half-planes shown in Fig. 2. The num-

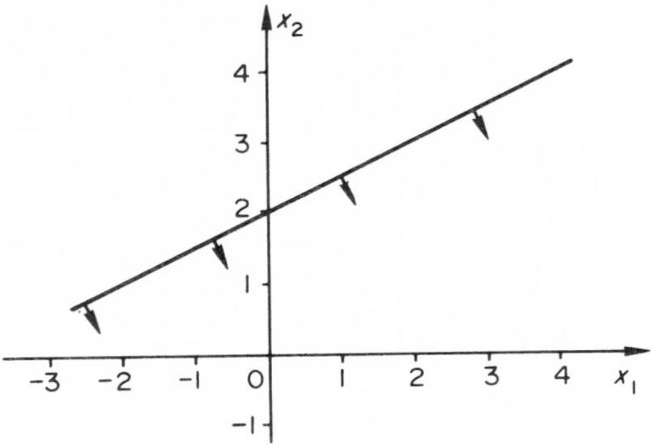

Figure 1

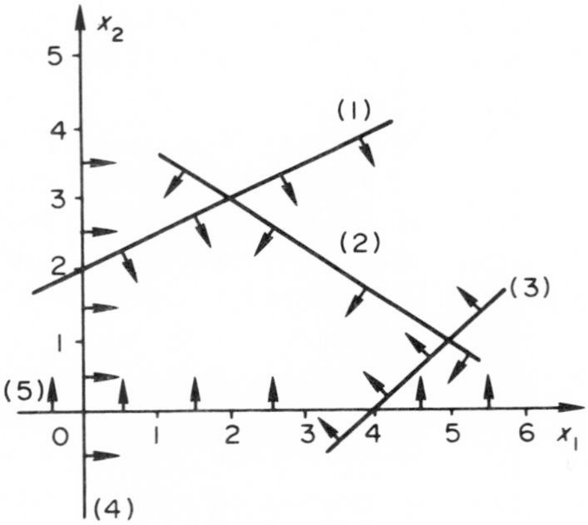

Figure 2

bers on the various lines in Fig. 2 refer to the constraints, which we number as follows: (1) $x_1 - 2x_2 \geqq -4$, (2) $2x_1 + 3x_2 \leqq 13$, (3) $x_1 - x_2 \leqq 4$, (4) $x_1 \geqq 0$, (5) $x_2 \geqq 0$. The set of all those points, each of which satisfies *all* of the constraints, is the common part, or *intersection*, of the five half-planes of Fig. 2. This set is shaded in Fig. 3. It consists of all points lying on or inside the five-sided polygon *ABCDE*. The coordinates of each corner point are found by solving the system consisting of the two equations of the lines meeting at that corner.

Now our problem is to determine at which point of the region *ABCDE* our function f, where $f(x_1, x_2) = -4x_1 + 3x_2$, attains its minimum value. We reason as follows: For each constant k, the equation $-4x_1 + 3x_2 = k$ represents a straight line. For example, the lines corresponding to $k = 0$, $k = -8$, $k = -16$, and $k = -24$ are shown in Fig. 4. Along each such line, the function f has a *constant* value, namely, the value of k corresponding to

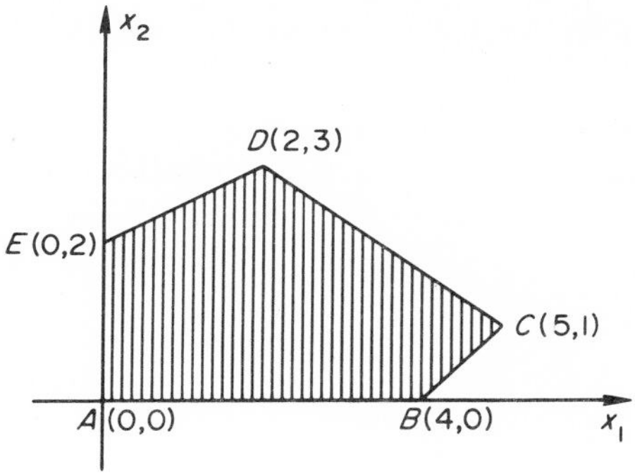

Figure 3

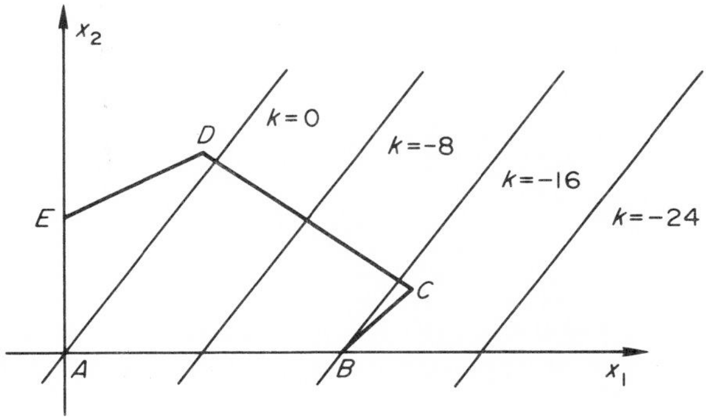

Figure 4

that line. Finding the minimum value that f attains on the region $ABCDE$ is equivalent to finding the smallest number k for which the line $-4x_1 + 3x_2 = k$ has at least one point in common with the region. From Fig. 4, we should guess that the smaller (algebraically) the value of k, the farther is the corresponding line to the right. This can also be verified by noting that the x_1 intercept, which is $-k/4$, increases as k decreases. Thus, by comparing the slopes of lines BC and $-4x_1 + 3x_2 = k$, we judge from Fig. 4 that the smallest number k for which the line $-4x_1 + 3x_2 = k$ has at least one point in common with the region $ABCDE$ is the value for which the line passes through C. This value is $k = -4 \cdot 5 + 3 \cdot 1 = -17$. Therefore, our function f attains its minimum value on the region $ABCDE$ at the point C (5, 1), and this minimum value is -17.

Had we been seeking the maximum value of f subject to the same constraints, we should have proceeded in a similar way. In that case, however, we should have sought the *largest* value of k for which the line $-4x_1 + 3x_2 = k$ crosses the region. Clearly, this is the value for which the line passes through E and is given by $k = -4 \cdot 0 + 3 \cdot 2 = 6$. Hence, the maximum value of f on the region is 6, and this value is attained only at the point E (0, 2).

Example 6. Now let us return to the problem as originally stated in Example 1, Section 1–1, and modify the function f slightly. Suppose we put $g(x_1, x_2) = -4x_1 + 4x_2$ and pose the problem of minimizing g subject to the same set of constraints. In Fig. 5, we have drawn a typical line

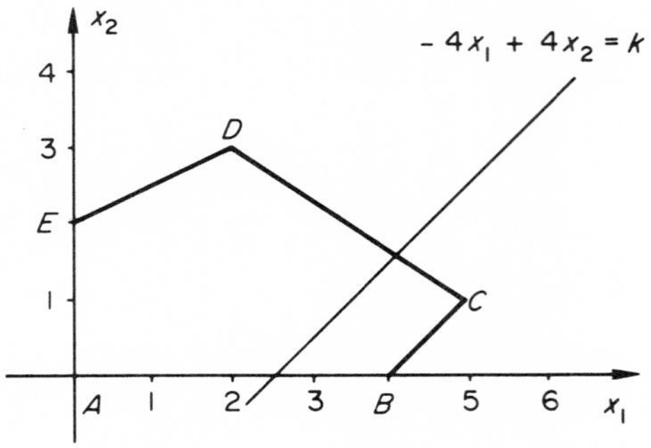

Figure 5

$-4x_1 + 4x_2 = k$. Each such line has slope 1 and hence is parallel to BC. As before, decreasing k "moves" the line to the right. Hence, the smallest value of k for which the line cuts the region determined by the constraints is the value for which it coincides with BC. This value can be found from either the coordinates of B or those of C and is given by $k = -4 \cdot 4 + 4 \cdot 0 = -16$. Thus, the minimum value of the function g is -16, and, in this case, the minimum value is attained not at just a single point of the polygon, but at *each* point of the side BC.

Next, consider the following problem, which illustrates a situation quite different from that in the preceding example:

Example 7. Maximize $2x_1 + x_2$ subject to the conditions

$$\begin{cases} x_1 - x_2 \geqq -1, \\ x_1 - 2x_2 \leqq 2, \\ x_1 \geqq 0, \qquad x_2 \geqq 0. \end{cases}$$

Proceeding as before, we sketch the set of all points (x_1, x_2) satisfying these conditions. This set is shown in Fig. 6, together with a typical line $2x_1 + x_2 = k$, for $k > 0$. Clearly, each line $2x_1 + x_2 = k$ for $k > 0$ crosses our region. This means that $2x_1 + x_2$ does not attain a maximum value on the set of points satisfying the constraints. Notice that this set is *unbounded,* i.e., for each $r > 0$, it contains points whose distance from the origin exceeds r. It should not be inferred from this, however, that, when the set of points

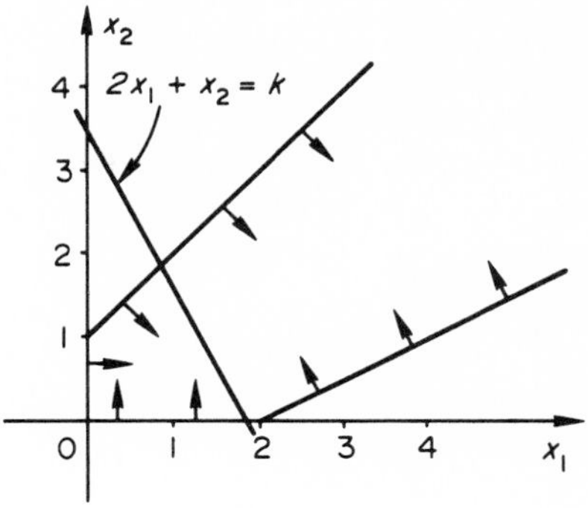

Figure 6

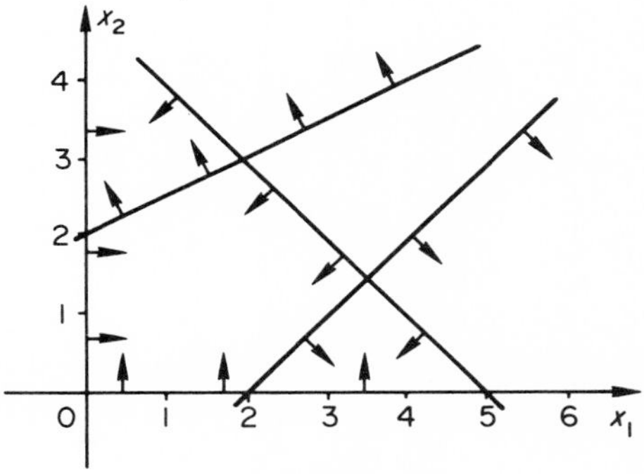

Figure 7

satisfying the constraints of a problem turns out to be unbounded, it is necessarily the case that the problem has no solution. For example, the problem of minimizing $2x_1 + x_2$ subject to the above constraints has a unique solution. What is it?

Finally let us consider the following example:

Example 8. Minimize $2x_1 - 3x_2$ subject to the constraints

$$\left\{\begin{aligned} x_1 - 2x_2 &\leqq -4, \\ x_1 + x_2 &\leqq 5, \\ x_1 - x_2 &\geqq 2, \\ x_1 \geqq 0, \quad & x_2 \geqq 0. \end{aligned}\right.$$

In Fig. 7 we have shown the half-planes determined by the five given inequalities. Clearly, no point of the plane lies in *every* half-plane, or, the way this is usually expressed, the intersection of the half-planes is *empty*. This means that our problem has no solution.

Each of the last two examples was a linear programming problem without a solution, but for quite different reasons. To distinguish between these cases and to facilitate general discussion, we introduce the terminology of feasible solution and optimal solutions. A *feasible solution* is simply a point whose coordinates satisfy all of the constraints. An *optimal solution* is a feasible solution at which the given function attains its *optimum* (i.e., maximum or minimum, depending on how the problem was stated) value. Thus, in Example 7 there were infinitely many feasible solutions, but no optimal solution; while in Example 8 there were no feasible solutions. In Example 5 there was a unique optimal solution, but in Example 6 there were infinitely many optimal solutions.

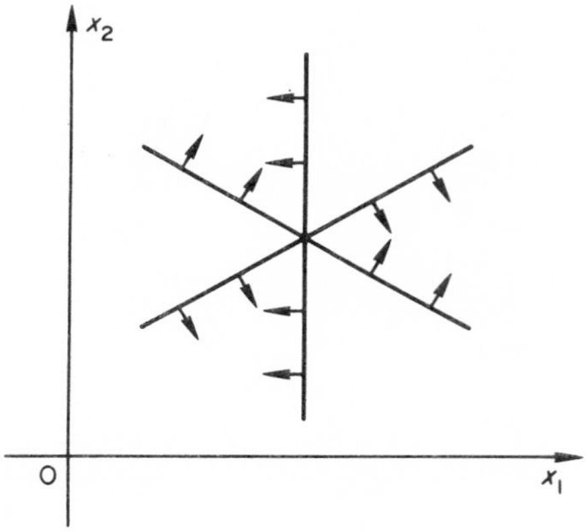

Figure 8

We now make a few general remarks about two-variable problems, which we justify by geometrical reasoning. A linear programming problem involving the optimization of a function f of two variables may have (i) no feasible solution, (ii) exactly one feasible solution, or (iii) infinitely many feasible solutions—there are no other possibilities. The first two cases are of little interest to us. Example 8 illustrated (i), and in Fig. 8 we have illustrated a situation in which there is exactly one point in the intersection of three closed half-planes. Of course, the one feasible solution is also optimal in such a case. If there is more than one feasible solution, then consider two different feasible solutions A and B. Any closed half-plane which contains both A and B will contain the line segment AB. Hence, this segment will be in the intersection of all the half-planes corresponding to the constraints of the problem, which means that each point of AB is a feasible solution. Thus, if there is more than one feasible solution, there are infinitely many. Hence, cases (i), (ii), and (iii), above, are the only possible cases.

If we have a problem with infinitely many feasible solutions, the set of all feasible solutions may be either bounded (as in Examples 5 and 6) or unbounded (as in Example 7). In the bounded case there must be at least one optimal solution. Put another way, this says that, if the set of feasible solutions is bounded, then there exist both a largest and a smallest value of k for which the line $f(x_1, x_2) = k$ meets the set of feasible solutions in at least one point. In the unbounded case, there may or may not be an optimal solution. In any event, if optimal solutions exist, they will be found only on the "boundary" of the set of all feasible solutions. (The term *boundary* will not be precisely defined here. The student doubtless has a good intuitive notion of its meaning. In Example 5, for instance, the boundary of the set of feasible solutions consists of the five segments AB, BC, CD, DE, and EA.) This seems clear geometrically, since, as the line $f(x_1, x_2) = k$ moves across the set S of feasible solutions in the direction of increasing k, for a maximizing problem, or decreasing k, for a minimizing problem, there will be a unique "last point" at which the line meets S (unique optimal solution) or the line will finally coincide with a portion of the boundary of S (infinitely many optimal solutions) or the line will forever meet the set S (no optimal solution).

EXERCISES

1. Find graphically both the maximum and minimum values (if such exist) of (a) $3x_1 + x_2$ and (b) $8x_1 - 2x_2$ subject to the constraints

$$\begin{cases} x_1 - 3x_2 \geqq -3, \\ 2x_1 + 3x_2 \geqq -6, \\ 2x_1 + x_2 \leqq 8, \\ 4x_1 - x_2 \leqq 16. \end{cases}$$

Determine all points at which these optimum values are attained.

2. Determine graphically the maximum and minimum values (if such exist) of $4x_2 - 3x_1$ subject to the constraints

$$\begin{cases} x_1 + 2 \geqq 0, \\ 3x_1 + 6 \geqq 2x_2, \\ x_2 - 3 \leqq 0, \\ 3x_1 + x_2 \leqq 9. \end{cases}$$

Also determine at what points the optimum values are attained.

3. Consider the problem of maximizing $x_2 - 2x_1$ subject to the constraints

$$\begin{cases} 3x_2 \leqq x_1 + 3, \\ x_2 - kx_1 \geqq 2 - 3k, \\ x_1 \geqq 0, \end{cases}$$

where k is some constant. Clearly, the solution depends on k. (a) Determine all values of k for which the set of feasible solutions is bounded, and find the optimal solution for each such value of k. (b) Determine all values of k for which the set of feasible solutions is unbounded. Does an optimal solution exist for each such case? If so, find all optimal solutions. (c) Does the position of the optimal solution vary continuously with k?

4. This problem is a special case of the general problem formulated in Example 3, Section 1–2, with the added restriction that the variables must be integers. Suppose the only resources needed to produce tables and chairs are labor and wood and that the quantities involved are as follows: 5 units of wood per table, 2 units of wood per chair, 4 units of labor per table, and 1 unit of labor per chair. Suppose also that a certain manufacturer of tables and chairs has available to him 60 units of wood and 40 units of labor. Determine how many chairs and tables he should produce for maximum profit if (a) there is \$5 profit on each table and \$3 on each chair; (b) there is \$6 profit on each table and \$2 on each chair.

5. Find the maximum value of (a) $x + 2y$, (b) $y - 3x$, (c) $x^2 + y^2$, and (d) $x - \frac{1}{81}y^2$ subject to the constraints

$$\begin{cases} x^3 \leqq 3y, \\ x^2 + y \leqq 6x, \\ y \geqq 0. \end{cases}$$

Hint: Although no part of this problem is a linear programming problem, each may be solved graphically by methods similar to those used for a linear problem.

6. Formulate the following problem as a linear programming problem: We wish to select a diet of minimum cost from a list of n foods in such a way that minimal requirements of m nutrients (vitamins and minerals) are either equaled or exceeded. We consider a fixed period of time. We are given (i) the number of units of each nutrient which is the minimal requirement for that period of time, (ii) the number of units of each nutrient supplied per unit of each food, and (iii) the cost per unit of each food. We assume that all food purchased will be consumed during the given period of time. Use the following notation: b_i = number of units of nutrient i which is the minimal requirement for the given period; a_{ij} = number of units of nutrient i supplied by one unit of food j; c_j = number of units of money which is the cost per unit of food j; x_j = number of units of food j to be purchased.

7. Formulate the following as a linear programming problem: A company manufactures three products, each of which utilizes some capacity in three manufacturing departments—assembly, inspection, and packing. The capacity requirements per unit of product in hours are shown in the table.

Product	*Production Time in Hours per Unit*		
	Assembly	*Inspection*	*Packing*
A	0.30	0.10	0.06
B	0.50	0.08	0.04
C	0.40	0.12	0.05

Available capacities per week are 1800 hours of assembly time, 800 hours of inspection time, and 700 hours of packing time. The profit per unit sold is \$0.20 for A, \$0.15 for B, and \$0.10 for C. All products produced can be sold for this profit. What should be the production rate per week for each product in order to maximize profits?

8. Suppose that in the previous problem the manufacturer had contracts which required him to produce at least 2000 units per week of product A and at least 1000 units per week of product C. Further suppose that he feels he cannot sell more than 1500 units per week of product B and more than 3000 units per week of product C. Reformulate the linear programming problem to reflect these additional constraints.

9. Two products are made by blending three raw materials according to specifications given in the accompanying table.

Product	*Material*		
	1	2	3
A	10%	≧30%	≦80%
B	≧30%	≧20%	≦60%

The quantities of raw materials available each week are 4000 pounds, 6000 pounds, and 10,000 pounds for materials 1, 2, and 3, respectively. Material costs per pound are \$3.00, \$2.00, and \$1.00, respectively. Product A sells for \$12.00 per pound and product B sells for \$15.00 per pound. All manufacturing costs, other than material, are assumed to be \$2.00 per pound regardless of the product or blend. The objective is to determine the blend to use for each product and the quantities of each to produce each week to obtain maximum profits. Formulate this as a linear programming problem.

10. Suppose that in the previous problem the specifications had been the following:

Product	*Material*		
	1	2	3
A	10%	20—40%	≦80%
B	≧30%	≧20%	≦60%

Reformulate the linear programming problem.

CHAPTER TWO

TOPICS FROM LINEAR ALGEBRA

In the preceding chapter we described how linear programming problems involving only two variables may be solved graphically. Before we can understand and apply the nongraphical "simplex" method for solving the general linear programming problem, to be presented in the next chapter, we must be familiar with certain concepts and techniques from the branch of mathematics known as *linear algebra*. It is the purpose of this chapter to present these topics, which include a brief introduction to matrices, systems of linear equations, and vectors.

2–1. *MATRICES.*

The language and notation of matrices will be convenient for us in our later discussions, but we shall require only a very little of the extensive subject known as *matrix algebra*. In this section we define the basic operations of matrix algebra and state and prove some of the elementary properties. Some additional definitions and properties appear in the exercises at the end of this and subsequent sections.

DEFINITION 1. A *matrix* is a rectangular array of numbers, written as follows:

$$\begin{pmatrix} a_{11} & a_{12} & \cdots & a_{1n} \\ a_{21} & a_{22} & \cdots & a_{2n} \\ \cdot & \cdot & & \cdot \\ \cdot & \cdot & & \cdot \\ \cdot & \cdot & & \cdot \\ a_{m1} & a_{m2} & \cdots & a_{mn} \end{pmatrix}$$

The horizontal arrays within the matrix are called the *rows*, and the vertical arrays are called the *columns* of the matrix. If a matrix has m rows and n columns, we say that it is an *m by n matrix*. In case $m = n$, we refer to the matrix as a *square matrix*. The numbers a_{ij} are called the *elements* of the matrix.

Example 1. Examples of matrices are the following:

$$\begin{pmatrix} 2 & -3 & 0 & 1 \\ 4 & 1 & -1 & 7 \\ 10 & 6 & 4 & 5 \end{pmatrix}, \quad \begin{pmatrix} 2 & 10 \\ 1 & 1 \\ 9 & 4 \\ 12 & -3 \end{pmatrix}, \quad \begin{pmatrix} 2 & 1 & 7 \\ 4 & 4 & 4 \\ 1 & -1 & 0 \end{pmatrix}.$$

The dimensions of these matrices are, from left to right, 3 by 4, 4 by 2, and 3 by 3.

There is no numerical "value" intrinsically associated with a matrix. It is possible, and for some purposes useful, to define for each *square* matrix a number called the *determinant* of the matrix. We do not use determinants in this text.

Matrices will frequently be denoted by boldface capital letters such as $\mathbf{A}, \mathbf{B}, \mathbf{C}, \ldots$. Also, if we say that $\mathbf{A} = (a_{ij})$ is an m by n matrix, or if we write $\mathbf{A} = (a_{ij})$, $(i = 1, \ldots, m; j = 1, \ldots, n)$, we simply mean that $\mathbf{A}$ is a matrix with m rows and n columns and that a_{ij} denotes the number in row i and column j. The rows of a matrix are always numbered consecutively from top to bottom, and the columns are numbered consecutively from left to right.

DEFINITION 2. Suppose $\mathbf{A} = (a_{ij})$ is an m by n matrix and $\mathbf{B} = (b_{ij})$ is a p by q matrix. We say that $\mathbf{A} = \mathbf{B}$ if, and only if, $m = p$, $n = q$, and $a_{ij} = b_{ij}$ for each i and j.

Example 2.

$$\begin{pmatrix} 2 & 1 & 3 \\ -1 & 4 & 6 \end{pmatrix} \neq \begin{pmatrix} 2 & 1 & -3 \\ -1 & 4 & 6 \end{pmatrix} \quad \text{and} \quad \begin{pmatrix} 3 & 4 \\ 5 & 6 \end{pmatrix} \neq \begin{pmatrix} 3 & 4 \\ 5 & 6 \\ 0 & 0 \end{pmatrix}.$$

In the first case, the matrices have the same dimensions, but their elements in the first row and third column are different. In the second case, the matrices do not have the same number of rows.

We next define the operation of matrix addition:

Definition 3. If $\mathbf{A} = (a_{ij})$ and $\mathbf{B} = (b_{ij})$ are m by n matrices, we define $\mathbf{A} + \mathbf{B}$ to be the m by n matrix $\mathbf{C} = (c_{ij})$, where $c_{ij} = a_{ij} + b_{ij}$ for each i and j.

Example 3. If

$$\mathbf{A} = \begin{pmatrix} 2 & 3 & -7 \\ 1 & 4 & 10 \end{pmatrix} \quad \text{and} \quad \mathbf{B} = \begin{pmatrix} 2 & -1 & 4 \\ 0 & 6 & -3 \end{pmatrix},$$

then

$$\mathbf{A} + \mathbf{B} = \begin{pmatrix} 4 & 2 & -3 \\ 1 & 10 & 7 \end{pmatrix}.$$

Note that $\mathbf{A} + \mathbf{B}$ is undefined if $\mathbf{A}$ and $\mathbf{B}$ have different dimensions. We next show that the order of terms in a sum is irrelevant:

Theorem 1. Matrix addition is commutative; i.e., if $\mathbf{A}$ and $\mathbf{B}$ are m by n matrices, then $\mathbf{A} + \mathbf{B} = \mathbf{B} + \mathbf{A}$.

Proof: Let $\mathbf{A} = (a_{ij})$ and $\mathbf{B} = (b_{ij})$ be m by n matrices; let $\mathbf{A} + \mathbf{B} = \mathbf{C}$ and $\mathbf{B} + \mathbf{A} = \mathbf{D}$. Then $\mathbf{C}$ and $\mathbf{D}$ are m by n matrices; say $\mathbf{C} = (c_{ij})$ and $\mathbf{D} = (d_{ij})$. By definition, we have $c_{ij} = a_{ij} + b_{ij}$ and $d_{ij} = b_{ij} + a_{ij}$. But $a_{ij} + b_{ij} = b_{ij} + a_{ij}$ since addition of numbers is commutative. Thus, $c_{ij} = d_{ij}$ for each i and j, and therefore $\mathbf{A} + \mathbf{B} = \mathbf{B} + \mathbf{A}$.

Another property of matrix addition relates to grouping the terms in a sum involving three matrices:

Theorem 2. Matrix addition is associative; i.e., if $\mathbf{A}$, $\mathbf{B}$, and $\mathbf{C}$ are m by n matrices, then

$$(\mathbf{A} + \mathbf{B}) + \mathbf{C} = \mathbf{A} + (\mathbf{B} + \mathbf{C}).$$

Proof: Let $\mathbf{A} = (a_{ij})$, $\mathbf{B} = (b_{ij})$, and $\mathbf{C} = (c_{ij})$ be m by n matrices. Let $\mathbf{A} + \mathbf{B} = \mathbf{D} = (d_{ij})$, and let $\mathbf{B} + \mathbf{C} = \mathbf{E} = (e_{ij})$. Then $\mathbf{D}$ and $\mathbf{E}$ are m by n matrices, and we have $d_{ij} = a_{ij} + b_{ij}$ and $e_{ij} = b_{ij} + c_{ij}$. We wish to prove that $\mathbf{D} + \mathbf{C} = \mathbf{A} + \mathbf{E}$. We know that $\mathbf{D} + \mathbf{C} = (f_{ij})$, where $f_{ij} = d_{ij} + c_{ij}$, and $\mathbf{A} + \mathbf{E} = (g_{ij})$, where $g_{ij} = a_{ij} + e_{ij}$. Using the fact that addition of numbers is associative, we have

$$f_{ij} = d_{ij} + c_{ij} = (a_{ij} + b_{ij}) + c_{ij} = a_{ij} + (b_{ij} + c_{ij}) = a_{ij} + e_{ij} = g_{ij}.$$

Therefore, $\mathbf{D} + \mathbf{C} = \mathbf{A} + \mathbf{E}$, and the proof is complete.

By using the corresponding property of addition of numbers, it can be proved that, in a sum involving any number of matrices, all having the same dimensions, the terms can be written in any order and grouped in any fashion whatsoever.

Definition 4. Let $\mathbf{0}_{mn}$ denote the m by n matrix (z_{ij}), where $z_{ij} = 0$ for each i and j. $\mathbf{0}_{mn}$ is called the *m by n zero matrix*.

Example 4.

$$\mathbf{0}_{21} = \begin{pmatrix} 0 \\ 0 \end{pmatrix}, \qquad \mathbf{0}_{34} = \begin{pmatrix} 0 & 0 & 0 & 0 \\ 0 & 0 & 0 & 0 \\ 0 & 0 & 0 & 0 \end{pmatrix}.$$

The following theorem, whose easy proof is left to the student, shows that the zero matrix plays a role in matrix algebra analogous to that of the number 0 in ordinary algebra:

THEOREM 3. For each m by n matrix $\mathbf{A}$, we have

$$\mathbf{A} + \mathbf{0}_{mn} = \mathbf{A}.$$

If x is a number, then $-x$, the negative of x, has the property that $x + (-x) = 0$. If $\mathbf{A} = (a_{ij})$ is an m by n matrix, then the m by n matrix $\mathbf{B} = (-a_{ij})$ has the analogous property that $\mathbf{A} + \mathbf{B} = \mathbf{0}_{mn}$. Hence, we make the following definition:

DEFINITION 5. The *negative* of an m by n matrix $\mathbf{A} = (a_{ij})$ is denoted by $-\mathbf{A}$ and is defined as follows: $-\mathbf{A} = (-a_{ij})$.

Example 5. If

$$\mathbf{A} = \begin{pmatrix} 2 & 3 \\ -5 & 4 \end{pmatrix}, \quad \text{then} \quad -\mathbf{A} = \begin{pmatrix} -2 & -3 \\ 5 & -4 \end{pmatrix}.$$

This leads to the operation of subtraction:

DEFINITION 6. If $\mathbf{A}$ and $\mathbf{B}$ are m by n matrices, we define $\mathbf{A} - \mathbf{B}$ to mean $\mathbf{A} + (-\mathbf{B})$.

It is easily seen that, if $\mathbf{A} = (a_{ij})$ and $\mathbf{B} = (b_{ij})$ are m by n matrices, then $\mathbf{A} - \mathbf{B} = (c_{ij})$, where $c_{ij} = a_{ij} - b_{ij}$.

Example 6.

$$\begin{pmatrix} 2 & 10 \\ 3 & -1 \\ 4 & 2 \end{pmatrix} - \begin{pmatrix} 0 & 3 \\ 1 & -3 \\ 7 & 6 \end{pmatrix} = \begin{pmatrix} 2 & 7 \\ 2 & 2 \\ -3 & -4 \end{pmatrix}.$$

Next we come to the operation of matrix multiplication. This operation is defined in what may seem at first to be a rather peculiar way. There are good reasons for this definition, however, though they are not at all obvious at this point. One of these reasons will be mentioned in Exercise 5 at the end of this section.

DEFINITION 7. Let $\mathbf{A} = (a_{ij})$ be an m by n matrix, and let $\mathbf{B} = (b_{ij})$ be an n by p matrix. We define the product $\mathbf{AB}$ to be the m by p matrix (c_{ij}), where

$$c_{ij} = \sum_{k=1}^{n} a_{ik}b_{kj}. \tag{1}$$

Equation (1) tells us that the element in the ith row and j^{th} column of the product matrix is obtained by multiplying the kth element of the ith row of **A** by the kth element of the jth column of **B** for each $k = 1, 2, \ldots, n$ and adding all these products together.

Example 7. Let

$$\mathbf{A} = \begin{pmatrix} 3 & 2 & 5 \\ -1 & 4 & 2 \end{pmatrix} \quad \text{and} \quad \mathbf{B} = \begin{pmatrix} 1 & -2 & 5 & 2 \\ 2 & 4 & 0 & -2 \\ 3 & 4 & 1 & 6 \end{pmatrix}.$$

Then **A** is 2 by 3 and **B** is 3 by 4, so **AB** is defined and will be a 2 by 4 matrix. The element in the first row and first column of **AB** is found by looking at the first row of **A** and the first column of **B**, multiplying their corresponding elements together, and adding the products. We get $3 \cdot 1 + 2 \cdot 2 + 5 \cdot 3$, or 22. The other elements are found similarly by considering each of the other seven combinations of a row from **A** and a column from **B**, multiplying corresponding elements together, and adding the products. The final result is

$$\mathbf{AB} = \begin{pmatrix} 3 & 2 & 5 \\ -1 & 4 & 2 \end{pmatrix} \begin{pmatrix} 1 & -2 & 5 & 2 \\ 2 & 4 & 0 & -2 \\ 3 & 4 & 1 & 6 \end{pmatrix} = \begin{pmatrix} 22 & 22 & 20 & 32 \\ 13 & 26 & -3 & 2 \end{pmatrix}.$$

Note that, in order for a product to be defined, the number of columns in the left-hand matrix must equal the number of rows in the right-hand matrix. For instance, in the preceding example, the product **BA** is undefined.

Matrix multiplication, unlike ordinary multiplication of numbers, is not commutative (see Exercise 2). However, it is associative, as we now show.

THEOREM 4. Let $\mathbf{A} = (a_{ij})$ be an m by n matrix; $\mathbf{B} = (b_{ij})$, an n by p matrix; and $\mathbf{C} = (c_{ij})$, a p by q matrix. Then the products **(AB)C** and **A(BC)** are each defined, and they are equal.

Proof: Let $\mathbf{AB} = \mathbf{D} = (d_{ij})$, and let $\mathbf{BC} = \mathbf{E} = (e_{ij})$. Then **D** is an m by p matrix, and **E** is an n by q matrix. Hence, $(\mathbf{AB})\mathbf{C} = \mathbf{DC}$ and $\mathbf{A}(\mathbf{BC}) = \mathbf{AE}$ are each defined, and each is an m by q matrix. Let $\mathbf{DC} = (f_{ij})$ and $\mathbf{AE} = (g_{ij})$; we must prove that $f_{ij} = g_{ij}$ for each i and j $(i = 1, \ldots, m; j = 1, \ldots, q)$. We have

$$\begin{aligned} f_{ij} &= \sum_{k=1}^{p} d_{ik}c_{kj} = \sum_{k=1}^{p} \left(\sum_{r=1}^{n} a_{ir}b_{rk} \right) c_{kj} \\ &= \sum_{k=1}^{p} \left(\sum_{r=1}^{n} a_{ir}b_{rk}c_{kj} \right) = \sum_{r=1}^{n} \left(\sum_{k=1}^{p} a_{ir}b_{rk}c_{kj} \right) \\ &= \sum_{r=1}^{n} a_{ir} \left(\sum_{k=1}^{p} b_{rk}c_{kj} \right) = \sum_{r=1}^{n} a_{ir}e_{rj} = g_{ij}, \end{aligned}$$

which completes the proof.

Thus, if the number of rows in **B** equals the number of columns in **A** and the number of rows in **C** equals the number of columns in **B**, the product

ABC is unambiguously defined. More generally, it can be proved that a product $\mathbf{A}_1\mathbf{A}_2\mathbf{A}_3 \ldots \mathbf{A}_n$ is unambiguously defined provided that, for each $i = 2, 3, \ldots, n$ the number of rows in $\mathbf{A}_i$ equals the number of columns in $\mathbf{A}_{i-1}$.

The final operation which we define is called *scalar multiplication:*

DEFINITION 8. Let $\mathbf{A} = (a_{ij})$ be an m by n matrix, and let α be a scalar (number). Then we define $\alpha\mathbf{A}$, or $\mathbf{A}\alpha$, to be the m by n matrix (b_{ij}), where $b_{ij} = \alpha a_{ij}$.

In other words, to multiply a matrix by a number, we multiply every element of the matrix by that number.

Example 8. If

$$\mathbf{A} = \begin{pmatrix} 3 & 5 & -1 \\ 1 & 7 & 0 \end{pmatrix} \quad \text{and} \quad \alpha = 2,$$

then

$$\alpha\mathbf{A} = 2\begin{pmatrix} 3 & 5 & -1 \\ 1 & 7 & 0 \end{pmatrix} = \begin{pmatrix} 6 & 10 & -2 \\ 2 & 14 & 0 \end{pmatrix}.$$

Some of the properties of scalar multiplication are given in the next theorem; the proof is left to the student.

THEOREM 5. Let **A** and **B** be m by n matrices, and let α and β be scalars. Then we have

$$\text{(i)} \qquad (\alpha + \beta)\mathbf{A} = \alpha\mathbf{A} + \beta\mathbf{A},$$
$$\text{(ii)} \qquad \alpha(\mathbf{A} + \mathbf{B}) = \alpha\mathbf{A} + \alpha\mathbf{B},$$
$$\text{(iii)} \qquad (\alpha\beta)\mathbf{A} = \alpha(\beta\mathbf{A}),$$
$$\text{(iv)} \qquad 1\mathbf{A} = \mathbf{A},$$
$$\text{(v)} \qquad (-1)\mathbf{A} = -\mathbf{A},$$
$$\text{(vi)} \qquad 0\mathbf{A} = \mathbf{0}_{mn}.$$

Further, if **A** is m by n and **B** is n by p, then

$$\text{(vii)} \qquad \mathbf{A}(\alpha\mathbf{B}) = (\alpha\mathbf{A})\mathbf{B} = \alpha(\mathbf{AB}).$$

In our subsequent work we shall frequently use matrices with a single column; these are given a special name, as indicated in the following definition:

DEFINITION 9. A matrix with m rows and one column is called an *m-dimensional column vector.*

Example 9. $\begin{pmatrix} 2 \\ 3 \\ -5 \end{pmatrix}$ is a three-dimensional column vector.

We shall use lower-case boldface letters such as **x**, **y**, etc., to represent column vectors, contrary to our usual policy of using capitals for matrices.

Also, for typographical convenience, we shall frequently write the elements of a column vector in a row, separated by commas, and enclosed by square brackets, rather than writing them in a column. For instance,

$$[2, 3, -5] = \begin{pmatrix} 2 \\ 3 \\ -5 \end{pmatrix}.$$

The subject of vectors, which is of great importance in linear programming, will be discussed in detail in Sections 2–3, 2–4, 2–5, and 2–6.

EXERCISES

1. Perform the indicated computations where possible; if some indicated operation is undefined, state this fact.

(a) $$\begin{pmatrix} 6 & 2 & -1 \\ 3 & 3 & 5 \end{pmatrix} + \begin{pmatrix} -2 & 14 & 10 \\ 7 & 0 & -5 \end{pmatrix}.$$

(b) $$\begin{pmatrix} 12 & 4 \\ 2 & 15 \\ -1 & 3 \end{pmatrix} - 4\begin{pmatrix} 1 & 0 \\ -1 & 2 \\ 6 & -2 \end{pmatrix}.$$

(c) $$\begin{pmatrix} 13 & 2 & -7 \\ 1 & 6 & 4 \end{pmatrix} + \begin{pmatrix} 0 & 0 \\ 0 & 0 \end{pmatrix}.$$

(d) $$\begin{pmatrix} 4 & 9 & 4 & 0 \\ -1 & 3 & 3 & 2 \end{pmatrix}\begin{pmatrix} 1 & 0 \\ -1 & 2 \\ 2 & 1 \\ 3 & 1 \end{pmatrix}.$$

(e) $$\begin{pmatrix} 2 & 5 \\ 1 & -1 \end{pmatrix}\left\{3\begin{pmatrix} 1 & 4 \\ 5 & 1 \end{pmatrix} - 2\begin{pmatrix} 1 & 4 \\ 5 & 1 \end{pmatrix}\right\}.$$

(f) $$\begin{pmatrix} 1 & 1 \\ 1 & 1 \end{pmatrix}\begin{pmatrix} -3 & 2 & 6 \\ 5 & 1 & 3 \end{pmatrix}\begin{pmatrix} 4 \\ 2 \\ -1 \end{pmatrix}.$$

(g) $$\begin{pmatrix} 1 & 0 & 0 \\ 0 & 1 & 0 \\ 0 & 0 & 1 \end{pmatrix}\begin{pmatrix} -5 & 6 & 3 \\ 1 & 2 & 9 \\ 8 & 6 & 7 \end{pmatrix}.$$

(h) $$\begin{pmatrix} 3 \\ 2 \\ -1 \end{pmatrix}(4 \quad 0 \quad 5).$$

(i) $$(4 \quad 0 \quad 5)\begin{pmatrix} 3 \\ 2 \\ -1 \end{pmatrix}.$$

(j) $$\begin{pmatrix} 3 & -2 & 4 \\ 6 & 1 & 1 \\ 3 & 2 & 2 \end{pmatrix} \left\{ \begin{pmatrix} 2 & 3 \\ -1 & 1 \\ 0 & 4 \end{pmatrix} + 5 \begin{pmatrix} -1 & 1 \\ 0 & 2 \\ -2 & 1 \end{pmatrix} \right\}.$$

2. If **A** is an m by n matrix, what must be the dimensions of a matrix **B** so that both **AB** and **BA** are defined? What relation between m and n must hold in order for **AB** and **BA** to have the same dimensions? If $\mathbf{A} = \begin{pmatrix} 2 & -1 \\ 1 & 3 \end{pmatrix}$ and $\mathbf{B} = \begin{pmatrix} 1 & 4 \\ -2 & 3 \end{pmatrix}$, compute both **AB** and **BA**. This example shows that, even if we have a pair of matrices **A** and **B** for which **AB** and **BA** are each defined and have the same dimensions, it may not be true that $\mathbf{AB} = \mathbf{BA}$. In other words, there is no commutative law for matrix multiplication.

3. One of the basic and most important properties of real numbers is that, if a and b are numbers such that $ab = 0$, then either $a = 0$ or $b = 0$. It might appear that the analogous statement for matrices would be that, if **A** is an m by n matrix, **B** is an n by p matrix, and $\mathbf{AB} = \mathbf{0}_{mp}$, then either $\mathbf{A} = \mathbf{0}_{mn}$ or $\mathbf{B} = \mathbf{0}_{np}$. Show, however, that this is false by finding 2 by 2 matrices **A** and **B**, neither equal to the zero matrix, whose product is the zero matrix.

Note: A property of square matrices which is analogous to the above property of numbers is found in Exercise 9 of Section 2–2.

4. Prove that matrix multiplication is distributive with respect to matrix addition, i.e., if **A** is an m by n matrix and **B** and **C** are n by p matrices, then $\mathbf{A}(\mathbf{B} + \mathbf{C}) = \mathbf{AB} + \mathbf{AC}$.

5. Let $\mathbf{A} = (a_{ij})$ be an m by n matrix; $\mathbf{x} = [x_1, x_2, \ldots, x_n]$, an n-dimensional column vector; and $\mathbf{b} = [b_1, b_2, \ldots, b_m]$, an m-dimensional column vector. Prove, using the definitions of matrix product and matrix equality, that $\mathbf{Ax} = \mathbf{b}$ if, and only if, the numbers $x_1, \ldots, x_n$ satisfy each of the following equations:

$$\begin{cases} a_{11}x_1 + a_{12}x_2 + \cdots + a_{1n}x_n = b_1, \\ a_{21}x_1 + a_{22}x_2 + \cdots + a_{2n}x_n = b_2, \\ \cdots \qquad \cdots \qquad \cdots, \\ a_{m1}x_1 + a_{m2}x_2 + \cdots + a_{mn}x_n = b_m. \end{cases}$$

Note: These equations can also be thought of as defining a transformation (function) whereby, to a given vector $\mathbf{x} = [x_1, \ldots, x_n]$, corresponds a uniquely determined vector $\mathbf{b} = [b_1, \ldots, b_m]$. This transformation is completely specified by the matrix **A**. The desire to be able to write, as the product **Ax**, the result of applying this transformation to **x** is a motivating factor behind the definition of matrix multiplication.

6. For each pair of positive integers (i, j), let δ_{ij} be defined as follows:

$$\delta_{ij} = \begin{cases} 0 & \text{if} \quad i \neq j \\ 1 & \text{if} \quad i = j. \end{cases}$$

For each positive integer n, let $\mathbf{I}_n$ denote the n by n matrix $\mathbf{I}_n = (\delta_{ij})$. For example,

$$\mathbf{I}_3 = \begin{pmatrix} 1 & 0 & 0 \\ 0 & 1 & 0 \\ 0 & 0 & 1 \end{pmatrix}.$$

Prove that, if **A** is any m by n matrix and **B** is any n by p matrix, then $\mathbf{AI}_n = \mathbf{A}$ and $\mathbf{I}_n\mathbf{B} = \mathbf{B}$. In particular, if **C** is any n by n matrix, then $\mathbf{CI}_n = \mathbf{I}_n\mathbf{C} = \mathbf{C}$. Thus, in the algebra of n by n matrices, $\mathbf{I}_n$ plays a role analogous to that of the number 1 in ordinary algebra. For this reason $\mathbf{I}_n$ is called the *identity matrix*, or *unit matrix, of order n*.

7. Suppose **A**, **B**, and **C** are matrices such that $\mathbf{AB} = \mathbf{C}$.
(a) If **A** is m by n and **C** has p columns, what are the dimensions of **B**?
(b) If the jth column of **B** is denoted by $\mathbf{b}_j$ and the jth column of **C**, by $\mathbf{c}_j$, prove that $\mathbf{Ab}_j = \mathbf{c}_j$.

2–2. *SYSTEMS OF LINEAR EQUATIONS.*

In Exercise 5 of the preceding section, the student was asked to prove that, if $\mathbf{A} = (a_{ij})$ is an m by n matrix, $\mathbf{x} = [x_1, x_2, \ldots, x_n]$ is an n-dimensional column vector, and $\mathbf{b} = [b_1, b_2, \ldots, b_m]$ is an m-dimensional column vector, then the matrix equality

$$\mathbf{Ax} = \mathbf{b} \tag{2}$$

holds if, and only if, the numbers $x_1, x_2, \ldots, x_n$ satisfy each of the equations

$$\begin{cases} a_{11}x_1 + a_{12}x_2 + \cdots + a_{1n}x_n = b_1, \\ a_{21}x_1 + a_{22}x_2 + \cdots + a_{2n}x_n = b_2, \\ \cdots \qquad \cdots \qquad \cdots, \\ a_{m1}x_1 + a_{m2}x_2 + \cdots + a_{mn}x_n = b_m. \end{cases} \tag{3}$$

This result follows from the definitions of matrix multiplication and matrix equality.

A set of equations of the form of (3) is called a system of m linear equations in n unknowns. A solution of (3) can be thought of as an ordered set of n numbers $x_1, x_2, \ldots, x_n$ which satisfies each of the m equations in the system. In view of the result of the exercise referred to above, we can regard (2) as a system of m linear equations in n unknowns and define a solution of such a system as a column vector x satisfying (2). We make things more precise with the following definition:

DEFINITION 10. Let **A** be a given m by n matrix, and let **b** be a given m-dimensional column vector. The problem of finding all n-dimensional column vectors **x** such that (2) holds is called a *system of m linear equations in n unknowns*. A column vector **x** for which (2) holds is called a *solution* of the system.

Example 10. The system of three equations in three unknowns

$$\begin{pmatrix} 2 & 1 & -1 \\ 1 & 4 & 1 \\ 1 & -1 & -1 \end{pmatrix}\begin{pmatrix} x_1 \\ x_2 \\ x_3 \end{pmatrix} = \begin{pmatrix} 1 \\ 3 \\ 0 \end{pmatrix},$$

when written in form (3), becomes

$$\begin{cases} 2x_1 + x_2 - x_3 = 1, \\ x_1 + 4x_2 + x_3 = 3, \\ x_1 - x_2 - x_3 = 0. \end{cases}$$

The student should verify that $\mathbf{x} = [3, -1, 4]$ is a solution of this system. At this point we are not concerned with the possibility that there might be other solutions.

Example 11. Let

$$\mathbf{A} = \begin{pmatrix} 2 & -3 & 1 & 1 \\ 1 & 4 & -2 & 5 \\ 0 & 0 & 0 & 0 \end{pmatrix}, \qquad \mathbf{b} = \begin{pmatrix} 10 \\ 7 \\ 6 \end{pmatrix}.$$

Then, for any column vector $\mathbf{x} = [x_1, x_2, x_3, x_4]$, we have

$$\mathbf{Ax} = \begin{pmatrix} 2x_1 - 3x_2 + x_3 + x_4 \\ x_1 + 4x_2 - 2x_3 + 5x_4 \\ 0 \end{pmatrix}.$$

Thus, there is no vector $\mathbf{x}$ for which $\mathbf{Ax} = \mathbf{b}$, and we say that the system has no solutions.

Example 12. Let

$$\mathbf{A} = \begin{pmatrix} 1 & 2 & -3 \\ 3 & 6 & -8 \\ 2 & 4 & -4 \end{pmatrix}, \qquad \mathbf{b} = \begin{pmatrix} 5 \\ 13 \\ 6 \end{pmatrix}.$$

The student should verify that, if k is any number, the vector $\mathbf{x} = [-2k - 1, k, -2]$ is a solution of the system $\mathbf{Ax} = \mathbf{b}$. Again, we are not concerned at present with the possibility of the existence of solutions other than those of this form.

The student having little or no experience with linear systems may be wondering how we obtained the solutions in Examples 10 and 12. The rest of this section will be devoted to explaining a general method for solving systems of linear equations, where, by *solving* a system, we mean the process of finding *all* of its solutions or showing that there are none. A fundamental notion which must be understood to follow the discussion is that of *equivalent systems*.

DEFINITION 11. Let **A** be an m_1 by n matrix, **C** an m_2 by n matrix, **b** an m_1-dimensional column vector, and **d** an m_2-dimensional column vector. The systems $\mathbf{Ax} = \mathbf{b}$ and $\mathbf{Cx} = \mathbf{d}$ are said to be *equivalent* if, and only if, each solution of one of them is a solution of the other.

Thus, two systems involving the same number of unknowns, but not necessarily the same number of equations, are said to be equivalent provided they have exactly the same collection of solutions. In particular, if neither system has any solution, they are equivalent.

The procedure we are going to describe for solving a system consists of replacing the given system by an equivalent system, then replacing that by another equivalent system, and so on, until we at last obtain a system whose form is so simple that either its solutions can be written down by inspection or we can see that it has no solutions. What we mean by "simple form" will be made precise later, but first consider the following examples:

Example 13.

$$\begin{cases} x_1 + 0x_2 + 0x_3 = -2, \\ 0x_1 + x_2 + 0x_3 = 5, \\ 0x_1 + 0x_2 + x_3 = 4. \end{cases}$$

Here $\mathbf{A} = \mathbf{I}_3$ (see Exercise 6, Section 2–1), and it is evident that the system has the unique (one and only one) solution $\mathbf{x} = [-2, 5, 4]$.

Example 14.

$$\begin{cases} 0x_1 + 2x_2 + 0x_3 - 2x_4 + x_5 = 1, \\ x_1 - x_2 + 0x_3 + 3x_4 + 0x_5 = 7, \\ 0x_1 + 4x_2 + x_3 + 8x_4 + 0x_5 = 10. \end{cases}$$

Here we notice that x_1 has been "eliminated from" (i.e., appears with a zero coefficient in) the first and third equations, x_3 has been eliminated from the first and second equations, and x_5 has been eliminated from the second and third equations. Hence, we can solve for x_1, x_3, and x_5 in terms of x_2 and x_4, obtaining

$$\begin{aligned} x_1 &= 7 + x_2 - 3x_4, \\ x_3 &= 10 - 4x_2 - 8x_4, \\ x_5 &= 1 - 2x_2 + 2x_4. \end{aligned} \tag{4}$$

Thus, if we assign values arbitrarily to x_2 and x_4 and then compute x_1, x_3, and x_5 from Eq. (4), we shall obtain a solution $\mathbf{x} = [x_1, x_2, x_3, x_4\ x_5]$ for the system. Conversely, each solution is obtainable in this way. Thus, we could say that the set of all solutions of the given system is the set of all five-dimensional column vectors **x** of the form

$$\mathbf{x} = [7 + c - 3d,\ c,\ 10 - 4c - 8d,\ d,\ 1 - 2c + 2d],$$

where c and d are real numbers.

We have said that our process of solving a system will consist of replacing the given system by an equivalent system and then replacing that system by another, and so on. At each stage, what we shall do is replace certain equations in the system by other equations in one of the three ways justified by the following theorem:

THEOREM 6. Given a system of m linear equations in n unknowns, we obtain an equivalent system of m linear equations in n unknowns if we do any one of the following:

I. Interchange two equations of the system.
II. Replace an equation of the given system with a nonzero multiple of itself, i.e., with the new equation which results when both sides of the original equation are multiplied by some nonzero number c.
III. Replace an equation by the sum of it and a multiple of another equation, where, by the sum of two equations, we mean the equation whose left-hand side is the sum of the two left-hand sides and whose right-hand side is the sum of the two right-hand sides.

We shall give a proof only for part III of this theorem. The arguments in the other two parts are very simple and are left to the student.

Proof of part III: Consider system (3) above. For convenience of discussion, suppose we replace the first equation in (3) by the sum of it and c times the second equation, where c is some constant. Then we obtain the following system:

$$(5)\begin{cases} (a_{11} + ca_{21})x_1 + (a_{12} + ca_{22})x_2 + \cdots + (a_{1n} + ca_{2n})x_n = b_1 + cb_2, \\ a_{21}x_1 + a_{22}x_2 + \cdots + a_{2n}x_n = b_2, \\ \cdots \qquad \cdots \qquad \cdots, \\ a_{m1}x_1 + a_{m2}x_2 + \cdots + a_{mn}x_n = b_m. \end{cases}$$

We have to show that systems (3) and (5) are equivalent. First, each solution of (3) is a solution of (5). For any solution of the first two equations of (3) will satisfy the first equation of (5), and the remaining equations in (5) are identical with the corresponding equations of (3). Thus we have shown that, if an operation of type III is performed upon a system, we do not lose any solutions. But, starting with system (5), we can perform upon it the operation of type III, which consists of replacing the first equation in (5) by it plus $-c$ times the second equation. This gives us back system (3), and, from what has just been proved, we have not lost any solutions. That is, every solution of (5) is a solution of (3). Therefore, (3) and (5) are equivalent. The same argument could be given for any pair of equations in the system, not just the first and second. This completes the proof that an operation of type III performed upon a given system yields an equivalent system.

Example 15. Consider the system

$$(6)\qquad \begin{cases} x_1 - 2x_2 + x_3 + 6x_4 = 10, \\ 3x_1 - 5x_2 - x_3 + 12x_4 = 25, \\ -2x_1 + 6x_2 + 4x_3 - 7x_4 = -15. \end{cases}$$

If we first replace the second equation by the sum of the second equation and -3 times the first equation, we obtain the system

$$(7)\qquad \begin{cases} x_1 - 2x_2 + x_3 + 6x_4 = 10, \\ x_2 - 4x_3 - 6x_4 = -5, \\ -2x_1 + 6x_2 + 4x_3 - 7x_4 = -15. \end{cases}$$

If, in (7), we replace the third equation by the sum of the third equation and two times the first equation, we obtain the system

$$(8)\qquad \begin{cases} x_1 - 2x_2 + x_3 + 6x_4 = 10, \\ x_2 - 4x_3 - 6x_4 = -5, \\ 2x_2 + 6x_3 + 5x_4 = 5. \end{cases}$$

We know by the theorem just proved that (6) is equivalent to (7) and (7) is equivalent to (8). Hence (6) is equivalent to (8). This example illustrates how we can use operations of type III to eliminate an unknown from all equations of the system except one.

It is clear from Definition 10 that the system referred to there is completely determined by the matrices **A** and **b** and that, by writing down those two matrices, we should be displaying all the information necessary to deal with this system. Thus in Example 15, for instance, knowing that

$$\mathbf{A} = \begin{pmatrix} 1 & -2 & 1 & 6 \\ 3 & -5 & -1 & 12 \\ -2 & 6 & 4 & -7 \end{pmatrix}, \qquad \mathbf{b} = \begin{pmatrix} 10 \\ 25 \\ -15 \end{pmatrix}$$

completely determines the problem. It is convenient to combine these matrices into a single matrix, called the augmented matrix, defined as follows:

DEFINITION 12. Let **A** be an m by n matrix and **b**, an m-dimensional column vector. For the system $\mathbf{Ax} = \mathbf{b}$, the matrix **A** is called the *coefficient matrix* and the m by $n + 1$ matrix $(\mathbf{A}\,|\,\mathbf{b})$, whose $(n + 1)$st column consists of the elements of **b**, is called the *augmented matrix.*

Example 16. In Example 15, the coefficient matrix and augmented matrix are, respectively,

$$\mathbf{A} = \begin{pmatrix} 1 & -2 & 1 & 6 \\ 3 & -5 & -1 & 12 \\ -2 & 6 & 4 & -7 \end{pmatrix} \quad \text{and} \quad (\mathbf{A}\,|\,\mathbf{b}) = \left(\begin{array}{cccc|c} 1 & -2 & 1 & 6 & 10 \\ 3 & -5 & -1 & 12 & 25 \\ -2 & 6 & 4 & -7 & -15 \end{array}\right).$$

The vertical bar between the last two columns of the augmented matrix can be thought of as a reminder of the fact that the role played by the last column is different from the roles of the other columns.

There is an obvious correspondence between a linear system and its augmented matrix, in which the ith equation of the system corresponds to the ith row of the matrix. It follows that each of our three basic operations upon systems, described in Theorem 6, has its counterpart in an operation performed upon the augmented matrix of the system. These operations, which will be referred to as the *elementary row transformations*, are as follows:

I. Interchange two rows of the augmented matrix.

II. Replace a row of the augmented matrix with a nonzero multiple of itself, i.e., with the row which results when each number in the original row is multiplied by some nonzero number c.

III. Replace a row by the sum of it and a multiple of another row, where the sum of two rows is calculated by adding them, term by term, as in matrix addition.

Example 17. The augmented matrix for system (6) of Example 15 is

$$\left(\begin{array}{rrrr|r} 1 & -2 & 1 & 6 & 10 \\ 3 & -5 & -1 & 12 & 25 \\ -2 & 6 & 4 & -7 & -15 \end{array}\right).$$

The operations of type III upon this matrix which correspond to those performed in Example 15 are, first, replace the second row by the sum of it and -3 times the first row and, second, replace the third row by the sum of it and two times the first row. The matrix obtained as a result of performing both of these operations is, of course, the augmented matrix for system (8), namely,

$$\left(\begin{array}{rrrr|r} 1 & -2 & 1 & 6 & 10 \\ 0 & 1 & -4 & -6 & -5 \\ 0 & 2 & 6 & 5 & 5 \end{array}\right).$$

We shall now describe exactly what we mean by the "simple form" to which we referred earlier. First we make a definition introducing some new notation:

DEFINITION 13. Let m be a positive integer. For each $i = 1, 2, \ldots, m$, we define $\mathbf{e}_i^m$ to be the m-dimensional column vector whose i^{th} element is 1 and each of whose other elements is 0. These column vectors are called the *m-dimensional unit vectors.*

Example 18. The three-dimensional unit vectors are

$$\mathbf{e}_1^3 = \begin{pmatrix} 1 \\ 0 \\ 0 \end{pmatrix}, \quad \mathbf{e}_2^3 = \begin{pmatrix} 0 \\ 1 \\ 0 \end{pmatrix}, \quad \mathbf{e}_3^3 = \begin{pmatrix} 0 \\ 0 \\ 1 \end{pmatrix}.$$

A system of equations will have the simple form referred to above provided that its augmented matrix is in *canonical form* according to the following definition:

DEFINITION 14. Let $\mathbf{A}$ be an m by n matrix. We say that $\mathbf{A}$ is in *canonical form* if, and only if, either (i) each of the m-dimensional unit vectors $\mathbf{e}_i^m$ $(i = 1, \ldots, m)$ appears as a column of $\mathbf{A}$ or (ii), for each i such that $\mathbf{e}_i^m$ is not a column of $\mathbf{A}$, the ith row of $\mathbf{A}$ contains only zeros. The augmented matrix $(\mathbf{A}|\mathbf{b})$ for the system $\mathbf{Ax} = \mathbf{b}$ is said to be in canonical form if, and only if, $\mathbf{A}$ is in canonical form.

Example 19. Each of the following is an example of an augmented matrix in canonical form:

$$\left(\begin{array}{ccc|c} 1 & 0 & 0 & -2 \\ 0 & 1 & 0 & 5 \\ 0 & 0 & 1 & 4 \end{array}\right), \qquad \left(\begin{array}{ccccc|c} 0 & 2 & 0 & -2 & 1 & 1 \\ 1 & -1 & 0 & 3 & 0 & 7 \\ 0 & 4 & 1 & 8 & 0 & 10 \end{array}\right),$$

(a) (b)

$$\left(\begin{array}{cccccc|c} 0 & 4 & 1 & 1 & 0 & 0 & 8 \\ 0 & 0 & 0 & 0 & 0 & 0 & 0 \\ 1 & 5 & -2 & 0 & 4 & 0 & -21 \\ 0 & -2 & 7 & 0 & 3 & 1 & 4 \end{array}\right), \qquad \left(\begin{array}{ccccc|c} 1 & 1 & 0 & 4 & 10 & 6 \\ 0 & 0 & 1 & -3 & 2 & 5 \\ 0 & 0 & 0 & 0 & 0 & 0 \\ 0 & 0 & 0 & 0 & 0 & 3 \end{array}\right).$$

(c) (d)

The solutions (or lack of solutions) of the corresponding systems can easily be determined from these matrices. Note that (a) and (b) are the augmented matrices for the systems in Examples 13 and 14, respectively, and we have previously indicated the solutions of these systems. From matrix (c), we see that

$$\begin{aligned} x_1 &= -21 - 5x_2 + 2x_3 - 4x_5, \\ x_4 &= 8 - 4x_2 - x_3, \\ x_6 &= 4 + 2x_2 - 7x_3 - 3x_5, \end{aligned}$$

where x_2, x_3, and x_5 are arbitrary. Therefore, the set of all solutions of the corresponding system is the set of all six-dimensional column vectors $\mathbf{x}$ of the form

$$\mathbf{x} = [-21 - 5a + 2b - 4c, a, b, 8 - 4a - b, c, 4 + 2a - 7b - 3c].$$

The system corresponding to matrix (*d*) has no solutions, since the last equation in that system is

$$0x_1 + 0x_2 + 0x_3 + 0x_4 + 0x_5 = 3,$$

which itself has no solutions.

We point out here that, for a given matrix $(\mathbf{A}|\mathbf{b})$, there will, except in trivial cases, be more than one matrix in canonical form which can be obtained from $(\mathbf{A}|\mathbf{b})$ by elementary row transformations. For instance, consider matrix (d) of Example 19. If we add -5 times the second row to the first row and then multiply the second row by $\frac{1}{2}$, we obtain

$$\left(\begin{array}{cccccc|c} 1 & 1 & -5 & 19 & 0 & & -19 \\ 0 & 0 & \frac{1}{2} & -\frac{3}{2} & 1 & & \frac{5}{2} \\ 0 & 0 & 0 & 0 & 0 & & 0 \\ 0 & 0 & 0 & 0 & 0 & & 3 \end{array}\right),$$

which is different from (d), but has the canonical form.

These examples indicate that, if, given a system of linear equations, we can find an equivalent system in canonical form, we can easily determine all solutions of our system. But how do we find such an equivalent system? For a given system of equations, there are usually many different ways in which this can be done. To prove that it *can* always be done, we now outline a procedure by which, starting with the augmented matrix $(\mathbf{A}|\mathbf{b})$ for any given system of m equations in n unknowns, we can obtain in a finite number of steps the augmented matrix of an equivalent system in canonical form. This procedure, incidentally, makes use of elementary row transformations of types II and III only. The steps are as follows:

Choose a nonzero element c_1 of $(\mathbf{A}|\mathbf{b})$, not in the $(n + 1)$st column. Let c_1 be in position (i_1, j_1) (row i_1, column j_1). Multiply row i_1 of $(\mathbf{A}|\mathbf{b})$ by $1/c_1$, so that in the new row i_1 there is a 1 in position (i_1, j_1). By adding suitable multiples of (new) row i_1 to the other rows, obtain another matrix in which column j_1 is the unit vector $\mathbf{e}_{i_1}^m$. In this matrix choose a nonzero c_2 in position (i_2, j_2), where $i_2 \neq i_1$ and $j_2 \neq n + 1$. (Of course, $j_2 \neq j_1$.) Multiply row i_2 by $1/c_2$, so that, in the new row i_2, there is a 1 in position (i_2, j_2). By adding suitable multiples of (new) row i_2 to the other rows, obtain another matrix in which column j_2 is the unit vector $\mathbf{e}_{i_2}^m$. Observe that, in this matrix, column j_1 will still be $\mathbf{e}_{i_1}^m$. Continue in this fashion until a matrix is obtained in which either (i) all of the unit vectors $\mathbf{e}_i^m$ $(i = 1, \ldots, m)$ appear among the first n columns, or (ii) there are no nonzero numbers in the first n columns except those in rows $i_1, i_2, \ldots,$ corresponding to unit vectors $\mathbf{e}_{i_1}^m, \mathbf{e}_{i_2}^m, \ldots,$ appearing among the first n columns. The matrix at that stage has the canonical form. We illustrate the process with two examples:

Example 20. Suppose we wish to solve the system

$$\begin{cases} 2x_1 + x_2 - 3x_3 + x_5 + x_6 = 4, \\ x_1 - x_2 + 2x_4 - x_5 - x_6 = 0, \\ 3x_1 + 2x_2 + 2x_3 + x_4 + x_5 = 1, \\ x_2 - x_3 - x_4 + 2x_5 - 3x_6 = 2. \end{cases}$$

We first write down the augmented matrix

$$\begin{pmatrix} 2 & 1 & -3 & 0 & 1 & \textcircled{1} & | & 4 \\ 1 & -1 & 0 & 2 & -1 & -1 & | & 0 \\ 3 & 2 & 2 & 1 & 1 & 0 & | & 1 \\ 0 & 1 & -1 & -1 & 2 & -3 & | & 2 \end{pmatrix}$$

and then proceed to perform a sequence of elementary row transformations as described above. At each stage we circle the nonzero element ($c_1, c_2, \ldots$) we have chosen. These elements are referred to as the *pivot elements.* Thus the circled 1 in the matrix above indicates that our first group of operations will consist of adding multiples of the first row to the other rows so that column six becomes $\mathbf{e}_1^4 = [1, 0, 0, 0]$. We proceed:

$$\begin{pmatrix} 2 & 1 & -3 & 0 & 1 & 1 & | & 4 \\ 3 & 0 & -3 & 2 & 0 & 0 & | & 4 \\ 3 & 2 & 2 & 1 & \textcircled{1} & 0 & | & 1 \\ 6 & 4 & -10 & -1 & 5 & 0 & | & 14 \end{pmatrix} \longrightarrow \begin{pmatrix} -1 & -1 & -5 & -1 & 0 & 1 & | & 3 \\ 3 & 0 & -3 & \textcircled{2} & 0 & 0 & | & 4 \\ 3 & 2 & 2 & 1 & 1 & 0 & | & 1 \\ -9 & -6 & -20 & -6 & 0 & 0 & | & 9 \end{pmatrix} \longrightarrow$$

$$\begin{pmatrix} \frac{1}{2} & -1 & -\frac{13}{2} & 0 & 0 & 1 & | & 5 \\ \frac{3}{2} & 0 & -\frac{3}{2} & 1 & 0 & 0 & | & 2 \\ \frac{3}{2} & 2 & \frac{7}{2} & 0 & 1 & 0 & | & -1 \\ 0 & \textcircled{-6} & -29 & 0 & 0 & 0 & | & 21 \end{pmatrix} \longrightarrow \begin{pmatrix} \frac{1}{2} & 0 & -\frac{5}{3} & 0 & 0 & 1 & | & \frac{3}{2} \\ \frac{3}{2} & 0 & -\frac{3}{2} & 1 & 0 & 0 & | & 2 \\ \frac{3}{2} & 0 & -\frac{37}{6} & 0 & 1 & 0 & | & 6 \\ 0 & 1 & \frac{29}{6} & 0 & 0 & 0 & | & -\frac{7}{2} \end{pmatrix}.$$

This last matrix is in canonical form, since the four unit vectors $\mathbf{e}_i^4$ ($i = 1, 2, 3, 4$) are among its first six columns. From it we see that

$$\begin{aligned} x_2 &= -\tfrac{7}{2} - \tfrac{29}{6}x_3, \\ x_4 &= 2 - \tfrac{3}{2}x_1 + \tfrac{3}{2}x_3, \\ x_5 &= 6 - \tfrac{3}{2}x_1 + \tfrac{37}{6}x_3, \\ x_6 &= \tfrac{3}{2} - \tfrac{1}{2}x_1 + \tfrac{5}{3}x_3 \end{aligned}$$

and hence that the set of all solutions of our original system is the set of all six-dimensional column vectors $\mathbf{x}$ of the form

$$\mathbf{x} = [a, -\tfrac{7}{2} - \tfrac{29}{6}b, b, 2 - \tfrac{3}{2}a + \tfrac{3}{2}b, 6 - \tfrac{3}{2}a + \tfrac{37}{6}b, \tfrac{3}{2} - \tfrac{1}{2}a + \tfrac{5}{3}b].$$

Example 21. Here we wish to solve the system

$$\begin{cases} 7x_1 + 21x_2 + 30x_3 + 6x_4 + 15x_5 = 44, \\ x_2 - 3x_3 - 3x_4 - 7x_5 = -13, \\ 3x_1 + 8x_2 + 12x_3 + 3x_4 + 7x_5 = 19, \\ x_1 + 6x_2 + 12x_3 + 3x_4 + 9x_5 = 23. \end{cases}$$

We write down the augmented matrix and proceed as before:

$$\left(\begin{array}{ccccc|c} 7 & 21 & 30 & 6 & 15 & 44 \\ 0 & 1 & -3 & -3 & -7 & -13 \\ 3 & 8 & 12 & \textcircled{3} & 7 & 19 \\ 1 & 6 & 12 & 3 & 9 & 23 \end{array}\right) \longrightarrow \left(\begin{array}{ccccc|c} 1 & 5 & 6 & 0 & 1 & 6 \\ \textcircled{3} & 9 & 9 & 0 & 0 & 6 \\ 1 & \frac{8}{3} & 4 & 1 & \frac{7}{3} & \frac{19}{3} \\ -2 & -2 & 0 & 0 & 2 & 4 \end{array}\right) \longrightarrow$$

$$\left(\begin{array}{ccccc|c} 0 & 2 & \textcircled{3} & 0 & 1 & 4 \\ 1 & 3 & 3 & 0 & 0 & 2 \\ 0 & -\frac{1}{3} & 1 & 1 & \frac{7}{3} & \frac{13}{3} \\ 0 & 4 & 6 & 0 & 2 & 8 \end{array}\right) \longrightarrow \left(\begin{array}{ccccc|c} 0 & \frac{2}{3} & 1 & 0 & \frac{1}{3} & \frac{4}{3} \\ 1 & 1 & 0 & 0 & -1 & -2 \\ 0 & -1 & 0 & 1 & 2 & 3 \\ 0 & 0 & 0 & 0 & 0 & 0 \end{array}\right).$$

This last matrix is in canonical form since the only missing unit vector is $\mathbf{e}_4^4 = [0, 0, 0, 1]$ and the fourth row of the coefficient part of the matrix contains only zeros. The system has solutions because there is also a zero in the (4, 6) position. We leave it to the student to describe explicitly (as in Example 20) the set of all solutions of the system.

We now summarize the relation between the nature of the set of all solutions of a system and the appearance of the final augmented matrix in canonical form found by a process such as that described above. Assume the original system involves m equations in n unknowns.

Case 1. Each of the unit vectors $\mathbf{e}_i^m$ $(i = 1, \ldots, m)$ appears among the first n columns of the final augmented matrix. (Hence, $m \leqq n$.)

(a) If $m = n$, the system has a unique solution.

(b) If $m < n$, the system has an infinite collection of solutions. If columns $j_1, j_2, \ldots, j_m$ are the unit vectors $\mathbf{e}_1^m, \mathbf{e}_2^m, \ldots, \mathbf{e}_m^m$, in some order, then we can solve our equations for $x_{j_1}, x_{j_2}, \ldots, x_{j_m}$ in terms of the remaining $n - m$ unknowns, which can therefore be thought of as arbitrary.

Case 2. At least one of the m unit vectors does not appear among the first n columns of the final augmented matrix, but, for each i such that $\mathbf{e}_i^m$ is missing, row i of the coefficient part of the matrix contains only zeros.

(a) If, for some i, each element in row i is zero except the element in column $n + 1$, which is nonzero, the system has no solutions.

(b) If (a) does not occur and *each* column is a different unit vector, there is a unique solution. (This could happen only if $n < m$.)

(c) If (a) does not occur and the number k of different unit vectors appearing is less than n, there will be infinitely many solutions. Any $n - k$ unknowns not corresponding to some chosen set of k columns containing k different unit vectors can be thought of as arbitrary.

Each of the assertions in this summary is evident when one imagines the equations corresponding to the canonical matrix written out. The student should do this for each case.

As the final topic in this section, let us discuss the application of the foregoing methods to the solution of the matrix equation

$$\text{(9)} \qquad \mathbf{AX} = \mathbf{B}.$$

In this equation, **A** and **B** are given matrices and **X** is unknown. Suppose $\mathbf{A} = (a_{ij})$ is m by n. Then **B** must also have m rows if there are to be any solutions. Hence, assume $\mathbf{B} = (b_{ij})$ is m by p. Then the dimensions of the unknown matrix $\mathbf{X} = (x_{ij})$ must be n by p. Equation (9) is equivalent, by the definition of matrix multiplication, to the system

$$\text{(10)} \qquad \sum_{k=1}^{n} a_{ik}x_{kj} = b_{ij} \qquad (i = 1, \ldots, m;\ j = 1, \ldots, p)$$

of mp equations in np unknowns. Thus, we could write down the augmented matrix for (10) and proceed in the usual way to reduce it to canonical form. However, there is a simpler and less cumbersome way of looking at the situation. Let the columns of **X** be denoted by $\mathbf{x}^{(1)}, \mathbf{x}^{(2)}, \ldots, \mathbf{x}^{(p)}$ and those of **B**, by $\mathbf{b}^{(1)}, \mathbf{b}^{(2)}, \ldots, \mathbf{b}^{(p)}$. Then Eq. (9) holds if, and only if, $\mathbf{Ax}^{(j)} = \mathbf{b}^{(j)}$ for each $j = 1, \ldots, p$. This is a direct consequence of the definition of matrix multiplication, for $\mathbf{x}^{(j)} = [x_{1j}, x_{2j}, \ldots, x_{nj}]$, and so the element in the ith row of $\mathbf{Ax}^{(j)}$ is $\sum_{k=1}^{n} a_{ik}x_{kj}$. Hence, $\mathbf{Ax}^{(j)} = \mathbf{b}^{(j)}$ holds for each $j = 1, \ldots, p$ if, and only if, (10) holds and this, in turn, is equivalent to (9). Thus (9) may be solved by solving each of the p systems $\mathbf{Ax}^{(j)} = \mathbf{b}^{(j)}$ $(j = 1, \ldots, p)$ of m equations in n unknowns. Since each of these systems has the same coefficient matrix **A**, we do not have to write down separately the augmented matrices $(\mathbf{A}\,|\,\mathbf{b}^{(1)}), (\mathbf{A}\,|\,\mathbf{b}^{(2)}), \ldots, (\mathbf{A}\,|\,\mathbf{b}^{(p)})$. Instead, we may simply write down the m by $(n + p)$ matrix $(\mathbf{A}\,|\,\mathbf{B})$, in which **A** and **B** are written side by side, and perform on it a sequence of elementary row transformations so as to reduce **A** to canonical form. Then, by considering individually each of the columns in the right-hand portion of the transformed matrix in conjunction with the left-hand portion, we may obtain the solutions of each of the systems $\mathbf{Ax}^{(j)} = \mathbf{b}^{(j)}$ and, hence, of (9). Of course, if any one of the systems $\mathbf{Ax}^{(j)} = \mathbf{b}^{(j)}$ has no solutions, then (9) has no solutions. We illustrate the procedure with the following example:

Example 22. Consider the matrix equation

$$\begin{pmatrix} 2 & 1 & 5 & -1 \\ -1 & 3 & 4 & 0 \\ 1 & 0 & 2 & 6 \end{pmatrix} \begin{pmatrix} x_{11} & x_{12} \\ x_{21} & x_{22} \\ x_{31} & x_{32} \\ x_{41} & x_{42} \end{pmatrix} = \begin{pmatrix} 8 & 7 \\ -6 & 1 \\ 4 & -10 \end{pmatrix}.$$

We solve it by following the procedure outlined above, circling the pivot element at each stage as usual:

$$(\mathbf{A}|\mathbf{B}) = \left(\begin{array}{rrrr|rr} 2 & \textcircled{1} & 5 & -1 & 8 & 7 \\ -1 & 3 & 4 & 0 & -6 & 1 \\ 1 & 0 & 2 & 6 & 4 & -10 \end{array}\right) \longrightarrow \left(\begin{array}{rrrr|rr} 2 & 1 & 5 & -1 & 8 & 7 \\ -7 & 0 & -11 & 3 & -30 & -20 \\ \textcircled{1} & 0 & 2 & 6 & 4 & -10 \end{array}\right) \longrightarrow$$

$$\left(\begin{array}{rrrr|rr} 0 & 1 & 1 & -13 & 0 & 27 \\ 0 & 0 & \textcircled{3} & 45 & -2 & -90 \\ 1 & 0 & 2 & 6 & 4 & -10 \end{array}\right) \longrightarrow \left(\begin{array}{rrrr|rr} 0 & 1 & 0 & -28 & \frac{2}{3} & 57 \\ 0 & 0 & 1 & 15 & -\frac{2}{3} & -30 \\ 1 & 0 & 0 & -24 & \frac{16}{3} & 50 \end{array}\right).$$

From the last matrix we see, ignoring column six, that

$$x_{11} = \tfrac{16}{3} + 24x_{41}$$
$$x_{21} = \tfrac{2}{3} + 28x_{41}$$
$$x_{31} = -\tfrac{2}{3} - 15x_{41}$$

and, ignoring column five, that

$$x_{12} = \quad 50 + 24x_{42}$$
$$x_{22} = \quad 57 + 28x_{42}$$
$$x_{32} = -30 - 15x_{42}.$$

Hence, a matrix **X** satisfies the given equation if, and only if, **X** has the form

$$\mathbf{X} = \begin{pmatrix} \frac{16}{3} + 24c & 50 + 24d \\ \frac{2}{3} + 28c & 57 + 28d \\ -\frac{2}{3} - 15c & -30 - 15d \end{pmatrix},$$

where c and d can be any numbers.

EXERCISES

1. For each of the following systems, find *all* solutions or else prove there are none, using the method explained in this section. For each system which has infinitely many solutions, describe the set of all solutions in a manner similar to that in Examples 14 and 20.

(a) $$\begin{cases} x_1 + 3x_2 + 7x_3 = 42, \\ x_1 + 4x_2 + 9x_3 = 55, \\ 2x_1 + 4x_2 + 11x_3 = 63. \end{cases}$$

(b) $$\begin{cases} 5x_1 + x_2 + 13x_3 = -5, \\ 6x_1 + x_2 + 13x_3 = -1, \\ 13x_1 + 2x_2 + 33x_3 = -12, \\ 16x_1 + 3x_2 + 42x_3 = -16. \end{cases}$$

(c) $$\begin{cases} 2x_1 + x_2 + x_3 - x_4 + 4x_5 = 14, \\ 7x_1 + 4x_2 + 3x_3 - 5x_4 + 12x_5 = 50, \\ x_1 - 2x_2 + 2x_3 + 4x_4 + 8x_5 = 0. \end{cases}$$

(d)
$$\begin{cases} 5x_1 - 6x_2 - 6x_3 + 3x_4 - 5x_5 - 3x_6 = 3, \\ 22x_1 - 24x_2 - 28x_3 + 15x_4 - 23x_5 - 17x_6 = 3, \\ -6x_1 + x_2 + 12x_3 - 9x_4 + 9x_5 + 14x_6 = 23, \\ 7x_1 - 15x_2 - 2x_3 - 3x_4 - 3x_5 + 9x_6 = 37. \end{cases}$$

(e)
$$\begin{cases} x_1 - x_2 + 3x_3 = 5, \\ 2x_1 - 2x_2 + 7x_3 = 12, \\ x_1 - x_2 + 4x_3 = 7, \\ x_1 - x_2 + x_3 = 1. \end{cases}$$

(f)
$$\begin{cases} x_1 + x_2 + x_3 + x_4 + x_5 = 0, \\ 4x_1 + 3x_2 + 4x_3 + 8x_4 + 5x_5 = 0, \\ 3x_1 + 3x_3 + 15x_4 + 6x_5 = 1. \end{cases}$$

(g)
$$\begin{cases} 2x_1 + x_2 = 0, \\ 9x_1 + 4x_2 - x_3 = 0, \\ 5x_1 + x_2 - 3x_3 = 0. \end{cases}$$

2. A system of linear equations is called *homogeneous* if every constant term is 0. An example is the system of Exercise 1(g). Explain why (a) every homogeneous system has at least one solution and (b) every homogeneous system with fewer equations than unknowns has infinitely many solutions.

3(a) Prove that, corresponding to each vector $\mathbf{x} = [x_1, x_2]$ whose components satisfy the conditions

(i)
$$\begin{cases} x_1 - 2x_2 \geqq -4, \\ 2x_1 + 3x_2 \leqq 13, \\ x_1 - x_2 \leqq 4, \\ x_1 \geqq 0, \quad x_2 \geqq 0, \end{cases}$$

(cf. Example 1, Chapter 1), there is a vector $\mathbf{x}' = [x_1, x_2, x_3, x_4, x_5]$ whose first two components are those of $\mathbf{x}$ and which satisfies the conditions

(ii)
$$\begin{cases} x_1 - 2x_2 - x_3 = -4, \\ 2x_1 + 3x_2 + x_4 = 13, \\ x_1 - x_2 + x_5 = 4, \\ x_j \geqq 0 \quad (j = 1, 2, 3, 4, 5), \end{cases}$$

and that, conversely, if $\mathbf{x}' = [x_1, x_2, x_3, x_4, x_5]$ is any solution of (ii), then its first two components determine a vector $\mathbf{x} = [x_1, x_2]$ satisfying (i).

(b) Solve the system of three equations in five unknowns appearing in (ii) in such a way that x_4 and x_5 are the arbitrary unknowns.

(c) Use the result of (b) to express $f(x_1, x_2) = -4x_1 + 3x_2$ in terms of x_4 and x_5. Call the result $g(x_4, x_5)$.

(d) Let S be the set of all numbers $f(x_1, x_2)$, where x_1 and x_2 are restricted by (i). Example 1, Chapter 1, was the problem of finding the smallest number in S. Let T be the set of all numbers $g(x_4, x_5)$, where $x_4 \geqq 0$ and $x_5 \geqq 0$. Prove that every number in S is also in T. Is the converse true?

(e) Simply by looking at the expression $g(x_4, x_5)$, determine the smallest number in T [i.e., the minimum value of $g(x_4, x_5)$ subject to $x_4 \geqq 0, x_5 \geqq 0$]. Explain why this number is the minimum value of $f(x_1, x_2)$ subject to (i).

Note: The method outlined in this exercise is not recommended as a general algebraic procedure, since one cannot predict in advance which unknowns should be chosen as arbitrary. To see what sort of difficulties may arise, solve the equations in (ii) so that x_3 and x_4 are arbitrary, and then try to proceed as before.

4. For each of the following pairs of matrices **A** and **B**, find all matrices **X** which satisfy the equation **AX** = **B** or show that there are none:

(a) $$\mathbf{A} = \begin{pmatrix} 2 & -1 & 4 \\ -3 & 2 & 0 \end{pmatrix}, \qquad \mathbf{B} = \begin{pmatrix} 3 & -5 \\ 2 & 4 \end{pmatrix}$$

(b) $$\mathbf{A} = \begin{pmatrix} 1 & -2 & 3 \\ 1 & -1 & 2 \\ 3 & -4 & 7 \end{pmatrix}, \qquad \mathbf{B} = \begin{pmatrix} -2 & 0 & 5 \\ 2 & 1 & 2 \\ 2 & 3 & 9 \end{pmatrix}$$

(c) $$\mathbf{A} = \begin{pmatrix} 1 & 3 & -1 \\ 1 & 2 & -2 \\ 1 & 5 & 2 \end{pmatrix}, \qquad \mathbf{B} = \begin{pmatrix} 0 & 3 & 1 \\ 0 & 4 & -1 \\ 2 & 2 & 6 \end{pmatrix}$$

(d) $$\mathbf{A} = \begin{pmatrix} 2 & 3 \\ -1 & 2 \end{pmatrix}, \qquad \mathbf{B} = \begin{pmatrix} 1 & 0 \\ 0 & 1 \end{pmatrix}$$

5. Let **A** be an n by n matrix, and let $\mathbf{I}_n$ be the n by n identity matrix (see Exercise 6, Section 2–1). An n by n matrix **B** is said to be a *right inverse* of **A** provided $\mathbf{AB} = \mathbf{I}_n$. Similarly, a *left inverse* of **A** is defined as an n by n matrix **C** such that $\mathbf{CA} = \mathbf{I}_n$. For each of the following matrices, find a right inverse or else prove that none exists. Also, show that each right inverse found is a left inverse.

(a) $$\begin{pmatrix} 1 & 3 & -1 \\ 1 & 2 & -2 \\ 1 & 5 & 2 \end{pmatrix}$$

(b) $$\begin{pmatrix} 0 & 1 & 1 \\ 1 & 1 & 0 \\ 1 & 0 & 1 \end{pmatrix}$$

(c) $$\begin{pmatrix} 1 & -2 & 3 \\ 1 & -1 & 2 \\ 3 & -4 & 7 \end{pmatrix}$$

(d) $$\begin{pmatrix} 2 & 0 & 0 & 0 \\ 0 & 3 & 0 & 0 \\ 0 & 0 & -4 & 0 \\ 0 & 0 & 0 & 5 \end{pmatrix}$$

6. Although we shall not do so, it can be proved that, if a square matrix **A** has a right inverse **B**, then **B** is also a left inverse of **A**. Taking this for granted, prove each of the following statements:

(a) If a square matrix **A** has a left inverse **B**, then **B** is also a right inverse of **A**.

(b) If $\mathbf{B}_1$ and $\mathbf{B}_2$ are right inverses of a square matrix **A**, then $\mathbf{B}_1 = \mathbf{B}_2$.

Note: A consequence of the results of this exercise is that, for a given square matrix **A**, either (i) **A** has neither a right nor a left inverse or (ii) there is exactly one matrix which is both a right and a left inverse of **A**. In case (ii), we refer to the uniquely determined right and left inverse simply as the *inverse* of **A** and denote it by $\mathbf{A}^{-1}$. A matrix for which (i) holds is called *singular;* one for which (ii) holds is called *nonsingular.*

7. Suppose $\mathbf{A}$ and $\mathbf{B}$ are *nonsingular* (see Note following Exercise 6) n by n matrices. Determine which one of the following statements is true, and prove it:
(a) The product $\mathbf{AB}$ may either be singular or nonsingular.
(b) The product $\mathbf{AB}$ is nonsingular, and we have $(\mathbf{AB})^{-1} = \mathbf{A}^{-1}\mathbf{B}^{-1}$.
(c) The product $\mathbf{AB}$ is nonsingular, and we have $(\mathbf{AB})^{-1} = \mathbf{B}^{-1}\mathbf{A}^{-1}$.

8(a) Suppose $\mathbf{A}$ is a nonsingular n by n matrix and $\mathbf{B}$ is any n by p matrix. Prove that the matrix equation $\mathbf{AX} = \mathbf{B}$ has a unique solution, and express this solution $\mathbf{X}$ in terms of $\mathbf{B}$ and $\mathbf{A}^{-1}$.
(b) Do Exercise 4(c) by first finding $\mathbf{A}^{-1}$ and then computing $\mathbf{X}$ by the formula of part (a).

9. Prove that, if the product of two square matrices is the zero matrix, then either (i) at least one of the matrices equals the zero matrix or (ii) each matrix is singular.

10. Let us say that a system of linear equations $\mathbf{Ax} = \mathbf{b}$ is in class N if it has no solutions, U if it has a unique solution, and I if it has infinitely many solutions. We know that each system falls into exactly one of these classes. Suppose we take a given system $\mathbf{Ax} = \mathbf{b}$ and replace $\mathbf{b}$ by a different column vector, say, $\mathbf{b}'$. Then the new system $\mathbf{Ax} = \mathbf{b}'$ will possibly belong to a class different from that of the original system. Determine which of the following class changes are possible and which are impossible (the symbol to the left of the arrow indicates the class of the original system):

$$N \longrightarrow U \qquad U \longrightarrow N \qquad I \longrightarrow N$$
$$N \longrightarrow I \qquad U \longrightarrow I \qquad I \longrightarrow U$$

2–3. *VECTORS.*

In Section 2–1 we defined a column vector as a matrix with only one column. Similarly, we define a row vector as a matrix having just one row. In solving physical problems dealing with forces, velocities, accelerations, and so on, we frequently deal with vectors which we represent by "arrows," or directed line segments. Thus, the term *vector* appears to be used in several different ways. These apparently diverse concepts, however, are unified in the mathematical structure known as a *vector space.*

Vectors (mostly column vectors) play a fundamental role in the treatment of the general linear programming problem in the next chapter and, because of this, we need to know some of their basic properties. These properties will be developed in subsequent sections. In the present section we attempt only to answer the question, "What is a vector?" The answer to this question is similar to the answer to the question, "What is a baseball player?" A baseball player is a member of a team which plays the game of baseball, this game being defined by its rather extensive list of rules. Similarly, a vector is a member of a set, known as a vector space, in which are defined certain operations which are subject to rules contained in a list of *axioms* or *postulates*. We now state in precise form the definition of a vector space. This will be followed by examples of particular vector spaces.

DEFINITION 15. A set $\mathscr{V}$ of objects is referred to as a *vector space*, and the members of $\mathscr{V}$ are referred to as *vectors* if, and only if, the following conditions are all satisfied:

V_1. There is defined in $\mathscr{V}$ an operation, called *vector addition* and denoted here by the ordinary addition symbol $+$, such that, if $\mathbf{x}$ and $\mathbf{y}$ are members of $\mathscr{V}$, then $\mathbf{x} + \mathbf{y}$ is a member of $\mathscr{V}$.

V_2. Vector addition has the following properties: (i) $\mathbf{x} + \mathbf{y} = \mathbf{y} + \mathbf{x}$ for each $\mathbf{x}$ and $\mathbf{y}$ in $\mathscr{V}$ (commutative law), and (ii) $(\mathbf{x} + \mathbf{y}) + \mathbf{z} = \mathbf{x} + (\mathbf{y} + \mathbf{z})$ for each $\mathbf{x}$, $\mathbf{y}$, and $\mathbf{z}$ in $\mathscr{V}$ (associative law).

V_3. There is a special member $\mathbf{0}$ of $\mathscr{V}$, called the *zero vector*, with the property that $\mathbf{x} + \mathbf{0} = \mathbf{x}$ for each $\mathbf{x}$ in $\mathscr{V}$.

V_4. With each member $\mathbf{x}$ of $\mathscr{V}$, there is associated a member of $\mathscr{V}$ called the *negative of* $\mathbf{x}$, denoted by $-\mathbf{x}$, with the property that $\mathbf{x} + (-\mathbf{x}) = \mathbf{0}$.

V_5. An operation known as *scalar multiplication* is defined, which associates with each real number α and each member $\mathbf{x}$ of $\mathscr{V}$ a unique member of $\mathscr{V}$ denoted by either $\alpha\mathbf{x}$ or $\mathbf{x}\alpha$.

V_6. Scalar multiplication has the following properties (α and β are real numbers; $\mathbf{x}$ and $\mathbf{y}$ are members of $\mathscr{V}$): (i) $(\alpha + \beta)\mathbf{x} = \alpha\mathbf{x} + \beta\mathbf{x}$, (ii) $\alpha(\mathbf{x} + \mathbf{y}) = \alpha\mathbf{x} + \alpha\mathbf{y}$, (iii) $(\alpha\beta)\mathbf{x} = \alpha(\beta\mathbf{x})$, (iv) $1\mathbf{x} = \mathbf{x}$, (v) $(-1)\mathbf{x} = -\mathbf{x}$, and (vi) $0\mathbf{x} = \mathbf{0}$.

Thus, there are three essential ingredients involved in the concept of a vector space: a set $\mathscr{V}$, a rule for adding together members of $\mathscr{V}$, and a rule for multiplying members of $\mathscr{V}$ by real numbers. If, in any particular situation, we have these three ingredients and if the conditions V_1 through V_6 are satisfied, then we have a vector space. We emphasize that the nature of the objects in $\mathscr{V}$ is not specified and is irrelevant. Whether or not a given set $\mathscr{V}$ forms a vector space or not depends entirely upon how the operations of vector addition and scalar multiplication are defined in $\mathscr{V}$.

Example 23. Let m and n be fixed positive integers, and let $\mathscr{V}$ be the set of all m by n matrices. We take Definition 3 as the rule for adding members of $\mathscr{V}$ (vector addition) and Definition 8 as the rule for multiplying members of $\mathscr{V}$ by real numbers (scalar multiplication). Having specified our three ingredients, we now have to check the requirements V_1 through V_6. V_1 is a consequence of Definition 3; V_2 follows from Theorems 1 and 2; the zero vector is the matrix $\mathbf{0}_{mn}$ given by Definition 4, and it has the property required in V_3 by Theorem 3; the negative of a matrix was defined in Definition 5, and this satisfies V_4; V_5 follows from Definition 8; and V_6 is a consequence of the first six parts of Theorem 5. Hence, the set of all m by n matrices, with the usual definitions of matrix addition and scalar multiplication, forms a vector space. Thus, it is correct, though not customary, to refer to any matrix as a vector. In particular, if $n = 1$, our set $\mathscr{V}$ is the set of all m by 1 matrices, to which we have already given the name *column vectors*. Since we now know that $\mathscr{V}$ is a vector space, our earlier terminology is justified. We shall denote this vector space by a special symbol, as follows:

DEFINITION 16. The vector space consisting of all m by 1 matrices, with the usual rules of matrix addition and scalar multiplication, is denoted by $\mathscr{V}_m$.

The members of $\mathscr{V}_1$ are 1 by 1 matrices, so that $\mathscr{V}_1$ is essentially the same as the set of all real numbers. Thus, the real numbers, with the usual operations of addition and multiplication, form a vector space.

Example 24. Let O be a fixed point in three-dimensional space. Let $\mathscr{V}$ be the set of all directed line segments $\overrightarrow{OA}$ whose initial point is O, and let $\mathscr{V}$ also include the point O itself. For convenience, we regard each single point Q as a directed line segment $\overrightarrow{QQ}$ of zero length which has the same direction as each line segment. The rule for determining the sum $\overrightarrow{OA} + \overrightarrow{OB}$ of two given members of $\mathscr{V}$ is as follows: Let $\overrightarrow{AB'}$ be a directed line segment with initial point A which has the same direction and length as $\overrightarrow{OB}$. Then we define $\overrightarrow{OA} + \overrightarrow{OB} = \overrightarrow{OB'}$. The rule for determining $\alpha\overrightarrow{OA}$, where α is a real number and $\overrightarrow{OA}$ is any member of $\mathscr{V}$, is as follows: If $\alpha \geqq 0$, then $\alpha\overrightarrow{OA} = \overrightarrow{OA'}$, where the direction of $\overrightarrow{OA'}$ is the same as that of $\overrightarrow{OA}$ and the length of $\overrightarrow{OA'}$ is α times the length of $\overrightarrow{OA}$; if $\alpha < 0$, then $\alpha\overrightarrow{OA} = \overrightarrow{OA''}$, where the direction of $\overrightarrow{OA''}$ is opposite to that of $\overrightarrow{OA}$ and the length of $\overrightarrow{OA''}$ is $|\alpha|$ times the length of $\overrightarrow{OA}$. Instead of verifying each of the requirements $V_1, \ldots, V_6$ directly, we establish a correspondence between this set $\mathscr{V}$, with its geometrically defined operations, and the vector space $\mathscr{V}_3$, with its algebraically defined operations. Let a cartesian coordinate system be chosen in three-dimensional space with origin at the fixed point O. Then, corresponding to each member $\overrightarrow{OA}$ of $\mathscr{V}$, we have the column vector $\mathbf{a} = [a_1, a_2, a_3]$ whose components are the coordinates of A relative to the chosen coordinate system. Now suppose $\overrightarrow{OA}$ and $\overrightarrow{OB}$ are members of $\mathscr{V}$, and let $\mathbf{a} = [a_2, a_2, a_3]$ and $\mathbf{b} = [b_1, b_2, b_3]$ be the corresponding members of $\mathscr{V}_3$. Let $\mathbf{b}' = [a_1 + b_1, a_2 + b_2, a_3 + b_3] = \mathbf{a} + \mathbf{b}$, and let B' be the point whose coordinates are the components of $\mathbf{b}'$. Then, by analytic geometry, $\overrightarrow{OB}$ and $\overrightarrow{AB'}$ have the same direction and length, so that $\overrightarrow{OA} + \overrightarrow{OB} = \overrightarrow{OB'}$ by our definition of addition in $\mathscr{V}$. But $\overrightarrow{OB'}$ corresponds to $\mathbf{b}' = \mathbf{a} + \mathbf{b}$. Thus, if $\overrightarrow{OA}$ corresponds to $\mathbf{a}$ and $\overrightarrow{OB}$ corresponds to $\mathbf{b}$, then $\overrightarrow{OA} + \overrightarrow{OB}$ corresponds to $\mathbf{a} + \mathbf{b}$. A similar situation exists with respect to scalar multiplication. Let

α be any real number; $\overrightarrow{OA}$, any member of $\mathscr{V}$; and $\mathbf{a} = [a_1, a_2, a_3]$, the column vector corresponding to $\overrightarrow{OA}$. Let $\mathbf{a}' = [\alpha a_1, \alpha a_2, \alpha a_3]$, and let A' be the point whose coordinates are the components of $\mathbf{a}'$. Then, using analytic geometry, we see that the direction of $\overrightarrow{OA'}$ is the same as that of $\overrightarrow{OA}$ if $\alpha \geqq 0$ and opposite to that of $\overrightarrow{OA}$ if $\alpha < 0$ and the length of $\overrightarrow{OA'}$ is $|\alpha|$ times the length of $\overrightarrow{OA}$ in each case. Hence, by our definition of scalar multiplication in $\mathscr{V}$, $\alpha\overrightarrow{OA} = \overrightarrow{OA'}$. Thus, if $\overrightarrow{OA}$ corresponds to $\mathbf{a}$ and α is any number, then $\alpha\overrightarrow{OA}$ corresponds to $\alpha\mathbf{a}$.

We have described here a rule which establishes a one-to-one correspondence between the members of $\mathscr{V}$ and those of $\mathscr{V}_3$ such that the operations of vector addition and scalar multiplication in the two sets are "preserved," as indicated in the following diagram:

$$\begin{array}{rcl} \mathscr{V} & & \mathscr{V}_3 \\ \overrightarrow{OA} & \longleftrightarrow & \mathbf{a} \\ \overrightarrow{OB} & \longleftrightarrow & \mathbf{b} \\ \overrightarrow{OA} + \overrightarrow{OB} & \longleftrightarrow & \mathbf{a} + \mathbf{b} \\ \alpha\overrightarrow{OA} & \longleftrightarrow & \alpha\mathbf{a} \end{array}$$

If the student will think it through, he will see that, as a consequence of this correspondence, the fact that $\mathscr{V}_3$ with its operations satisfies $V_1, \ldots, V_6$ implies that $\mathscr{V}$ with its operations also satisfies $V_1, \ldots, V_6$ and hence is a vector space.

Our final example is quite different in nature from the preceding two:

Example 25. Let S be some set of real numbers, and let $\mathscr{F}$ be the collection of all real-valued functions defined on S. If f and g are members of $\mathscr{F}$, we define $f + g$ to be the function h defined on S by the rule $h(x) = f(x) + g(x)$. If α is a real number and f is a member of $\mathscr{F}$, we define αf to be the function k defined on S by the rule $k(x) = \alpha f(x)$. The zero vector in $\mathscr{F}$ is the function ϕ such that $\phi(x) = 0$ for each x in S. The negative $-f$ of a member f of $\mathscr{F}$ is the function g defined by $g(x) = -f(x)$ for each x in S. That the requirements $V_1, \ldots, V_6$ are satisfied now follows easily by use of the corresponding properties of real numbers. We leave it to the student to supply the details himself.

These examples, together with others appearing in the exercises, should make clear the generality of the term *vector*. We have seen that such diverse mathematical objects as matrices, directed line segments, and real-valued functions of a real variable may be classed as vectors. The main point to keep in mind is that we cannot decide whether a given set forms a vector space until we know how the two rules of operation, vector addition and scalar multiplication, are defined in that set. Knowing this, we then have to check the requirements $V_1, \ldots, V_6$.

EXERCISES

In each of the following, a set $\mathscr{V}$ is specified and rules for vector addition and scalar multiplication are given. In each case, you are to determine whether the given set, with the operations defined, forms a vector space. In case it does not, determine which of the conditions $V_1, \ldots, V_6$ of Definition 15 are not satisfied.

1. $\mathscr{V}$ is the set of all complex numbers, $a + bi$; vector addition is ordinary addition of complex numbers and scalar multiplication is ordinary multiplication.
2. $\mathscr{V}$ is the set of all integers; vector addition is ordinary addition, and scalar multiplication is ordinary multiplication.
3. $\mathscr{V}$ consists of the integer 0 only; vector addition is ordinary addition, and scalar multiplication is ordinary multiplication.
4. $\mathscr{V}$ consists of all scalar multiples of a fixed vector $\mathbf{a} = [a_1, a_2, a_3]$ in $\mathscr{V}_3$; vector addition and scalar multiplication are defined as in $\mathscr{V}_3$.
5. $\mathscr{V}$ is the set of all 2 by 2 matrices of the form

$$\begin{pmatrix} a & b \\ c & 0 \end{pmatrix};$$

the operations are the ordinary operations of matrix algebra.

6. $\mathscr{V}$ consists of all vectors of the form $c_1\mathbf{u}_1 + c_2\mathbf{u}_2$, where $\mathbf{u}_1$ and $\mathbf{u}_2$ are fixed vectors in some vector space $\mathscr{U}$ and c_1 and c_2 are real numbers; vector addition and scalar multiplication are defined as in $\mathscr{U}$.
7. $\mathscr{V}$ is any subset of a vector space $\mathscr{U}$ with the properties that, if $\mathbf{u}_1$ and $\mathbf{u}_2$ belong to $\mathscr{V}$, then so also does $\mathbf{u}_1 + \mathbf{u}_2$ and, for each $\mathbf{u}$ in $\mathscr{V}$ and each scalar α, $\alpha\mathbf{u}$ also is in $\mathscr{V}$, the operations being defined as in $\mathscr{U}$.
8. $\mathscr{V}$ is the collection of all real-valued functions f such that (i) f is defined and twice differentiable at each point of some fixed interval I and (ii) $f''(x) - f(x) = 0$ for each x in I; vector addition and scalar multiplication are defined as in Example 25.
9. $\mathscr{V}$ is the set of all column vectors $\mathbf{x} = [x_1, \ldots, x_n]$ which satisfy the system $\mathbf{Ax} = \mathbf{b}$, where $\mathbf{A}$ is a given m by n matrix and (a) $\mathbf{b} = \mathbf{0}$, (b) $\mathbf{b} \neq \mathbf{0}$.

2–4. *LINEAR COMBINATIONS; LINEAR INDEPENDENCE AND DEPENDENCE.*

In this and the following two sections we explain some of the basic terminology of vector spaces and develop some fundamental properties which we shall need in the next chapter. Most, though not all, of our examples will be drawn from the vector spaces $\mathscr{V}_m$ $(m = 1, 2, 3, \ldots)$, for it is with column vectors that we shall be mainly concerned in the next chapter.

One of the terms which we use most frequently is *linear combination of vectors.* This is defined as follows:

DEFINITION 17. If $\mathbf{v}_1, \mathbf{v}_2, \ldots, \mathbf{v}_n$ are vectors in a vector space $\mathscr{V}$ and $c_1, c_2, \ldots, c_n$ are numbers, then $c_1\mathbf{v}_1 + c_2\mathbf{v}_2 + \cdots + c_n\mathbf{v}_n$ is called a *linear combination* of $\mathbf{v}_1, \mathbf{v}_2, \ldots, \mathbf{v}_n$.

Note that, by parts V_1 and V_5 of Definition 15, $c_1\mathbf{v}_1 + c_2\mathbf{v}_2 + \cdots + c_n\mathbf{v}_n$ belongs to $\mathscr{V}$. In case $n = 1$, we usually say *scalar multiple* rather than *linear combination.*

Example 26. In $\mathscr{V}_4$ let $\mathbf{v}_1 = [-1, 0, 2, 3]$, $\mathbf{v}_2 = [1, 1, 0, 1]$, $\mathbf{v}_3 = [3, 2, 5, 1]$, and $\mathbf{v}_4 = [7, 6, 26, 11]$. Then $\mathbf{v}_4$ is a linear combination of $\mathbf{v}_1$, $\mathbf{v}_2$, and $\mathbf{v}_3$, since

$$3\mathbf{v}_1 - 2\mathbf{v}_2 + 4\mathbf{v}_3 = 3\begin{pmatrix}-1\\0\\2\\3\end{pmatrix} - 2\begin{pmatrix}1\\1\\0\\1\end{pmatrix} + 4\begin{pmatrix}3\\2\\5\\1\end{pmatrix} = \begin{pmatrix}7\\6\\26\\11\end{pmatrix} = \mathbf{v}_4.$$

Example 27. Consider the vector space $\mathscr{V}$ of directed line segments defined in Example 24. Let $\overrightarrow{OA}$ and $\overrightarrow{OB}$ be two nonzero vectors in $\mathscr{V}$ which have neither the same nor opposite directions. Then each linear combination of $\overrightarrow{OA}$ and $\overrightarrow{OB}$ is a vector lying in the plane determined by $\overrightarrow{OA}$ and $\overrightarrow{OB}$. Conversely, if $\overrightarrow{OC}$ is any vector lying in the plane of $\overrightarrow{OA}$ and $\overrightarrow{OB}$, then $\overrightarrow{OC}$ is a linear combination of $\overrightarrow{OA}$ and $\overrightarrow{OB}$. To see this, draw lines through C parallel to $\overrightarrow{OA}$ and $\overrightarrow{OB}$. These will determine points of intersection A' and B' as shown in Fig. 9. Now $\overrightarrow{OA'}$ is a scalar multiple of $\overrightarrow{OA}$, $\overrightarrow{OB'}$ is a scalar multiple of $\overrightarrow{OB}$, and, by construction, $\overrightarrow{OC} = \overrightarrow{OA'} + \overrightarrow{OB'}$. Hence, there are scalars c_1 and c_2 such that $\overrightarrow{OC} = c_1\overrightarrow{OA} + c_2\overrightarrow{OB}$, i.e., $\overrightarrow{OC}$ is a linear combination of $\overrightarrow{OA}$ and $\overrightarrow{OB}$.

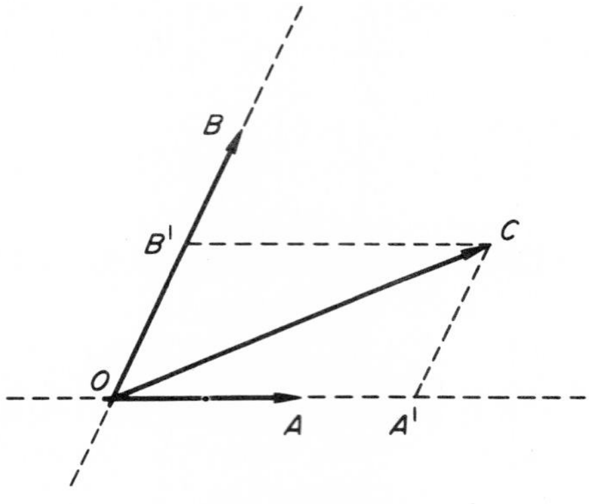

Figure 9

Example 28. Let $\mathscr{F}$ be the vector space, defined in Example 25, consisting of all real-valued functions defined on a set S of real numbers. Let

$f_1(x) = 1$, $f_2(x) = \cos 2x$, and $f_3(x) = \cos^2 x$ for each x in S. Then each of the functions f_1, f_2, and f_3 is a linear combination of the other two. For, from trigonometry, we know that $\cos 2x = 2\cos^2 x - 1$ for each x. Hence,

$$f_2 = 2f_3 - f_1, \tag{11}$$

and Eq. (11) can be solved also for f_3 and f_1.

In Section 2–2 we defined a system of m linear equations in n unknowns as the problem of finding all n-dimensional column vectors $\mathbf{x}$ such that $\mathbf{Ax} = \mathbf{b}$, where $\mathbf{A}$ is a given m by n matrix and $\mathbf{b}$ is a given m-dimensional column vector. We wish now to explain, in terms of linear combinations of vectors, another way of looking at this problem, a point of view which will prove useful later. Let $\mathbf{A} = (a_{ij})$ be an m by n matrix, and let its columns be called $\mathbf{a}_1, \mathbf{a}_2, \ldots, \mathbf{a}_n$. Then $\mathbf{a}_j = [a_{1j}, a_{2j}, \ldots, a_{mj}]$ for each $j = 1, 2, \ldots, n$. Let $\mathbf{b} = [b_1, b_2, \ldots, b_m]$ be a given m-dimensional column vector. Then the problem of finding all column vectors $\mathbf{x}$ satisfying $\mathbf{Ax} = \mathbf{b}$ is equivalent to the problem of finding all linear combinations of $\mathbf{a}_1, \mathbf{a}_2, \ldots, \mathbf{a}_n$ which equal $\mathbf{b}$. For, if $\mathbf{x} = [x_1, x_2, \ldots, x_n]$ satisfies $\mathbf{Ax} = \mathbf{b}$, then we have

$$\left\{\begin{array}{l} a_{11}x_1 + a_{12}x_2 + \cdots + a_{1n}x_n = b_1, \\ a_{21}x_1 + a_{22}x_2 + \cdots + a_{2n}x_n = b_2, \\ \cdots \qquad \cdots \qquad \cdots, \\ a_{m1}x_1 + a_{m2}x_2 + \cdots + a_{mn}x_n = b_m. \end{array}\right. \tag{12}$$

Hence,

$$x_1\begin{pmatrix} a_{11} \\ a_{21} \\ \cdot \\ \cdot \\ \cdot \\ a_{m1} \end{pmatrix} + x_2\begin{pmatrix} a_{12} \\ a_{22} \\ \cdot \\ \cdot \\ \cdot \\ a_{m2} \end{pmatrix} + \cdots x_n\begin{pmatrix} a_{1n} \\ a_{2n} \\ \cdot \\ \cdot \\ \cdot \\ a_{mn} \end{pmatrix} = \begin{pmatrix} b_1 \\ b_2 \\ \cdot \\ \cdot \\ \cdot \\ b_m \end{pmatrix}, \tag{13}$$

or

$$x_1\mathbf{a}_1 + x_2\mathbf{a}_2 + \cdots + x_n\mathbf{a}_n = \mathbf{b}, \tag{14}$$

which expresses $\mathbf{b}$ as a linear combination of $\mathbf{a}_1, \mathbf{a}_2, \ldots, \mathbf{a}_n$. Conversely, given a linear combination of $\mathbf{a}_1, \mathbf{a}_2, \ldots, \mathbf{a}_n$ equaling $\mathbf{b}$, as in (14), the coefficients $x_1, x_2, \ldots, x_n$ will satisfy (12) and hence can be taken as components of a column vector $\mathbf{x} = [x_1, x_2, \ldots, x_n]$ which will satisfy $\mathbf{Ax} = \mathbf{b}$.

Example 29. Let $\mathbf{a}_1 = [2, -1, 3]$, $\mathbf{a}_2 = [0, 1, 1]$, $\mathbf{a}_3 = [6, -4, 2]$, and $\mathbf{b} = [10, 8, -3]$, and suppose we wish to express $\mathbf{b}$ as a linear combination of $\mathbf{a}_1$, $\mathbf{a}_2$, and $\mathbf{a}_3$. The problem of finding all numbers x_1, x_2, x_3 such that

$$x_1\begin{pmatrix} 2 \\ -1 \\ 3 \end{pmatrix} + x_2\begin{pmatrix} 0 \\ 1 \\ 1 \end{pmatrix} + x_3\begin{pmatrix} 6 \\ -4 \\ 2 \end{pmatrix} = \begin{pmatrix} 10 \\ 8 \\ -3 \end{pmatrix}$$

is equivalent to solving the system

$$\begin{cases} 2x_1 + 6x_3 = 10, \\ -x_1 + x_2 - 4x_3 = 8, \\ 3x_1 + x_2 + 2x_3 = -3. \end{cases}$$

We leave it to the student to verify that this system has the unique solution $\mathbf{x} = [-21/2, 109/6, 31/6]$. Hence, we have

$$\mathbf{b} = -\tfrac{21}{2}\mathbf{a}_1 + \tfrac{109}{6}\mathbf{a}_2 + \tfrac{31}{6}\mathbf{a}_3.$$

The matrix equation $\mathbf{AX} = \mathbf{B}$, discussed in Section 2–2, can now be thought of as the problem of expressing each of the columns of **B** as a linear combination of the columns of **A**. (See Exercises 1 and 2 for numerical examples.) We shall discuss this interpretation further in Section 2–6.

If $\mathbf{v}_1, \mathbf{v}_2, \ldots, \mathbf{v}_n$ are vectors in any vector space $\mathscr{V}$, then the zero vector $\mathbf{0}$ in $\mathscr{V}$ can be expressed as a linear combination of $\mathbf{v}_1, \mathbf{v}_2, \ldots, \mathbf{v}_n$, because we have

$$\mathbf{0} = 0\mathbf{v}_1 + 0\mathbf{v}_2 + \cdots + 0\mathbf{v}_n. \tag{15}$$

In some cases, (15) may be the only way in which $\mathbf{0}$ may be expressed as a linear combination of a given set of vectors $\mathbf{v}_1, \mathbf{v}_2, \ldots, \mathbf{v}_n$, while in other cases there may be other ways. Our next definition, which is an important one, provides us with labels to distinguish the two cases:

DEFINITION 18. Let $\mathbf{v}_1, \mathbf{v}_2, \ldots, \mathbf{v}_n$ be vectors in a vector space $\mathscr{V}$, and let $\mathbf{0}$ denote the zero vector in $\mathscr{V}$. We say that the vectors $\mathbf{v}_1, \mathbf{v}_2, \ldots, \mathbf{v}_n$ are *linearly independent*, or that they form a *linearly independent set of vectors*, if, and only if, the only linear combination of $\mathbf{v}_1, \mathbf{v}_2, \ldots, \mathbf{v}_n$ which equals the zero vector is the trivial one given by (15). We say the vectors $\mathbf{v}_1, \mathbf{v}_2, \ldots, \mathbf{v}_n$ are *linearly dependent*, or that they form a *linearly dependent set of vectors*, if, and only if, (15) is not the only way of expressing $\mathbf{0}$ as a linear combination of $\mathbf{v}_1, \mathbf{v}_2, \ldots, \mathbf{v}_n$, i.e., we can write

$$\mathbf{0} = c_1\mathbf{v}_1 + c_2\mathbf{v}_2 + \cdots + c_n\mathbf{v}_n, \tag{16}$$

where at least one of the numbers $c_1, c_2 \ldots, c_n$ is not zero.

Example 30. The unit vectors $\mathbf{e}_1^2 = [1, 0]$ and $\mathbf{e}_2^2 = [0, 1]$ in $\mathscr{V}_2$ are linearly independent. For, if c_1 and c_2 are any two numbers, we have

$$c_1\mathbf{e}_1^2 + c_2\mathbf{e}_2^2 = [c_1, c_2].$$

Hence, $c_1\mathbf{e}_1^2 + c_2\mathbf{e}_2^2 = \mathbf{0}$ if, and only if, $c_1 = c_2 = 0$. More generally, in each space $\mathscr{V}_m$, the unit vectors $\mathbf{e}_1^m, \mathbf{e}_2^m, \ldots, \mathbf{e}_m^m$ are linearly independent. We leave it to the student to verify this by the same type of argument as in the case $m = 2$.

Example 31. The vectors $\mathbf{v}_1 = [-1, 2, 4]$ and $\mathbf{v}_2 = [3, -6, -12]$ in $\mathscr{V}_3$ are linearly dependent, for we have $\mathbf{v}_2 = -3\mathbf{v}_1$ and hence $3\mathbf{v}_1 + \mathbf{v}_2 = \mathbf{0}$. Of course, it is also true that $0\mathbf{v}_1 + 0\mathbf{v}_2 = \mathbf{0}$, but, since there is another, nontrivial, way of expressing $\mathbf{0}$ as a linear combination of $\mathbf{v}_1$ and $\mathbf{v}_2$, they are linearly dependent.

Example 32. The four vectors $\mathbf{v}_1, \mathbf{v}_2, \mathbf{v}_3, \mathbf{v}_4$ of Example 26 are linearly dependent since we have $3\mathbf{v}_1 - 2\mathbf{v}_2 + 4\mathbf{v}_3 - \mathbf{v}_4 = \mathbf{0}$. Suppose we wish to know whether the first three of these vectors, $\mathbf{v}_1, \mathbf{v}_2$, and $\mathbf{v}_3$, also form a linearly dependent set. Then we have to determine whether there are numbers x_1, x_2, x_3, not each zero, such that

$$x_1\begin{pmatrix}-1\\0\\2\\3\end{pmatrix} + x_2\begin{pmatrix}1\\1\\0\\1\end{pmatrix} + x_3\begin{pmatrix}3\\2\\5\\1\end{pmatrix} = \begin{pmatrix}0\\0\\0\\0\end{pmatrix}.$$

In other words, we have to determine whether the homogeneous system

$$\begin{cases} -x_1 + x_2 + 3x_3 = 0, \\ \quad\;\; x_2 + 2x_3 = 0, \\ 2x_1 \quad\;\; + 5x_3 = 0, \\ 3x_1 + x_2 + \;\; x_3 = 0 \end{cases}$$

has any nontrivial solutions. We leave it to the student to show, by the method of Section 2–2, that this system has only the trivial solution $x_1 = x_2 = x_3 = 0$. Therefore, $\mathbf{v}_1, \mathbf{v}_2$, and $\mathbf{v}_3$ are linearly independent.

Example 33. The functions f_1, f_2, f_3 defined in Example 28 are linearly dependent in the vector space $\mathscr{F}$ of Example 25 because we have

$$f_1 + f_2 - 2f_3 = \phi,$$

where ϕ here denotes the function such that $\phi(x) = 0$ for each x in S. On the other hand, the functions g_1, g_2, and g_3, where $g_1(x) = 1$, $g_2(x) = x$, $g_3(x) = x^2$ for each x in S, are linearly independent in $\mathscr{F}$ if we assume S contains more than two numbers. For suppose c_1, c_2, and c_3 are numbers such that

$$c_1g_1 + c_2g_2 + c_3g_3 = \phi. \tag{17}$$

Then

$$c_1 + c_2x + c_3x^2 = 0 \tag{18}$$

for each x in S. But, if any one of the numbers c_1, c_2, c_3 is different from 0, then (18) can hold for, at most, two different values of x and so cannot hold for all x in S. Therefore, if (17) holds, we must have $c_1 = c_2 = c_3 = 0$.

In the preceding examples we have encountered several instances of the following general problem: Given vectors $\mathbf{v}_1, \mathbf{v}_2, \ldots, \mathbf{v}_n$ in a vector space $\mathscr{V}$, determine whether or not these vectors are linearly independent. The methods used to solve this problem will, in general, vary from one vector space to another. However, in each space $\mathscr{V}_m$, the problem is equivalent to solving a homogeneous system of linear equations. Example 32 illustrated this. In general, given vectors $\mathbf{v}_1, \mathbf{v}_2, \ldots, \mathbf{v}_n$ in $\mathscr{V}_m$, where $\mathbf{v}_j = [a_{1j}, a_{2j}, \ldots, a_{mj}]$ $(j = 1, \ldots, n)$, to determine whether or not these vectors are linearly independent, we solve the system $\mathbf{Ax} = \mathbf{0}$, where $\mathbf{0}$ is the zero vector in $\mathscr{V}_m$ and $\mathbf{A} = (a_{ij})$ is the m by n matrix whose columns are $\mathbf{v}_1, \mathbf{v}_2, \ldots, \mathbf{v}_n$. If this system has only the trivial solution $x_1 = x_2 = \cdots = x_n = 0$, the given vectors are linearly independent. If this system has nontrivial solutions, the given vectors are linearly dependent and, from the solutions of the system, we can determine all linear combinations of $\mathbf{v}_1, \mathbf{v}_2, \ldots, \mathbf{v}_n$ which equal $\mathbf{0}$. The latter case is illustrated in the next example:

Example 34. Given the vectors $\mathbf{v}_1 = [1, 1, 3, 3]$, $\mathbf{v}_2 = [5, 6, 18, 19]$, $\mathbf{v}_3 = [2, 0, 1, 0]$, $\mathbf{v}_4 = [1, -2, -2, -1]$, and $\mathbf{v}_5 = [1, 5, 15, 20]$ in $\mathscr{V}_4$, we wish to determine whether or not they are linearly independent. The system $\mathbf{Ax} = \mathbf{0}$ which we have to consider in this case is a homogeneous system of four equations in five unknowns which, according to Exercise 2, Section 2–2, we can predict in advance will have infinitely many solutions. Thus, the given vectors are linearly dependent. If we wish to determine all linear combinations of them which equal $\mathbf{0}$, then we must solve the following system:

$$(19)\qquad \begin{cases} x_1 + 5x_2 + 2x_3 + x_4 + x_5 = 0, \\ x_1 + 6x_2 - 2x_4 + 5x_5 = 0, \\ 3x_1 + 18x_2 + x_3 - 2x_4 + 15x_5 = 0, \\ 3x_1 + 19x_2 - x_4 + 20x_5 = 0. \end{cases}$$

By a properly chosen sequence of elementary row transformations, it is possible to transform the augmented matrix for (19) into the following matrix in canonical form:

$$(20)\qquad \left(\begin{array}{ccccc|c} 1 & 0 & 0 & -32 & 0 & 0 \\ 0 & 1 & 0 & 5 & 0 & 0 \\ 0 & 0 & 1 & 4 & 0 & 0 \\ 0 & 0 & 0 & 0 & 1 & 0 \end{array}\right).$$

From (20) we see that the set of all solutions of (19) is the set of all column vectors $\mathbf{x}$ of the form

$$\mathbf{x} = [32k, -5k, -4k, k, 0].$$

Thus, for each number k, we have

$$(21)\qquad 32k\mathbf{v}_1 - 5k\mathbf{v}_2 - 4k\mathbf{v}_3 + k\mathbf{v}_4 + 0\mathbf{v}_5 = \mathbf{0},$$

and only those linear combinations of the given vectors which have the form of the left side of (21) will equal $\mathbf{0}$.

The situation in the above example, in which there are infinitely many nontrivial linear combinations of the given vectors which equal the zero vector, is not special. For, if $\mathbf{v}_1, \mathbf{v}_2, \ldots, \mathbf{v}_n$ are linearly dependent vectors in any vector space $\mathscr{V}$ and if $c_1\mathbf{v}_1 + c_2\mathbf{v}_2 + \cdots + c_n\mathbf{v}_n$ is one nontrivial linear combination of them which equals $\mathbf{0}$, then so is $kc_1\mathbf{v}_1 + \cdots + kc_n\mathbf{v}_n$ for each nonzero number k. On the other hand, if $\mathbf{v}_1, \mathbf{v}_2, \ldots, \mathbf{v}_n$ are linearly independent, then there is one, and only one, linear combination of them which equals the zero vector, namely, the trivial combination with each coefficient zero. Thus, we have proved that a set of vectors $\mathbf{v}_1, \mathbf{v}_2, \ldots, \mathbf{v}_n$ in a vector space $\mathscr{V}$ is linearly independent if, and only if, the zero vector in $\mathscr{V}$ can be expressed uniquely as a linear combination of $\mathbf{v}_1, \mathbf{v}_2, \ldots, \mathbf{v}_n$.

One of the basic reasons for the importance of the property of linear independence is that this uniqueness of linear combinations carries over to vectors other than the zero vector. This fact is contained in the next theorem:

THEOREM 7. Vectors $\mathbf{v}_1, \mathbf{v}_2, \ldots, \mathbf{v}_n$ in a vector space $\mathscr{V}$ are linearly independent if, and only if, the equality

$$c_1\mathbf{v}_1 + c_2\mathbf{v}_2 + \cdots + c_n\mathbf{v}_n = d_1\mathbf{v}_1 + d_2\mathbf{v}_2 + \cdots + d_n\mathbf{v}_n, \tag{22}$$

in which each c_i and d_i is a scalar, implies that $c_i = d_i$ for each $i = 1, 2, \ldots, n$.

Proof: Suppose first that $\mathbf{v}_1, \mathbf{v}_2, \ldots, \mathbf{v}_n$ are linearly independent and that an equality of form (22) holds. Then, by transposing, we obtain

$$(c_1 - d_1)\mathbf{v}_1 + (c_2 - d_2)\mathbf{v}_2 + \cdots + (c_n - d_n)\mathbf{v}_n = \mathbf{0}. \tag{23}$$

Since the vectors $\mathbf{v}_1, \mathbf{v}_2, \ldots, \mathbf{v}_n$ are linearly independent, Eq. (23) implies that $c_i - d_i = 0$, and hence that $c_i = d_i$, for each $i = 1, 2, \ldots, n$.

Conversely, suppose we have vectors $\mathbf{v}_1, \mathbf{v}_2, \ldots, \mathbf{v}_n$ for which equality (22) implies $c_i = d_i$ for each $i = 1, 2, \ldots, n$. Then, from

$$c_1\mathbf{v}_1 + c_2\mathbf{v}_2 + \cdots + c_n\mathbf{v}_n = \mathbf{0} = 0\mathbf{v}_1 + 0\mathbf{v}_2 + \cdots + 0\mathbf{v}_n,$$

we can conclude that $c_i = 0$ $(i = 1, 2, \ldots, n)$ and, hence, that the vectors $\mathbf{v}_1, \mathbf{v}_2, \ldots, \mathbf{v}_n$ are linearly independent.

We can conclude from this theorem that, if we have a linearly independent set of vectors $\mathbf{v}_1, \mathbf{v}_2, \ldots, \mathbf{v}_n$ in a vector space $\mathscr{V}$ and *if* we can express a given vector $\mathbf{b}$ in $\mathscr{V}$ as a linear combination of $\mathbf{v}_1, \mathbf{v}_2, \ldots, \mathbf{v}_n$, then this expression is unique. But we must realize that there *may* be some vectors in $\mathscr{V}$ which cannot be expressed as linear combinations of $\mathbf{v}_1, \mathbf{v}_2, \ldots, \mathbf{v}_n$ at all. This point will be discussed further in the next section (see also Exercise 4 in the present section).

The final theorem in this section gives us another characterization of linear dependence. Its proof is left to the student [Exercise 8, parts (a) and (b)].

THEOREM 8. A set of vectors $\mathbf{v}_1, \mathbf{v}_2, \ldots, \mathbf{v}_n$ in a vector space $\mathscr{V}$ is linearly dependent if, and only if, at least one of the vectors $\mathbf{v}_i$ can be expressed as a linear combination of the remaining vectors in the set.

EXERCISES

1. Let $\mathbf{a}_1 = [1, 1, -2]$, $\mathbf{a}_2 = [-5, -3, 4]$, $\mathbf{a}_3 = [4, 3, -5]$, and $\mathbf{a}_4 = [15, 11, -18]$. Express each of the following vectors as a linear combination of $\mathbf{a}_1, \mathbf{a}_2, \mathbf{a}_3, \mathbf{a}_4$ if possible, and determine which vector(s) cannot be so expressed: $\mathbf{b}_1 = [36, 29, -51]$, $\mathbf{b}_2 = [11, 9, -15]$, $\mathbf{b}_3 = [2, 3, -7]$. Do this by writing down a single matrix and then performing a certain sequence of elementary row transformations.

2. Let $\mathbf{a}_1 = [2, 7, 4]$, $\mathbf{a}_2 = [0, 2, 1]$, $\mathbf{a}_3 = [-7, -1, 1]$, $\mathbf{a}_4 = [3, 5, 2]$, $\mathbf{a}_5 = [2, 13, 7]$, $\mathbf{a}_6 = [12, 9, 2]$, and $\mathbf{a}_7 = [-2, 1, 1]$. Express each of these vectors as a linear combination of $\mathbf{a}_2$, $\mathbf{a}_4$, and $\mathbf{a}_7$.

3. For each of the following sets of vectors, determine whether the set is linearly dependent or linearly independent. In case of dependence, find all linear combinations of the given vectors which equal the zero vector.
(a) $\mathbf{v}_1 = [3, 4]$, $\mathbf{v}_2 = [5, 6]$.
(b) $\mathbf{v}_1 = [1, 0, 0]$, $\mathbf{v}_2 = [1, 1, 0]$, $\mathbf{v}_3 = [1, 1, 1]$.
(c) $\mathbf{v}_1 = [-2, 1, 3]$, $\mathbf{v}_2 = [0, 0, 1]$, $\mathbf{v}_3 = [4, -3, 0]$, $\mathbf{v}_4 = [2, 2, 2]$.
(d) $\mathbf{v}_1 = [1, 1, 0]$, $\mathbf{v}_2 = [0, 1, 1]$, $\mathbf{v}_3 = [0, 0, 0]$.
(e) $\mathbf{v}_1 = [1, 2, -1, 3, -2]$, $\mathbf{v}_2 = [1, 3, 2, 4, -2]$, $\mathbf{v}_3 = [1, -1, -10, 0, -2]$, $\mathbf{v}_4 = [-4, -6, 11, -11, 7]$, $\mathbf{v}_5 = [-3, -5, 7, -9, 5]$, $\mathbf{v}_6 = [5, 12, 4, 15, -6]$, $\mathbf{v}_7 = [-1, 2, 14, -2, -15]$, $\mathbf{v}_8 = [-9, -18, 4, -24, 0]$.
(f) $\mathbf{v}_1 = [-1, 4, 1]$, $\mathbf{v}_2 = [-3, -3, 1]$, $\mathbf{v}_3 = [0, 8, 1]$.

4. Let $\mathbf{v}_1 = [11, -2, 3, 4]$, $\mathbf{v}_2 = [21, -3, 5, 10]$, and $\mathbf{v}_3 = [2, -1, 1, 1]$. Prove that a vector $\mathbf{x} = [x_1, x_2, x_3, x_4]$ in $\mathscr{V}_4$ can be expressed uniquely as a linear combination of $\mathbf{v}_1, \mathbf{v}_2$, and $\mathbf{v}_3$ if, and only if, $3x_1 - 14x_2 - 19x_3 - x_4 = 0$. Thus, the given vectors are linearly independent, but many vectors in $\mathscr{V}_4$ cannot be expressed as linear combinations of them.

5. Let $\mathscr{F}$ be the vector space of Example 25, Section 2–3, and, for this exercise, assume that S is a nondegenerate interval of real numbers. Let f_1 and f_2 be the members of $\mathscr{F}$ defined by the rules

$$f_1(x) = \cos x, \qquad f_2(x) = \sin x,$$

for each x in S. Prove that f_1 and f_2 are linearly independent.
Hint: Start by assuming $c_1 \cos x + c_2 \sin x = 0$ for each x in S. Then differentiate both sides with respect to x. Now, for any fixed x in S, think of the equations you have obtained as being a system of two equations in the two unknowns c_1 and c_2.

6. Suppose $\mathbf{v}_1, \mathbf{v}_2, \ldots, \mathbf{v}_n$ are linearly independent vectors in a vector space $\mathscr{V}$, and let $\alpha_1, \alpha_2, \ldots, \alpha_n$ be nonzero numbers. Prove that the vectors $\alpha_1\mathbf{v}_1, \alpha_2\mathbf{v}_2, \ldots, \alpha_n\mathbf{v}_n$ are also linearly independent.

7. Let $\mathbf{v}_1, \mathbf{v}_2, \ldots, \mathbf{v}_n$ $(n > 1)$ be vectors in a vector space $\mathscr{V}$.
(a) Suppose that, for some $k (1 \leq k < n)$, the set of vectors $\mathbf{v}_1, \ldots, \mathbf{v}_k$ is linearly dependent. Prove that the vectors $\mathbf{v}_1, \mathbf{v}_2, \ldots, \mathbf{v}_n$ must also be linearly

dependent. In other words, if some subset of a given set of vectors is dependent, then the given set is dependent.
(b) As a special case of (a), prove that, if the given set of vectors contains the zero vector, then that set is linearly dependent.
(c) Prove that, if $\mathbf{v}_1, \mathbf{v}_2, \ldots, \mathbf{v}_n$ are linearly independent and k satisfies $1 \leq k < n$, then the vectors $\mathbf{v}_1, \ldots, \mathbf{v}_k$ are linearly independent. In other words, each subset of an independent set is independent.
8. Let $\mathbf{v}_1, \mathbf{v}_2, \ldots, \mathbf{v}_n$ be vectors in a vector space $\mathscr{V}$.
(a) Suppose at least one of these vectors, say $\mathbf{v}_1$ for convenience, can be expressed as a linear combination of the other vectors: $\mathbf{v}_1 = c_2\mathbf{v}_2 + c_3\mathbf{v}_3 + \cdots + c_n\mathbf{v}_n$. Prove that the given vectors are linearly dependent.
(b) Suppose we know that the given vectors are linearly dependent. Let $c_1\mathbf{v}_1 + c_2\mathbf{v}_2 + \cdots + c_n\mathbf{v}_n$ be a nontrivial linear combination of them, which equals the zero vector. Prove that each vector $\mathbf{v}_i$ for which $c_i \neq 0$ can be expressed as a linear combination of the remaining vectors.
(c) Given an equality of the form

$$c_1\mathbf{v}_1 + c_2\mathbf{v}_2 + \cdots + c_n\mathbf{v}_n = \mathbf{0},$$

we know that $c_i \neq 0$ implies that $\mathbf{v}_i$ can be expressed as a linear combination of the remaining vectors. Does $c_i = 0$ imply that $\mathbf{v}_i$ *cannot* be expressed as a linear combination of the remaining vectors? Either prove that it does, or give an example which shows that the implication need not hold.
Note: Parts (a) and (b) of this exercise constitute a proof of Theorem 8.
9. Let $\mathbf{v}_1, \mathbf{v}_2, \ldots, \mathbf{v}_n$ be vectors in a vector space $\mathscr{V}$. Let $\mathscr{V}'$ be the collection of all vectors in $\mathscr{V}$, each of which is a linear combination of $\mathbf{v}_1, \mathbf{v}_2, \ldots, \mathbf{v}_n$, and let vector addition and scalar multiplication be defined in $\mathscr{V}'$ just as they are in $\mathscr{V}$. Prove that $\mathscr{V}'$ is a vector space. (Exercise 6, Section 2–3, was a special case of this. In turn, the situation here is a special case of that described in Exercise 7, Section 2–3.)
10. Suppose the vectors $\mathbf{v}_1, \mathbf{v}_2, \mathbf{v}_3$ in a vector space $\mathscr{V}$ are linearly independent.
(a) Prove that the vectors $\mathbf{v}_1, \mathbf{v}_1 + \mathbf{v}_2$, and $\mathbf{v}_1 + \mathbf{v}_2 + \mathbf{v}_3$ are also linearly independent.
(b) More generally, what conditions on the scalars a, b_1, b_2, c_1, c_2, and c_3 are necessary and sufficient for the linear independence of the vectors $a\mathbf{v}_1, b_1\mathbf{v}_1 + b_2\mathbf{v}_2$, and $c_1\mathbf{v}_1 + c_2\mathbf{v}_2 + c_3\mathbf{v}_3$?
11. Let $\mathscr{V}$ be the vector space defined in Exercise 8 of Section 2–3. Let $f_1(x) = e^x$ and $f_2(x) = e^{-x}$ for each x in the interval I. Prove that f_1 and f_2 are members of $\mathscr{V}$ and that they are linearly independent.
12. Let $\mathbf{v}_1, \mathbf{v}_2, \ldots, \mathbf{v}_n$ be vectors in a vector space $\mathscr{V}$. Prove that, if there exists a vector $\mathbf{v}$ in $\mathscr{V}$ such that $\mathbf{v}$ can be expressed in one, and only one, way as a linear combination of $\mathbf{v}_1, \mathbf{v}_2, \ldots, \mathbf{v}_n$, then the vectors $\mathbf{v}_1, \mathbf{v}_2, \ldots, \mathbf{v}_n$ are linearly independent. (This is a strengthening of the "if" part of Theorem 7, Section 2–4.)

2–5. *BASES FOR A VECTOR SPACE.*

Every vector in $\mathscr{V}_3$ can be written as a linear combination of the three unit vectors $\mathbf{e}_1^3 = [1, 0, 0]$, $\mathbf{e}_2^3 = [0, 1, 0]$, and $\mathbf{e}_3^3 = [0, 0, 1]$. For, if $\mathbf{x} = [x_1, x_2, x_3]$ is any vector in $\mathscr{V}_3$, then we have

$$\mathbf{x} = \begin{pmatrix} x_1 \\ x_2 \\ x_3 \end{pmatrix} = x_1\begin{pmatrix} 1 \\ 0 \\ 0 \end{pmatrix} + x_2\begin{pmatrix} 0 \\ 1 \\ 0 \end{pmatrix} + x_3\begin{pmatrix} 0 \\ 0 \\ 1 \end{pmatrix} = x_1\mathbf{e}_1^3 + x_2\mathbf{e}_2^3 + x_3\mathbf{e}_3^3.$$

Likewise, if $\mathbf{v}_1 = [6, 9, 7]$, $\mathbf{v}_2 = [2, 4, 3]$, $\mathbf{v}_3 = [1, 1, 1]$, and $\mathbf{v}_4 = [10, 10, 9]$, then each vector in $\mathscr{V}_3$ can be written as a linear combination of $\mathbf{v}_1, \mathbf{v}_2, \mathbf{v}_3$, and $\mathbf{v}_4$. To show this, let $\mathbf{x} = [x_1, x_2, x_3]$ be any vector in $\mathscr{V}_3$ and consider the augmented matrix

(24) $$\left(\begin{array}{cccc|c} 6 & 2 & 1 & 10 & x_1 \\ 9 & 4 & 1 & 10 & x_2 \\ 7 & 3 & 1 & 9 & x_3 \end{array}\right).$$

By a properly chosen sequence of elementary row transformations, matrix (24) reduces to the matrix

(25) $$\left(\begin{array}{cccc|c} 1 & 0 & 0 & 2 & x_1' \\ 0 & 1 & 0 & -3 & x_2' \\ 0 & 0 & 1 & 4 & x_3' \end{array}\right),$$

where x_1', x_2', and x_3' are numbers which will depend on x_1, x_2, and x_3. From (25) we see that, if k is any number, then

(26) $$\mathbf{x} = (x_1' - 2k)\mathbf{v}_1 + (x_2' + 3k)\mathbf{v}_2 + (x_3' - 4k)\mathbf{v}_3 + k\mathbf{v}_4,$$

which shows that each vector in $\mathscr{V}_3$ can be expressed (in infinitely many ways) as a linear combination of $\mathbf{v}_1, \mathbf{v}_2, \mathbf{v}_3, \mathbf{v}_4$. Each of the two sets of vectors just considered—$\mathbf{e}_1^3, \mathbf{e}_2^3, \mathbf{e}_3^3$ and $\mathbf{v}_1, \mathbf{v}_2, \mathbf{v}_3, \mathbf{v}_4$—has thus been shown to have the property that each vector in $\mathscr{V}_3$ can be expressed as a linear combination of the vectors in that set. In the following definition, we give a name to this property of a set of vectors:

Definition 19. A set of vectors $\mathbf{v}_1, \mathbf{v}_2, \ldots, \mathbf{v}_n$ in a vector space $\mathscr{V}$ is said to *span* $\mathscr{V}$ if, and only if, each vector in $\mathscr{V}$ can be expressed as a linear combination of $\mathbf{v}_1, \mathbf{v}_2, \ldots, \mathbf{v}_n$.

According to this definition, then, each of the sets of vectors $\mathbf{e}_1^3, \mathbf{e}_2^3, \mathbf{e}_3^3$ and $\mathbf{v}_1, \mathbf{v}_2, \mathbf{v}_3, \mathbf{v}_4$ spans $\mathscr{V}_3$. Now the first set, consisting of the three unit vectors, has the additional property that, if any one of its members is removed from the set, the remaining two vectors will *not* span $\mathscr{V}_3$. For, if $\mathbf{e}_i^3$ is removed, then each linear combination of the remaining two vectors will have i^{th} component zero and hence these two vectors cannot span $\mathscr{V}_3$. The second set, however, does not have this property. For, if we remove $\mathbf{v}_4$ from the set, we can see from (25), ignoring the fourth column, that each vector in $\mathscr{V}_3$ can be uniquely expressed as a linear combination of $\mathbf{v}_1$, $\mathbf{v}_2$, and $\mathbf{v}_3$. This property, possessed by the set of three unit vectors in $\mathscr{V}_3$, but not by the set of vectors $\mathbf{v}_1, \mathbf{v}_2, \mathbf{v}_3, \mathbf{v}_4$, is so important that a set of vectors having it is given a special name, as follows:

DEFINITION 20. A set of vectors $\mathbf{v}_1, \mathbf{v}_2, \ldots, \mathbf{v}_n$ in a vector space $\mathcal{V}$ is said to be a *basis* for $\mathcal{V}$ if, and only if, (i) the vectors $\mathbf{v}_1, \mathbf{v}_2, \ldots, \mathbf{v}_n$ span $\mathcal{V}$ and (ii), if any one of the vectors $\mathbf{v}_i$ is removed from the set, the remaining vectors do not span $\mathcal{V}$.

Note: An equivalent form of this definition appears in Exercise 5 at the end of this section.

Thus the vectors $\mathbf{e}_1^3$, $\mathbf{e}_2^3$, and $\mathbf{e}_3^3$ form a basis for $\mathcal{V}_3$, and, more generally, the m unit vectors $\mathbf{e}_1^m, \mathbf{e}_2^m, \ldots, \mathbf{e}_m^m$ form a basis for $\mathcal{V}_m$. We shall refer to this basis as the unit basis for $\mathcal{V}_m$. As we shall see, the unit basis is not by any means the only basis for $\mathcal{V}_m$. In fact, each *nondegenerate* vector space, i.e., each vector space containing more than one vector, has infinitely many different bases. (A *degenerate* vector space consists of a zero vector only, and that zero vector forms the one and only basis for the space—a very trivial situation.)

The rest of this section is devoted to a discussion of properties of bases for vector spaces. Except for Theorem 10, a special case of which is proved in detail, we give only outlines of proofs. Supplying the missing details is left to the student, and, in fact, these proofs are to be regarded as the chief exercises associated with this section. They consist of fairly straightforward arguments based on the pertinent definitions and previous results. A few additional exercises appear at the end of the section.

The first theorem shows us that, although it was not mentioned in the definition of a basis, the concept of linear independence is intimately associated with the concept of basis.

THEOREM 9. If the vectors $\mathbf{v}_1, \mathbf{v}_2, \ldots, \mathbf{v}_n$ form a basis for a nondegenerate vector space $\mathcal{V}$, then these vectors are linearly independent.

Outline of proof: It is sufficient to prove that no linearly dependent set of vectors forms a basis for $\mathcal{V}$. This can be done by starting with a dependent set $\mathbf{v}_1, \mathbf{v}_2, \ldots, \mathbf{v}_n$ which spans $\mathcal{V}$ and proving, by use of Theorem 8 of Section 2–4, that there is at least one vector $\mathbf{v}_i$ which can be removed from the set so that the remaining $n - 1$ vectors span $\mathcal{V}$.

Theorem 9 says that each basis of a vector space is a linearly independent set of vectors, but it does *not* say that each linearly independent set of vectors in a vector space $\mathcal{V}$ is a basis for $\mathcal{V}$. The latter statement, in fact, is not true, as we pointed out at the end of Section 2–4. The next theorem sheds some light on the question of conditions under which a given set of linearly independent vectors in a vector space $\mathcal{V}$ will form a basis for $\mathcal{V}$.

THEOREM 10. Suppose $\mathcal{V}$ is a vector space which has a basis consisting of n vectors. Then any set of n linearly independent vectors in $\mathcal{V}$ is a basis for $\mathcal{V}$.

Note: For the sake of simplicity and ease of comprehension, we shall give a proof of this theorem only for the case $n = 3$. It will be evident that a similar proof could be given for any positive integer n.

Proof for case $n = 3$: We are given a vector space $\mathscr{V}$ which has a basis consisting of three vectors, say $\mathbf{v}_1$, $\mathbf{v}_2$, and $\mathbf{v}_3$. Let $\mathbf{u}_1$, $\mathbf{u}_2$, and $\mathbf{u}_3$ be any set of three linearly independent vectors in $\mathscr{V}$. We wish to prove that the vectors $\mathbf{u}_1, \mathbf{u}_2, \mathbf{u}_3$ also form a basis for $\mathscr{V}$, which means that we must show that they satisfy requirements (i) and (ii) of Definition 20.

Consider first the requirement (i). We have to show that each vector in $\mathscr{V}$ can be expressed as a linear combination of $\mathbf{u}_1$, $\mathbf{u}_2$, and $\mathbf{u}_3$. We know that each vector in $\mathscr{V}$ is a linear combination of $\mathbf{v}_1, \mathbf{v}_2, \mathbf{v}_3$, and so, in particular, we can write

(27) $$\mathbf{u}_1 = a_1\mathbf{v}_1 + a_2\mathbf{v}_2 + a_3\mathbf{v}_3,$$

where a_1, a_2, and a_3 are suitably chosen scalars. Now none of the vectors $\mathbf{u}_1, \mathbf{u}_2, \mathbf{u}_3$ is the zero vector, for $\mathbf{u}_i = \mathbf{0}$ would imply linear dependence of $\mathbf{u}_1$, $\mathbf{u}_2$, and $\mathbf{u}_3$ (see Exercise 6(b), Section 2–4). Hence, at least one of the coefficients in (27) must be different from zero, say $a_3 \neq 0$, for convenience. Then we can solve Eq. (27) for $\mathbf{v}_3$, obtaining an expression of the form

(28) $$\mathbf{v}_3 = a_1'\mathbf{v}_1 + a_2'\mathbf{v}_2 + a_3'\mathbf{u}_1.$$

(The formulas for a_1', a_2', and a_3' in terms of a_1, a_2, and a_3 are easy to see, but are of no particular concern to us.)

Now any given vector $\mathbf{v}$ in $\mathscr{V}$ can be expressed as a linear combination of $\mathbf{v}_1, \mathbf{v}_2, \mathbf{v}_3$, say

(29) $$\mathbf{v} = t_1\mathbf{v}_1 + t_2\mathbf{v}_2 + t_3\mathbf{v}_3.$$

If, in (29), we replace $\mathbf{v}_3$ by the right-hand side of (28) and combine terms, we obtain an expression for $\mathbf{v}$ as a linear combination of $\mathbf{v}_1$, $\mathbf{v}_2$, and $\mathbf{u}_1$:

(30) $$\mathbf{v} = (t_1 + t_3a_1')\mathbf{v}_1 + (t_2 + t_3a_2')\mathbf{v}_2 + t_3a_3'\mathbf{u}_1.$$

This proves that one of the basis vectors (we called it $\mathbf{v}_3$ for convenience) can be removed and replaced by $\mathbf{u}_1$ so that the resulting set of three vectors spans $\mathscr{V}$. Perhaps the plan of the proof is now apparent. We are next going to show that one of the two remaining original basis vectors ($\mathbf{v}_1$ and $\mathbf{v}_2$ in our notation) can be removed and replaced by $\mathbf{u}_2$ so that the resulting set of three vectors spans $\mathscr{V}$. This set will include both $\mathbf{u}_1$ and $\mathbf{u}_2$. Finally, we show that the remaining one of the original basis vectors can be removed and replaced by $\mathbf{u}_3$ and that the resulting set, which will consist of $\mathbf{u}_1$, $\mathbf{u}_2$, and $\mathbf{u}_3$, spans $\mathscr{V}$.

Continuing, since $\mathbf{v}_1$, $\mathbf{v}_2$, and $\mathbf{u}_1$ span $\mathscr{V}$, we can write

(31) $$\mathbf{u}_2 = b_1\mathbf{v}_1 + b_2\mathbf{v}_2 + b_3\mathbf{u}_1.$$

Now at least one of b_1 and b_2 must be different from zero, since otherwise (31) would reduce to $\mathbf{u}_2 = b_3\mathbf{u}_1$, contrary to the independence of $\mathbf{u}_1$, $\mathbf{u}_2$, and $\mathbf{u}_3$. For convenience, assume $b_2 \neq 0$, and solve (31) for $\mathbf{v}_2$, obtaining an expression of the form

(32) $$\mathbf{v}_2 = b_1'\mathbf{v}_1 + b_2'\mathbf{u}_1 + b_3'\mathbf{u}_2.$$

If we consider an arbitrary vector $\mathbf{v}$ in $\mathscr{V}$, express $\mathbf{v}$ as a linear combination of $\mathbf{v}_1$, $\mathbf{v}_2$, and $\mathbf{u}_1$, and then replace $\mathbf{v}_2$ by the right-hand side of (32), we obtain an expression of $\mathbf{v}$ as a linear combination of $\mathbf{v}_1$, $\mathbf{u}_1$, and $\mathbf{u}_2$. Thus, the vectors $\mathbf{v}_1$, $\mathbf{u}_1$, and $\mathbf{u}_2$ span $\mathscr{V}$. Hence, we can write

(33) $$\mathbf{u}_3 = c_1\mathbf{v}_1 + c_2\mathbf{u}_1 + c_3\mathbf{u}_2,$$

and we must have $c_1 \neq 0$ or else (33) would reduce to $\mathbf{u}_3 = c_2\mathbf{u}_1 + c_3\mathbf{u}_2$, contradicting the independence of $\mathbf{u}_1, \mathbf{u}_2, \mathbf{u}_3$. Solving (33) for $\mathbf{v}_1$, we obtain an expression of the form

(34) $$\mathbf{v}_1 = c_1'\mathbf{u}_1 + c_2'\mathbf{u}_2 + c_3'\mathbf{u}_3.$$

If we consider an arbitrary vector $\mathbf{v}$ in $\mathscr{V}$, express $\mathbf{v}$ as a linear combination of $\mathbf{v}_1$, $\mathbf{u}_1$, and $\mathbf{u}_2$, and then replace $\mathbf{v}_1$ by the right-hand side of (34), we obtain an expression of $\mathbf{v}$ as a linear combination of $\mathbf{u}_1$, $\mathbf{u}_2$, and $\mathbf{u}_3$. Therefore, the vectors $\mathbf{u}_1, \mathbf{u}_2, \mathbf{u}_3$ span $\mathscr{V}$, and the first part of the proof is complete.

The proof that $\mathbf{u}_1, \mathbf{u}_2, \mathbf{u}_3$ satisfy requirement (ii) of Definition 20 is much easier. Since they are linearly independent, no one of them can be expressed as a linear combination of the other two. Hence, no two of them span $\mathscr{V}$.

Example 35. We observed earlier in this section that the three unit vectors $\mathbf{e}_1^3$, $\mathbf{e}_2^3$, and $\mathbf{e}_3^3$ form a basis for $\mathscr{V}_3$. From Theorem 10 it follows that any linearly independent set of three vectors in $\mathscr{V}_3$ will also form a basis for $\mathscr{V}_3$. For instance, the vectors $\mathbf{v}_1$, $\mathbf{v}_2$, and $\mathbf{v}_3$ defined near the beginning of the section constitute a basis, since from the first three columns of matrix (25) we can see that they are linearly independent.

There are three properties of bases that follow fairly easily from Theorems 9 and 10, which we now list as corollaries:

COROLLARY 1. If a vector space $\mathscr{V}$ has a basis consisting of n vectors, then any set of $n + 1$ (or more) vectors in $\mathscr{V}$ is linearly dependent.

Outline of proof: Suppose there were a set of $n + 1$ linearly independent vectors $\mathbf{v}_1, \mathbf{v}_2, \ldots, \mathbf{v}_{n+1}$ in $\mathscr{V}$. Use the result of Exercise 6(c), Section 2–4, and Theorem 10 to prove that $\mathbf{v}_{n+1}$ can be expressed as a linear combination of $\mathbf{v}_1, \ldots, \mathbf{v}_n$ and thus reach a contradiction.

Theorem 10 says that, if a vector space $\mathscr{V}$ has one basis consisting of n (linearly independent) vectors, then each set of n linearly independent vectors in $\mathscr{V}$ forms a basis for $\mathscr{V}$. But is it true that *each basis* for $\mathscr{V}$ must contain exactly n vectors? We should naturally expect this to be the case, and indeed it is, as the next corollary shows:

COROLLARY 2. If a vector space $\mathscr{V}$ has one basis containing exactly n vectors, then every basis for $\mathscr{V}$ contains exactly n vectors. Equivalently, any two bases for $\mathscr{V}$ contain the same number of vectors.

Outline of proof: Assuming $\mathscr{V}$ has two bases containing different numbers of vectors, use Theorem 9 and Corollary 1 to arrive at a contradiction.

The number of vectors in a basis for a vector space is thus uniquely determined and is referred to as the *dimension* of the space:

DEFINITION 21. A nondegenerate vector space $\mathscr{V}$ is said to be *n-dimensional*, or to have *dimension n*, if, and only if, $\mathscr{V}$ has a basis of n vectors. A degenerate vector space is said to have dimension zero.

For instance, $\mathscr{V}_n$ is n-dimensional, since we know that the n unit vectors $\mathbf{e}_1^n, \ldots, \mathbf{e}_n^n$ form a basis for $\mathscr{V}_n$. This is in accord with our earlier definition of n by 1 matrices as n-dimensional column vectors. A vector space which has no basis is not assigned a dimension (see Exercise 4 for an example of such a space).

The next corollary is an application of the preceding results to $\mathscr{V}_n$:

COROLLARY 3. A set of vectors in $\mathscr{V}_n$ forms a basis for $\mathscr{V}_n$ if, and only if, it is a set of n linearly independent vectors.

Outline of proof: As we have seen previously, the unit basis, consisting of $\mathbf{e}_1^n, \mathbf{e}_2^n, \ldots, \mathbf{e}_n^n$, is one basis for $\mathscr{V}_n$. Now apply Theorems 9 and 10 and Corollary 2.

The next theorem, which is an easy consequence of previous results, expresses one of the most important properties of a basis:

THEOREM 11. If vectors $\mathbf{v}_1, \mathbf{v}_2, \ldots, \mathbf{v}_n$ form a basis for a nondegenerate vector space $\mathscr{V}$, then each vector in $\mathscr{V}$ can be expressed in exactly one way as a linear combination of $\mathbf{v}_1, \mathbf{v}_2, \ldots, \mathbf{v}_n$.

Outline of proof: Use Definition 20 and Theorem 7.

We conclude this section with a theorem which will be used in connection with the geometric interpretation of the simplex method in the next chapter. It provides the answer to the general question of which the following is a special case: Suppose we have a set of ten vectors and we know, for some reason, that among these can be found six linearly independent vectors. We find, by some means, two linearly independent vectors. Can we now be sure that four other vectors exist among the remaining eight to complete a linearly independent set of six, or does it depend on the way in which the first two are chosen?

THEOREM 12. Let $\mathbf{v}_1, \mathbf{v}_2, \ldots, \mathbf{v}_n$ $(n > 2)$ be vectors in some vector space $\mathscr{V}$, and assume that among these vectors are m linearly independent vectors $(2 \leqq m < n)$. Then, given any k of the vectors $(1 \leqq k < m)$ which are independent, a set of $m - k$ vectors can be chosen from among the remaining $n - k$ vectors which, when adjoined to the given set of k vectors, will yield a set of m linearly independent vectors.

Outline of proof: Assume that the maximum number of vectors which can be adjoined to the given k vectors is r, where $r < m - k$. Get a contradiction by showing that each of the n vectors must be a linear combination of such a set of $k + r$ vectors and, hence, that the $(k + r)$-dimensional space which they span contains more than $k + r$ linearly independent vectors.

EXERCISES

1. Classify each of the following sets of vectors in one of three ways: (i) a basis for $\mathcal{V}_3$, (ii) a set which is not a basis for $\mathcal{V}_3$, but spans $\mathcal{V}_3$, or (iii) a set which is not a basis for $\mathcal{V}_3$, and does not span $\mathcal{V}_3$.
(a) $\mathbf{v}_1 = [9, -3, 4]$, $\mathbf{v}_2 = [-11, 3, -5]$, $\mathbf{v}_3 = [2, -1, 1]$.
(b) $\mathbf{v}_1 = [2, 0, 11]$, $\mathbf{v}_2 = [18, -7, 6]$.
(c) $\mathbf{v}_1 = [10, 33, 16]$, $\mathbf{v}_2 = [4, 13, 6]$, $\mathbf{v}_3 = [-15, -49, -23]$, $\mathbf{v}_4 = [-5, -17, -9]$, $\mathbf{v}_5 = [1, 3, 1]$.
(d) $\mathbf{v}_1 = [-2, 4, 1]$, $\mathbf{v}_2 = [-5, 11, 3]$, $\mathbf{v}_3 = [-8, 18, 5]$.
(e) $\mathbf{v}_1 = [0, 3, 1]$, $\mathbf{v}_2 = [1, 1, -3]$, $\mathbf{v}_3 = [2, 0, -1]$, $\mathbf{v}_4 = [-1, 2, 1]$.

2. The complex numbers, with the operations of addition and scalar multiplication defined as usual, form a vector space. Give an example of a basis for this space. What is the dimension of this space?

3. The set $\mathcal{V}$ defined in Exercise 5, Section 2–3, is a vector space. Give an example of a basis for it, and state its dimension.

4. The two preceding exercises and the situation in $\mathcal{V}_n$ might leave one with the impression that, for any given vector space $\mathcal{V}$, there will be some integer n for which $\mathcal{V}$ has a basis consisting of n vectors. This exercise shows that this is not the case. Let $\mathcal{F}$ be the vector space of Example 25, Section 2–3, where we now take S to be the entire set of real numbers. For each integer $i = 1, 2, \ldots$, let f_i be the function defined on S by the rule $f_i(x) = x^{i-1}$.
(a) Prove that, for each positive integer n, the functions $f_1, f_2, \ldots, f_n$ are linearly independent.
(b) Assuming $\mathcal{F}$ has a basis, which result of this section is directly contradicted by the result of part (a)?

5. Let $\mathbf{v}_1, \mathbf{v}_2, \ldots, \mathbf{v}_n$ be vectors in a nondegenerate vector space $\mathcal{V}$. Prove that they form a basis for $\mathcal{V}$ if, and only if, they are linearly independent and span $\mathcal{V}$.

2–6. *COLUMN SPACES; CHANGE OF BASIS; BASIC SOLUTIONS.*

According to Exercise 9, Section 2–4, if $\mathbf{v}_1, \mathbf{v}_2, \ldots, \mathbf{v}_n$ are vectors in a vector space $\mathcal{V}$, then the set $\mathcal{V}'$ of all linear combinations of $\mathbf{v}_1, \mathbf{v}_2, \ldots, \mathbf{v}_n$ (with the operations of vector addition and scalar multiplication defined just as they are in $\mathcal{V}$) is itself a vector space. Since it is contained in $\mathcal{V}$ and is spanned by $\mathbf{v}_1, \mathbf{v}_2, \ldots, \mathbf{v}_n$, $\mathcal{V}'$ is called the *subspace of* $\mathcal{V}$ *spanned by* $\mathbf{v}_1, \mathbf{v}_2, \ldots, \mathbf{v}_n$. We are now going to consider a special case of this general situation.

Definition 22. Let $\mathbf{A}$ be an m by n matrix, and regard the columns of $\mathbf{A}$ as vectors $\mathbf{a}_1, \mathbf{a}_2, \ldots, \mathbf{a}_n$ in $\mathscr{V}_m$. Then the subspace of $\mathscr{V}_m$ which is spanned by $\mathbf{a}_1, \mathbf{a}_2, \ldots, \mathbf{a}_n$ is called the *column space of* $\mathbf{A}$.

In Section 2–2 we learned how to reduce any matrix to canonical form. Let us now see what this reduction to canonical form can tell us about the column space of the matrix. First we consider a particular numerical example:

Example 36. Suppose

$$\mathbf{A} = \begin{pmatrix} -3 & 4 & 27 & -1 & -7 & -25 & 5 \\ 28 & 1 & -8 & 1 & 12 & 32 & -3 \\ 45 & 3 & 1 & 2 & 17 & 44 & -3 \\ 22 & 1 & -3 & 1 & 9 & 24 & -2 \end{pmatrix},$$

and let the columns of $\mathbf{A}$ be called $\mathbf{a}_1, \mathbf{a}_2, \ldots, \mathbf{a}_7$. There is a sequence of elementary row transformations which will transform $\mathbf{A}$ into the following matrix $\mathbf{A}^*$ in canonical form:

$$\mathbf{A}^* = \begin{pmatrix} 2 & 0 & -1 & 0 & 1 & 3 & 0 \\ 3 & 1 & 4 & 0 & 0 & -2 & 0 \\ 0 & 0 & 2 & 0 & 0 & 1 & 1 \\ 1 & 0 & 6 & 1 & 0 & 1 & 0 \end{pmatrix}.$$

Note that the columns $\mathbf{a}_2$, $\mathbf{a}_4$, $\mathbf{a}_5$, and $\mathbf{a}_7$ have been transformed into the unit vectors $\mathbf{e}_2^4$, $\mathbf{e}_4^4$, $\mathbf{e}_1^4$, and $\mathbf{e}_3^4$, respectively. Let $\mathbf{A}_1$ be a matrix whose columns are $\mathbf{a}_2$, $\mathbf{a}_4$, $\mathbf{a}_5$, and $\mathbf{a}_7$ in some order, and let $\mathbf{B}_1$ be a matrix whose columns are the remaining columns of $\mathbf{A}$. For definiteness, let

$$\mathbf{A}_1 = \begin{pmatrix} 4 & -1 & -7 & 5 \\ 1 & 1 & 12 & -3 \\ 3 & 2 & 17 & -3 \\ 1 & 1 & 9 & -2 \end{pmatrix}, \qquad \mathbf{B}_1 = \begin{pmatrix} -3 & 27 & -25 \\ 28 & -8 & 32 \\ 45 & 1 & 44 \\ 22 & -3 & 24 \end{pmatrix}.$$

Suppose we wish to solve the matrix equation $\mathbf{A}_1\mathbf{X} = \mathbf{B}_1$. Then we could write down the matrix $(\mathbf{A}_1|\mathbf{B}_1)$ and apply to it the same sequence of row transformations used to obtain $\mathbf{A}^*$ from $\mathbf{A}$. The resulting matrix would be the same as $\mathbf{A}^*$, except that the columns would be rearranged. In fact, the result would be

$$(\mathbf{A}_1^*|\mathbf{B}_1^*) = \left(\begin{array}{cccc|ccc} 0 & 0 & 1 & 0 & 2 & -1 & 3 \\ 1 & 0 & 0 & 0 & 3 & 4 & -2 \\ 0 & 0 & 0 & 1 & 0 & 2 & 1 \\ 0 & 1 & 0 & 0 & 1 & 6 & 1 \end{array}\right).$$

As we saw in Section 2–4, what we have done here may be thought of as expressing the columns of $\mathbf{B}_1$ as linear combinations of the columns of $\mathbf{A}_1$. Thus,

$$\begin{aligned} \mathbf{a}_1 &= 2\mathbf{a}_5 + 3\mathbf{a}_2 + 0\mathbf{a}_7 + \mathbf{a}_4, \\ \mathbf{a}_3 &= -\mathbf{a}_5 + 4\mathbf{a}_2 + 2\mathbf{a}_7 + 6\mathbf{a}_4, \\ \mathbf{a}_6 &= 3\mathbf{a}_5 - 2\mathbf{a}_2 + \mathbf{a}_7 + \mathbf{a}_4. \end{aligned} \tag{35}$$

It is clear also that the vectors $\mathbf{a}_2$, $\mathbf{a}_4$, $\mathbf{a}_5$, and $\mathbf{a}_7$ are linearly independent and hence form a basis for $\mathscr{V}_4$, which, in this case, is the column space of **A**. Note that Eqs. (35) can be read directly from $\mathbf{A}^*$. It is not necessary, in practice, to rearrange the columns.

In general, suppose we start with an m by n nonzero matrix **A**. By applying a certain sequence of elementary row transformations, we shall obtain a matrix $\mathbf{A}^*$ in canonical form. Let k be the number of distinct m-dimensional unit vectors which appear among the columns of $\mathbf{A}^*$, let $\mathbf{A}_1$ be an m by k matrix (a *submatrix* of **A**) whose columns are the columns of **A** which are transformed into these k unit vectors, and let $\mathbf{B}_1$ be an m by $(n-k)$ matrix whose columns are the remaining columns of **A**. If we apply to $(\mathbf{A}_1 \mid \mathbf{B}_1)$ the same sequence of row transformations used to obtain $\mathbf{A}^*$ from **A**, plus (possibly) some additional row interchanges, we obtain a matrix with the following appearance:

$$\begin{array}{r} k\left\{\begin{array}{c} \\ \\ \\ \\ \\ \end{array}\right. \\ m-k\left\{\begin{array}{c} \\ \\ \\ \\ \end{array}\right. \end{array} \left(\begin{array}{cccc|ccc} \multicolumn{4}{c|}{\overbrace{\hphantom{1\;0\;\cdots\;0}}^{k}} & \multicolumn{3}{c}{\overbrace{\hphantom{*\;\cdots\;*}}^{n-k}} \\ 1 & 0 & \cdots & 0 & * & \cdots & * \\ 0 & 1 & \cdots & 0 & * & \cdots & * \\ \vdots & \vdots & & \vdots & \vdots & & \vdots \\ 0 & 0 & \cdots & 1 & * & \cdots & * \\ 0 & 0 & \cdots & 0 & 0 & \cdots & 0 \\ \vdots & \vdots & & \vdots & \vdots & & \vdots \\ 0 & 0 & \cdots & 0 & 0 & \cdots & 0 \end{array}\right) \tag{36}$$

The asterisks simply denote the (possibly) nonzero numbers which will appear in the last $n-k$ columns of (36). From this matrix it is evident that the columns of $\mathbf{A}_1$ are linearly independent and that each of the columns not in $\mathbf{A}_1$ can be uniquely expressed as a linear combination of them. Thus, any linear combination of the columns of **A** can be written as a linear combination of the columns of $\mathbf{A}_1$. Therefore, the columns of $\mathbf{A}_1$ span the column space of **A**, are linearly independent, and so (see Exercise 5, Section 2–5) they form a basis for the column space of **A**. Consequently, no matter what sequence of row transformations is used to transform **A** into a canonical matrix $\mathbf{A}^*$, those columns of **A** which transform into the distinct unit vectors appearing in **A** will constitute a basis for the column space of **A**. This implies in particular that, no matter what sequence of row operations is used, the same number of distinct unit vectors will appear in the resulting canonical matrix. This number is the dimension of the column space and is also given another name, as follows:

DEFINITION 23. The dimension of the column space of a matrix **A** is called the *rank of* **A** (written *rank* **A**).

Thus, the rank of the matrix **A** in Example 36 is 4. Notice that the rank of a matrix can also be thought of as the maximum number of linearly independent columns in the matrix. It cannot exceed the smaller of the two dimensions of the matrix.

We now give another example to illustrate further the ideas discussed above:

Example 37. Suppose a given 4 by 6 matrix **A** with columns $\mathbf{a}_1, \mathbf{a}_2, \ldots, \mathbf{a}_6$ is transformed by elementary row operations into the matrix

$$\mathbf{A}^* = \begin{pmatrix} 0 & -2 & 1 & 3 & 0 & 6 \\ 0 & 0 & 0 & 0 & 0 & 0 \\ 1 & 4 & 0 & 5 & 0 & 4 \\ 0 & 10 & 0 & -2 & 1 & 7 \end{pmatrix}.$$

Then the rank of **A** is 3, the vectors $\mathbf{a}_1$, $\mathbf{a}_3$, and $\mathbf{a}_5$ form a basis for the column space of **A**, and the columns of **A** are expressed in terms of this basis as follows:

$$\begin{aligned}
\mathbf{a}_1 &= 0\mathbf{a}_3 + 1\mathbf{a}_1 + 0\mathbf{a}_5, \\
\mathbf{a}_2 &= -2\mathbf{a}_3 + 4\mathbf{a}_1 + 10\mathbf{a}_5, \\
\mathbf{a}_3 &= 1\mathbf{a}_3 + 0\mathbf{a}_1 + 0\mathbf{a}_5, \\
\mathbf{a}_4 &= 3\mathbf{a}_3 + 5\mathbf{a}_1 - 2\mathbf{a}_5, \\
\mathbf{a}_5 &= 0\mathbf{a}_3 + 0\mathbf{a}_1 + 1\mathbf{a}_5, \\
\mathbf{a}_6 &= 6\mathbf{a}_3 + 4\mathbf{a}_1 + 7\mathbf{a}_5.
\end{aligned}$$

In general, for a given matrix **A**, many different bases for its column space can be found among its columns. Once we have determined one basis by reducing **A** to canonical form, as just described, we could start over with the original matrix **A**, use a different sequence of transformations, and (possibly) obtain a different basis. However, there is a more efficient and systematic procedure for determining other bases from a known basis, which we are now going to describe and which is the heart of the simplex computational process to be discussed in the next chapter. The procedure is the same as that used in the proof of Theorem 10. Starting with a known basis chosen from the columns of **A**, we replace one of the basis vectors with one of the columns of **A** not in the initial basis, then replace one of the vectors in the new basis with a column of **A** not in the new basis, and so on, changing just one vector at a time. The following theorem makes clear just which replacements are possible for a given basis:

THEOREM 13. Suppose the vectors $\mathbf{v}_1, \mathbf{v}_2, \ldots, \mathbf{v}_n$ form a basis for a nondegenerate vector space $\mathscr{V}$. Let $\mathbf{v}$ be any vector in $\mathscr{V}$, and let $c_1, c_2, \ldots, c_n$ be the uniquely determined numbers such that

$$\mathbf{v} = c_1\mathbf{v}_1 + c_2\mathbf{v}_2 + \cdots + c_n\mathbf{v}_n. \tag{37}$$

Suppose we remove the vector $\mathbf{v}_i$ from the basis and replace it by the vector $\mathbf{v}$. Then the resulting set of vectors is a basis for $\mathscr{V}$ if, and only if, $c_i \neq 0$.

Proof: For convenience of notation, assume $i = 1$, i.e., $\mathbf{v}_1$ is removed from the basis and replaced by $\mathbf{v}$. Then we wish to prove that the vectors $\mathbf{v}, \mathbf{v}_2, \ldots, \mathbf{v}_n$ form a basis if, and only if, $c_1 \neq 0$.

Suppose first that $c_1 = 0$. Then, from (37), we have

$$\mathbf{v} = c_2\mathbf{v}_2 + \cdots + c_n\mathbf{v}_n,$$

which implies that the vectors $\mathbf{v}, \mathbf{v}_2, \ldots, \mathbf{v}_n$ are linearly dependent and so do *not* form a basis for $\mathscr{V}$.

Now suppose that $c_1 \neq 0$. To prove that $\mathbf{v}, \mathbf{v}_2, \ldots, \mathbf{v}_n$ form a basis, it is sufficient to prove that they are linearly independent (see Theorem 10). Suppose an equation of the form

$$b_1\mathbf{v} + b_2\mathbf{v}_2 + \cdots + b_n\mathbf{v}_n = \mathbf{0} \tag{38}$$

holds. If $b_1 \neq 0$, then we can solve (38) for $\mathbf{v}$, obtaining an expression of the form

$$\mathbf{v} = d_2\mathbf{v}_2 + \cdots + d_n\mathbf{v}_n. \tag{39}$$

But (37) and (39) are contradictory, since $c_1 \neq 0$ and Theorem 11 says that $\mathbf{v}$ can be expressed in *exactly one way* as a linear combination of the basis vectors $\mathbf{v}_1, \mathbf{v}_2, \ldots, \mathbf{v}_n$. Hence, we must have $b_1 = 0$. But then (38) becomes

$$b_2\mathbf{v}_2 + \cdots + b_n\mathbf{v}_n = \mathbf{0},$$

which implies $b_2 = \cdots = b_n = 0$, because the vectors $\mathbf{v}_2, \ldots, \mathbf{v}_n$ are linearly independent. Thus (38) holds only if $b_1 = b_2 = \cdots = b_n = 0$, which means that the vectors $\mathbf{v}, \mathbf{v}_2, \ldots, \mathbf{v}_n$ are linearly independent. This completes the proof.

To illustrate the computational process for replacing a basis vector by another vector, let us return to Example 36. We have already found that the columns $\mathbf{a}_2$, $\mathbf{a}_4$, $\mathbf{a}_5$, and $\mathbf{a}_7$ of the original matrix $\mathbf{A}$ form a basis for $\mathscr{V}_4$. Suppose we wish to insert $\mathbf{a}_1$ into the basis in place of one of these four vectors. Which of the vectors $\mathbf{a}_2, \mathbf{a}_4, \mathbf{a}_5, \mathbf{a}_7$ can be replaced by $\mathbf{a}_1$? According to the theorem just proved, to answer this question we must first express $\mathbf{a}_1$ as a linear combination of $\mathbf{a}_2$, $\mathbf{a}_4$, $\mathbf{a}_5$, and $\mathbf{a}_7$. Then $\mathbf{a}_1$ can replace any one of these vectors which appears with a nonzero coefficient in that linear combination. The first of Eqs. (35) tells us that $\mathbf{a}_1$ can replace any one of the three vectors $\mathbf{a}_5$, $\mathbf{a}_2$, and $\mathbf{a}_4$, but not $\mathbf{a}_7$. Suppose we decide to insert $\mathbf{a}_1$ into the basis in place of $\mathbf{a}_2$ and we wish to determine the coefficients of each of the columns of **A** relative to this new basis consisting of $\mathbf{a}_1$, $\mathbf{a}_4$, $\mathbf{a}_5$, and $\mathbf{a}_7$. This amounts to solving the matrix equation $\mathbf{A}_2\mathbf{X} = \mathbf{B}_2$, where $\mathbf{A}_2$ denotes a matrix whose columns are $\mathbf{a}_1$, $\mathbf{a}_4$, $\mathbf{a}_5$, and $\mathbf{a}_7$ and $\mathbf{B}_2$ is a matrix composed of the remaining columns of **A**. Since, in the matrix $\mathbf{A}^*$ obtained in Example 36, the columns $\mathbf{a}_4$, $\mathbf{a}_5$, and $\mathbf{a}_7$ of $\mathbf{A}_2$ have already been transformed into the unit vectors $\mathbf{e}_4^4$, $\mathbf{e}_1^4$, and $\mathbf{e}_3^4$, respectively, it remains only to perform a sequence of row operations which will transform $\mathbf{a}_1$ into $\mathbf{e}_2^4$. This requires using the element 3 of column one of **A** as pivot element and performing some row transformations of types II and III, as follows:

$$(40)\qquad \begin{pmatrix} 2 & 0 & -1 & 0 & 1 & 3 & 0 \\ \textcircled{3} & 1 & 4 & 0 & 0 & -2 & 0 \\ 0 & 0 & 2 & 0 & 0 & 1 & 1 \\ 1 & 0 & 6 & 1 & 0 & 1 & 0 \end{pmatrix} \longrightarrow \begin{pmatrix} 0 & -\frac{2}{3} & -\frac{11}{3} & 0 & 1 & \frac{13}{3} & 0 \\ 1 & \frac{1}{3} & \frac{4}{3} & 0 & 0 & -\frac{2}{3} & 0 \\ 0 & 0 & 2 & 0 & 0 & 1 & 1 \\ 0 & -\frac{1}{3} & \frac{14}{3} & 1 & 0 & \frac{5}{3} & 0 \end{pmatrix}.$$

From the second matrix in (40), we see that

$$(41)\qquad \begin{aligned} \mathbf{a}_1 &= 0\mathbf{a}_5 + 1\mathbf{a}_1 + 0\mathbf{a}_7 + 0\mathbf{a}_4, \\ \mathbf{a}_2 &= -\tfrac{2}{3}\mathbf{a}_5 + \tfrac{1}{3}\mathbf{a}_1 + 0\mathbf{a}_7 - \tfrac{1}{3}\mathbf{a}_4, \\ \mathbf{a}_3 &= -\tfrac{11}{3}\mathbf{a}_5 + \tfrac{4}{3}\mathbf{a}_1 + 2\mathbf{a}_7 + \tfrac{14}{3}\mathbf{a}_4, \\ \mathbf{a}_4 &= 0\mathbf{a}_5 + 0\mathbf{a}_1 + 0\mathbf{a}_7 + 1\mathbf{a}_4, \\ \mathbf{a}_5 &= 1\mathbf{a}_5 + 0\mathbf{a}_1 + 0\mathbf{a}_7 + 0\mathbf{a}_4, \\ \mathbf{a}_6 &= \tfrac{13}{3}\mathbf{a}_5 - \tfrac{2}{3}\mathbf{a}_1 + 1\mathbf{a}_7 + \tfrac{5}{3}\mathbf{a}_4, \\ \mathbf{a}_7 &= 0\mathbf{a}_5 + 0\mathbf{a}_1 + 1\mathbf{a}_7 + 0\mathbf{a}_4. \end{aligned}$$

We can display our results more clearly and keep better track of our changes of basis, if we label the rows and columns of our matrices as indicated below, which is just a rewriting of (40):

(42)

Basis	$\mathbf{a}_1$	$\mathbf{a}_2$	$\mathbf{a}_3$	$\mathbf{a}_4$	$\mathbf{a}_5$	$\mathbf{a}_6$	$\mathbf{a}_7$
$\mathbf{a}_5$	2	0	−1	0	1	3	0
$\mathbf{a}_2$	(3)	1	4	0	0	−2	0
$\mathbf{a}_7$	0	0	2	0	0	1	1
$\mathbf{a}_4$	1	0	6	1	0	1	0
$\mathbf{a}_5$	0	$-\frac{2}{3}$	$-\frac{11}{3}$	0	1	$\frac{13}{3}$	0
$\mathbf{a}_1$	1	$\frac{1}{3}$	$\frac{4}{3}$	0	0	$-\frac{2}{3}$	0
$\mathbf{a}_7$	0	0	2	0	0	1	1
$\mathbf{a}_4$	0	$-\frac{1}{3}$	$\frac{14}{3}$	1	0	$\frac{5}{3}$	0

We shall refer to arrays such as these as *tableaux*. The number appearing in such a tableau in the row labeled $\mathbf{a}_i$ and the column labeled $\mathbf{a}_j$ is the coefficient, say c_{ij}, of the vector $\mathbf{a}_i$ in the expression of $\mathbf{a}_j$ as a linear combination of the basis vectors. If, and only if, c_{ij} is not zero and $\mathbf{a}_j$ is not in that particular basis, then $\mathbf{a}_j$ can replace $\mathbf{a}_i$ to form a new basis. The computational procedure for obtaining the coefficients of the various columns relative to this new basis (assuming $c_{ij} \neq 0$) consists of using c_{ij} as the pivot element and performing the usual sequence of row transformations of types II and III.

As another example, we indicate a change of basis in Example 37 in which $\mathbf{a}_2$ replaces $\mathbf{a}_3$:

(43)

Basis	$\mathbf{a}_1$	$\mathbf{a}_2$	$\mathbf{a}_3$	$\mathbf{a}_4$	$\mathbf{a}_5$	$\mathbf{a}_6$
$\mathbf{a}_3$	0	(-2)	1	3	0	6
$\mathbf{a}_1$	1	4	0	5	0	4
$\mathbf{a}_5$	0	10	0	-2	1	7

Basis	$\mathbf{a}_1$	$\mathbf{a}_2$	$\mathbf{a}_3$	$\mathbf{a}_4$	$\mathbf{a}_5$	$\mathbf{a}_6$
$\mathbf{a}_2$	0	1	$-\frac{1}{2}$	$-\frac{3}{2}$	0	-3
$\mathbf{a}_1$	1	0	2	11	0	16
$\mathbf{a}_5$	0	0	5	13	1	37

From the second of these tableaux, we read the following information:

$$
\begin{aligned}
\mathbf{a}_1 &= 0\mathbf{a}_2 + 1\mathbf{a}_1 + 0\mathbf{a}_5,\\
\mathbf{a}_2 &= 1\mathbf{a}_2 + 0\mathbf{a}_1 + 0\mathbf{a}_5,\\
\mathbf{a}_3 &= -\tfrac{1}{2}\mathbf{a}_2 + 2\mathbf{a}_1 + 5\mathbf{a}_5,\\
\mathbf{a}_4 &= -\tfrac{3}{2}\mathbf{a}_2 + 11\mathbf{a}_1 + 13\mathbf{a}_5,\\
\mathbf{a}_5 &= 0\mathbf{a}_2 + 0\mathbf{a}_1 + 1\mathbf{a}_5,\\
\mathbf{a}_6 &= -3\mathbf{a}_2 + 16\mathbf{a}_1 + 37\mathbf{a}_5.
\end{aligned}
$$

Now let us consider a linear system $\mathbf{Ax} = \mathbf{b}$ in the light of the above discussion. At least one solution exists if, and only if, $\mathbf{b}$ is a linear combination of the columns of $\mathbf{A}$, i.e., $\mathbf{b}$ is in the column space of $\mathbf{A}$. From this the following theorem follows easily. The details of its proof are left to the student.

THEOREM 14. A linear system $\mathbf{Ax} = \mathbf{b}$ has at least one solution if, and only if, the column spaces of the coefficient matrix $\mathbf{A}$ and the augmented matrix $(\mathbf{A}\,|\,\mathbf{b})$ are the same.

In terms of *rank*, we can state necessary and sufficient conditions for solvability of a linear system as follows:

THEOREM 15. A linear system $\mathbf{Ax} = \mathbf{b}$ has at least one solution if, and only if, its coefficient matrix $\mathbf{A}$ and its augmented matrix $(\mathbf{A}|\mathbf{b})$ have the same rank.

Proof: If a system $\mathbf{Ax} = \mathbf{b}$ is known to have at least one solution, then, by Theorem 14, the column spaces of $\mathbf{A}$ and $(\mathbf{A}|\mathbf{b})$ are identical. Hence, rank $\mathbf{A}$ = rank $(\mathbf{A}\,|\,\mathbf{b})$.

Now suppose we have a system $\mathbf{Ax} = \mathbf{b}$ which has no solution. We wish to show that rank $\mathbf{A} \neq$ rank $(\mathbf{A}\,|\,\mathbf{b})$. If $\mathbf{A}$ is a zero matrix, then $\mathbf{b} \neq \mathbf{0}$ and we have $0 = \text{rank } \mathbf{A} < 1 = \text{rank } (\mathbf{A}|\mathbf{b})$. Hence, suppose $\mathbf{A}$ is nonzero. For convenience, suppose the columns $\mathbf{a}_1, \ldots, \mathbf{a}_k$ of $\mathbf{A}$ form a basis for the column space of $\mathbf{A}$. Then the vectors $\mathbf{a}_1, \ldots, \mathbf{a}_k, \mathbf{b}$ form a linearly independent set. To prove this, suppose

(44) $$c_1\mathbf{a}_1 + \cdots + c_k\mathbf{a}_k + c_{k+1}\mathbf{b} = \mathbf{0}.$$

Then we must have $c_{k+1} = 0$, or else, from (44), we could express $\mathbf{b}$ as a linear combination of $\mathbf{a}_1, \ldots, \mathbf{a}_k$, contrary to our supposition that $\mathbf{Ax} = \mathbf{b}$ has no solution. But, with $c_{k+1} = 0$, (44) reduces to

$$c_1\mathbf{a}_1 + \cdots + c_k\mathbf{a}_k = \mathbf{0},$$

which implies $c_i = 0$ $(i = 1, \ldots, k)$ because of the independence of $\mathbf{a}_1, \ldots, \mathbf{a}_k$. Thus, (44) holds only if $c_i = 0$ $(i = 1, \ldots, k + 1)$, which proves that $\mathbf{a}_1, \ldots, \mathbf{a}_k$, and $\mathbf{b}$ form a linearly independent set. Since $\mathbf{a}_1, \ldots, \mathbf{a}_k$ span the column space of $\mathbf{A}$, it follows that $\mathbf{a}_1, \ldots, \mathbf{a}_k, \mathbf{b}$ span the column space of $(\mathbf{A} \mid \mathbf{b})$ and hence form a basis for this column space. Therefore, if $\mathbf{Ax} = \mathbf{b}$ has no solution, we have

$$\text{Rank } (\mathbf{A} \mid \mathbf{b}) = 1 + \text{rank } \mathbf{A} \neq \text{rank } \mathbf{A},$$

which completes the proof.

For any system $\mathbf{Ax} = \mathbf{b}$, it is evident that rank $\mathbf{A} \leqq$ rank $(\mathbf{A} \mid \mathbf{b})$. What we have just proved is that solutions exist if, and only if, the equality holds. When we reduce the augmented matrix $(\mathbf{A} \mid \mathbf{b})$ to canonical form, we automatically determine the ranks of $\mathbf{A}$ and $(\mathbf{A} \mid \mathbf{b})$, bases for the column spaces of $\mathbf{A}$ and $(\mathbf{A} \mid \mathbf{b})$ (their common basis if solutions exist), and all linear combinations of the columns of $\mathbf{A}$ which equal $\mathbf{b}$. If we denote by $(\mathbf{A}^* \mid \mathbf{b}^*)$ the canonical augmented matrix into which $(\mathbf{A} \mid \mathbf{b})$ is transformed and if we assume rank $\mathbf{A}$ = rank $(\mathbf{A} \mid \mathbf{b})$, then we know that the elements of $\mathbf{b}^*$ are the coefficients of $\mathbf{b}$ relative to the particular basis determined by our sequence of row transformations. These numbers determine one solution of our system—one in which each arbitrary unknown is assigned the value 0. If the rank of $\mathbf{A}$ equals the number of equations, such a solution is called a *basic solution.* Basic solutions play an important role in the simplex process; they are precisely defined as follows:

DEFINITION 24. Let $\mathbf{Ax} = \mathbf{b}$ be a system of m equations in n unknowns in which rank $\mathbf{A} = m$. A *basic solution* of $\mathbf{Ax} = \mathbf{b}$ is a solution $\mathbf{x} = [x_1, x_2, \ldots, x_n]$ obtained in the following way: Select a basis for $\mathscr{V}_m$ from the columns $\mathbf{a}_1, \mathbf{a}_2, \ldots, \mathbf{a}_n$ of $\mathbf{A}$, and express $\mathbf{b}$ as a linear combination of these basis vectors. For each j such that $\mathbf{a}_j$ is in the basis selected, let x_j be the coefficient of $\mathbf{a}_j$ in this linear combination. For each j such that $\mathbf{a}_j$ is not in the basis selected, let $x_j = 0$. The unknowns corresponding to basis vectors are called *basic variables;* the remaining unknowns are called *nonbasic variables.*

As an illustration, let us find some basic solutions in a numerical example:

Example 38. Consider the system

$$\begin{cases} 3x_1 - 14x_2 + 40x_3 + 9x_4 + x_5 = 10, \\ x_1 - 2x_2 + 13x_3 + 2x_4 + x_5 = 12, \\ 2x_1 - 7x_2 + 25x_3 + 5x_4 + x_5 = 12. \end{cases}$$

By a properly chosen sequence of row transformations, its augmented matrix can be transformed into the following matrix:

$$\left(\begin{array}{ccccc|c} 0 & -2 & 3 & 1 & 0 & -2 \\ 1 & 1 & 3 & 0 & 0 & 6 \\ 0 & 1 & 4 & 0 & 1 & 10 \end{array}\right).$$

From this we see that $\mathbf{b} = -2\mathbf{a}_4 + 6\mathbf{a}_1 + 10\mathbf{a}_5$ if we label the columns in the usual way. Hence, one basic solution is $\mathbf{x} = [6, 0, 0, -2, 10]$. To obtain other basic solutions, we have to find other bases among the columns of **A** and determine the coefficients of **b** relative to these bases. We illustrate by making a change of basis, using the technique and the tableau format described earlier in this section:

(45)

Basis	$\mathbf{a}_1$	$\mathbf{a}_2$	$\mathbf{a}_3$	$\mathbf{a}_4$	$\mathbf{a}_5$	$\mathbf{b}$
$\mathbf{a}_4$	0	−2	3	1	0	−2
$\mathbf{a}_1$	1	(1)	3	0	0	6
$\mathbf{a}_5$	0	1	4	0	1	10

Basis	$\mathbf{a}_1$	$\mathbf{a}_2$	$\mathbf{a}_3$	$\mathbf{a}_4$	$\mathbf{a}_5$	$\mathbf{b}$
$\mathbf{a}_4$	2	0	9	1	0	10
$\mathbf{a}_2$	1	1	3	0	0	6
$\mathbf{a}_5$	−1	0	1	0	1	4

The tableau on the left in (45) exhibits the basic solution $\mathbf{x} = [6, 0, 0, -2, 10]$ already found. The one on the right exhibits another basic solution, $\mathbf{x} = [0, 6, 0, 10, 4]$, found by inserting the vector $\mathbf{a}_2$ into the basis in place of $\mathbf{a}_1$. In Exercise 7, the student is asked to continue the computations and find other basic solutions.

Notice that, for a system $\mathbf{Ax} = \mathbf{b}$ with m equations and n unknowns, no basic solution exists if rank $\mathbf{A} < m$. If rank $\mathbf{A} = m$, there will be as many basic solutions as there are sets of m linearly independent vectors which can be found among the n columns of **A**. This cannot exceed (but need not equal) the number of combinations of n objects taken m at a time, which is $n!/m!(n-m)!$. In Example 38 ($m = 3$, $n = 5$), this number is $5!/3!2! = 10$. We leave it to the student to determine whether 10 basic solutions actually exist.

A basic solution of a system of m equations in n unknowns is an n-dimensional column vector with at least $n - m$ zero components, since each component corresponding to a nonbasis vector is zero. If, in addition, at least one of the components corresponding to a basis vector is zero, then the solution is called a *degenerate* basic solution. Otherwise, it is called a *nondegenerate* basic solution. If $m = 3$ and we picture the vectors geometrically as directed line segments, then a degenerate basic solution is one for which **b** lies in the plane determined by two of the basis vectors (or on the line determined by one of the basis vectors if there are two extra zeros) and a nondegenerate basic solution is one for which this is not the case.

EXERCISES

1. In Example 37, suppose that $\mathbf{a}_1 = [2, -5, 1, 4]$, $\mathbf{a}_3 = [0, 1, 1, 2]$, and $\mathbf{a}_5 = [6, 0, -1, 2]$. Find the original matrix $\mathbf{A}$.

2. Determine the rank of each of the following matrices:

(a) $\begin{pmatrix} 2 & 5 & -4 \\ 0 & 1 & 2 \\ 0 & 0 & 6 \end{pmatrix}$ (b) $\begin{pmatrix} 0 & 3 \\ 0 & 0 \end{pmatrix}$

(c) $\begin{pmatrix} 3 & -2 & 6 & 1 & 2 \\ 0 & 0 & 0 & -1 & 1 \\ 0 & 0 & 0 & 3 & -2 \\ 1 & 0 & 0 & 1 & 0 \end{pmatrix}$ (d) $\begin{pmatrix} 2 & -1 \\ 0 & 0 \\ -4 & 2 \\ 2 & 5 \end{pmatrix}$

3. The following tableau displays the coefficients of six column vectors $\mathbf{a}_1, \ldots, \mathbf{a}_6$ relative to a basis composed of $\mathbf{a}_4$, $\mathbf{a}_2$, and $\mathbf{a}_5$. Insert first $\mathbf{a}_1$ for $\mathbf{a}_5$ and then $\mathbf{a}_3$ for $\mathbf{a}_4$ and so obtain a tableau displaying the coefficients of $\mathbf{a}_1, \ldots, \mathbf{a}_6$ relative to $\mathbf{a}_3$, $\mathbf{a}_2$, and $\mathbf{a}_1$. Why cannot the replacement of $\mathbf{a}_4$ by $\mathbf{a}_3$ be made first?

Basis	$\mathbf{a}_1$	$\mathbf{a}_2$	$\mathbf{a}_3$	$\mathbf{a}_4$	$\mathbf{a}_5$	$\mathbf{a}_6$
$\mathbf{a}_4$	2	0	0	1	0	2
$\mathbf{a}_2$	5	1	3	0	0	0
$\mathbf{a}_5$	−1	0	4	0	1	6

4. Starting with the first tableau in (42), determine all tableaux corresponding to bases containing $\mathbf{a}_5$, $\mathbf{a}_2$, and $\mathbf{a}_4$.

5. Continuing the computation begun in (43), determine all tableaux corresponding to bases containing $\mathbf{a}_1$ and $\mathbf{a}_5$.

6. Suppose $\mathbf{A}$ is an m by n matrix with $m < n$, rank $\mathbf{A} = m$, and columns $\mathbf{a}_1, \mathbf{a}_2, \ldots, \mathbf{a}_n$. Suppose that columns $\mathbf{a}_1, \ldots, \mathbf{a}_m$ form a basis for the column space of $\mathbf{A}$, and, for each $i = 1, \ldots, m$ and $j = 1, \ldots, n$, let y_{ij} be the coefficient of $\mathbf{a}_i$ in the expression of $\mathbf{a}_j$ as a linear combination of $\mathbf{a}_1, \ldots, \mathbf{a}_m$; i.e., we have

$$\mathbf{a}_j = \sum_{i=1}^{m} y_{ij}\mathbf{a}_i = y_{1j}\mathbf{a}_1 + y_{2j}\mathbf{a}_2 + \cdots + y_{mj}\mathbf{a}_m \tag{46}$$

for each $j = 1, 2, \ldots, n$.

(a) In order that $\mathbf{a}_r$, where $r > m$, can replace $\mathbf{a}_1$ in the basis, what must be true?

(b) Assuming this condition is satisfied, express $\mathbf{a}_1$ as a linear combination of $\mathbf{a}_r, \mathbf{a}_2, \ldots, \mathbf{a}_m$.

(c) Substitute the expression for $\mathbf{a}_1$ found in (b) into (46), and combine terms to obtain the following expression for $\mathbf{a}_j$ in terms of the basis $\mathbf{a}_r, \mathbf{a}_2, \ldots, \mathbf{a}_m$:

(47) $$\mathbf{a}_j = \frac{y_{1j}}{y_{1r}}\mathbf{a}_r + \sum_{i=2}^{m}\left(y_{ij} - \frac{y_{ir}}{y_{1r}}y_{1j}\right)\mathbf{a}_i.$$

(d) Verify that (47) is in agreement with the results obtained from the following tableau by suitable row transformations:

Basis	$\mathbf{a}_1$	$\mathbf{a}_2$	$\cdots$	$\mathbf{a}_i$	$\cdots$	$\mathbf{a}_m$	$\cdots$	$\mathbf{a}_r$	$\cdots$	$\mathbf{a}_j$	$\cdots$
$\mathbf{a}_1$	1	0	$\cdots$	0	$\cdots$	0	$\cdots$	y_{1r}	$\cdots$	y_{1j}	$\cdots$
$\mathbf{a}_2$	0	1	$\cdots$	0	$\cdots$	0	$\cdots$	y_{2r}	$\cdots$	y_{2j}	$\cdots$
$\vdots$	$\vdots$	$\vdots$		$\vdots$		$\vdots$		$\vdots$		$\vdots$	
$\mathbf{a}_i$	0	0	$\cdots$	1	$\cdots$	0	$\cdots$	y_{ir}	$\cdots$	y_{ij}	$\cdots$
$\vdots$	$\vdots$	$\vdots$		$\vdots$		$\vdots$		$\vdots$		$\vdots$	
$\mathbf{a}_m$	0	0	$\cdots$	0	$\cdots$	1	$\cdots$	y_{mr}	$\cdots$	y_{mj}	$\cdots$

7. Continue the computations begun in (45), and determine all basic solutions in which one of the basic variables is x_5.

8. For the system

$$\begin{cases} 6x_1 - x_2 + 14x_3 - 20x_4 + 7x_5 = -16, \\ 2x_1 + x_2 - 5x_3 + 10x_4 - 3x_5 = 11, \\ x_1 + x_2 - 7x_3 + 12x_4 - 4x_5 = 13, \end{cases}$$

first find the basic solution in which x_1 and x_4 are zero. Then, by making a change of basis, find the basic solution in which x_1 and x_5 are zero. Use the tableau format, as in Example 38.

9. Find all basic solutions of the system

$$\begin{cases} x_1 + 2x_2 - x_3 + 2x_4 = 0, \\ 4x_1 + 9x_2 - 3x_3 + 11x_4 = 1, \\ x_1 + 5x_2 + 3x_3 + 9x_4 = 5. \end{cases}$$

10. The following tableau displays a basic solution of a certain system $\mathbf{Ax} = \mathbf{b}$ of three equations in five unknowns:

Basis	$\mathbf{a}_1$	$\mathbf{a}_2$	$\mathbf{a}_3$	$\mathbf{a}_4$	$\mathbf{a}_5$	$\mathbf{b}$
$\mathbf{a}_3$	0	0	1	2	1	2
$\mathbf{a}_1$	1	0	0	3	1	1
$\mathbf{a}_2$	0	1	0	3	2	4

Note that the basic variables are all positive. Successively insert $\mathbf{a}_5$ and $\mathbf{a}_4$ into the basis, and determine the vector to be removed in each case so that the basic variables in each solution are positive. Write down the two new basic solutions which you find.

11. We have considered the problem of making a change of basis only in the vector spaces $\mathscr{V}_m$, but actually the procedure we have described can be used in any vector space with a basis. If we know one basis for a vector space $\mathscr{V}$ and we are considering a finite collection of vectors in $\mathscr{V}$, each of which has a known expression in terms of these basis vectors, this information can be displayed in a tableau and changes of basis can be made by operating on this tableau in exactly the manner described in this section. As an illustration, let $\mathscr{V}$ be the vector space of all polynomials $Ax^2 + Bx + C$ with real coefficients A, B, and C. Algebraic operations are defined in the ordinary way. One basis for $\mathscr{V}$ consists of functions e_1, e_2, e_3, where $e_1(x) = 1$, $e_2(x) = x$, and $e_3(x) = x^2$. Let v_1, v_2, and v_3 be the functions defined as follows: $v_1(x) = 1 + x$, $v_2(x) = 1 + x + x^2$, and $v_3(x) = 3x^2 - 2x + 4$. Complete the following tableau, and then, by making appropriate changes of basis, express v_3 as a linear combination of e_1, v_1, and v_2:

Basis	e_1	e_2	e_3	v_1	v_2	v_3
e_1	1	0	0			
e_2	0	1	0			
e_3	0	0	1			

CHAPTER THREE

ALGEBRAIC SOLUTION OF LINEAR PROGRAMMING PROBLEMS

We are now ready to apply some of the basic linear algebra contained in the preceding chapter to the solution of linear programming problems involving any number of variables. The procedure to be explained is an iterative one and is known as the *simplex method*. Roughly described, it consists of first obtaining one feasible solution of the given problem and then determining a succession of new feasible solutions in such a way that the values of the linear function which we are trying to maximize or minimize progressively improve. This is analogous to the geometrical method, explained in Chapter 1, of solving two-variable problems by moving a line across the set of feasible solutions in the direction which improves the function to be optimized.

3-1. *RE-STATEMENT OF THE PROBLEM; BASIC DEFINITIONS.*

The linear programming problem was stated in Section 1-1, but for convenience of reference we restate the problem here together with definitions of some basic terms associated with linear programming problems.

DEFINITION 1. By a linear programming problem, we mean a problem of the following type: Given real numbers $c_1, c_2, \ldots, c_n, b_1, b_2, \ldots, b_m$, and a_{ij} $(i = 1, \ldots, m; j = 1, \ldots, n)$ we wish to maximize (or minimize) the function z of n real variables defined by

$$z(x_1, x_2, \ldots, x_n) = c_1x_1 + c_2x_2 + \cdots + c_nx_n$$

subject to the conditions

$$(1) \quad \begin{cases} a_{11}x_1 + a_{12}x_2 + \cdots + a_{1n}x_n \ (\leqq, =, \geqq)\ b_1 \\ a_{21}x_1 + a_{22}x_2 + \cdots + a_{2n}x_n \ (\leqq, =, \geqq)\ b_2 \\ \cdots \quad \cdots \quad \cdots \quad \cdots \\ a_{m1}x_1 + a_{m2}x_2 + \cdots + a_{mn}x_n \ (\leqq, =, \geqq)\ b_m, \end{cases}$$

where, in each line of (1), exactly one of the symbols $\leqq$, $=$, and $\geqq$ appears. The function z is called the *objective function.* Conditions (1) are referred to as the *constraints.* A *feasible solution* of the problem is an n-dimensional column vector $\mathbf{x} = [x_1, x_2, \ldots, x_n]$ whose components satisfy all of constraints (1). An *optimal solution* of the problem is a feasible solution for which the corresponding value of the objective function is a maximum (in the case of a maximizing problem) or a minimum (in the case of a minimizing problem), considering all possible values of the objective function corresponding to feasible solutions. By the *solution* of the problem, we shall mean the determination of an optimal solution and the corresponding value of the objective function, or the proof that no feasible solutions exist, or the proof that, although feasible solutions exist, there is no optimal solution.

The methods to be described in this chapter will enable us to solve any linear programming problem, but it is convenient to restrict ourselves at first to consideration of problems of the special kind named in the following definition:

DEFINITION 2. A linear programming problem whose set of constraints (1) includes the inequalities $x_j \geqq 0$ $(j = 1, \ldots, n)$ will be called a *linear programming problem with nonnegativity restrictions.*

Examples 1 and 2 of Section 1–1 are illustrations of linear programming problems with nonnegativity restrictions. We shall see later that, given any linear programming problem, we can formulate a related problem with nonnegativity restrictions whose solution yields the solution of the given problem. However, still another special type of problem must be defined before we can begin describing the algebraic process for solving problems with nonnegativity restrictions.

DEFINITION 3. A linear programming problem of the following type is said to be in *standard form:*

Given numbers $c_1, c_2, \ldots, c_n, b_1, b_2, \ldots, b_m$, where each $b_i \geqq 0$ $(i = 1, \ldots, m)$, and a_{ij} $(i = 1, \ldots, m; j = 1, \ldots, n)$, we wish to maximize (or minimize) the function z given by

$$z(x_1, x_2, \ldots, x_n) = c_1x_1 + c_2x_2 + \cdots + c_nx_n$$

subject to the conditions

$$(2) \quad \begin{cases} a_{11}x_1 + a_{12}x_2 + \cdots + a_{1n}x_n = b_1, \\ a_{21}x_1 + a_{22}x_2 + \cdots + a_{2n}x_n = b_2, \\ \cdots \quad \cdots \quad \cdots \quad \cdots \\ a_{m1}x_1 + a_{m2}x_2 + \cdots + a_{mn}x_n = b_m, \\ x_j \geqq 0 \qquad (j = 1, 2, \ldots, n). \end{cases}$$

Thus a problem is in standard form if it is a problem with nonnegativity restrictions whose constraints (except for the nonnegativity restrictions) consist of a system of linear equations with nonnegative constant terms. Now, it might seem at first as though the problem stated in Definition 3 is too special to be of any use in solving the general linear programming problem. However, any problem with nonnegativity restrictions, and hence any linear programming problem, can be solved by formulating and solving a related problem in standard form. We shall now illustrate with a numerical example the formulation of the related problem in standard form for a given problem with nonnegativity restrictions.

Example 1. Suppose the given problem is to maximize $z = 5x_1 - x_2 + 2x_3$ subject to the constraints

$$(3) \quad \begin{cases} x_1 - 3x_2 - x_3 \leqq 8, \\ 2x_1 + x_2 - 2x_3 \geqq 5, \\ x_1 - 6x_2 + x_3 \geqq -7, \\ -x_1 + 2x_2 + 5x_3 \leqq 6, \\ x_j \geqq 0 \qquad (j = 1, 2, 3). \end{cases}$$

Since we want the constants on the right to be nonnegative, we first multiply both sides of the third inequality by -1. (Remember that multiplying both sides of an inequality by a negative number reverses its sense.) Thus our problem may be stated in the following equivalent form:

Maximize $z = 5x_1 - x_2 + 2x_3$ subject to

$$(4) \quad \begin{cases} x_1 - 3x_2 - x_3 \leqq 8, \\ 2x_1 + x_2 - 2x_3 \geqq 5, \\ -x_1 + 6x_2 - x_3 \leqq 7, \\ -x_1 + 2x_2 + 5x_3 \leqq 6, \\ x_j \geqq 0 \qquad (j = 1, 2, 3). \end{cases}$$

Our conversion of the first four inequalities in (4) to equations will be based upon the following properties of inequalities: If a and b are real numbers, then (i) $a \leqq b$ if, and only if, there is a nonnegative number c such that $a + c = b$ and (ii) $a \geqq b$ if, and only if, there is a nonnegative number c such that $a - c = b$. Thus, given x_1, x_2, and x_3, the first of the inequalities in (4) holds if, and only if, there is a nonnegative number x_4 such that

$$x_1 - 3x_2 - x_3 + x_4 = 8,$$

and the second inequality holds if, and only if, there is a nonnegative number x_5 such that

$$2x_1 + x_2 - 2x_3 - x_5 = 5.$$

Proceeding in a similiar way with the third and fourth inequalities in (4), we finally obtain the related problem mentioned above:

Maximize $z' = 5x_1 - x_2 + 2x_3 + 0x_4 + 0x_5 + 0x_6 + 0x_7$ subject to

$$(5) \quad \begin{cases} x_1 - 3x_2 - x_3 + x_4 = 8, \\ 2x_1 + x_2 - 2x_3 - x_5 = 5, \\ -x_1 + 6x_2 - x_3 + x_6 = 7, \\ -x_1 + 2x_2 + 5x_3 + x_7 = 6, \\ x_j \geqq 0 \quad (j = 1, 2, \ldots, 7). \end{cases}$$

Note that the two problems are technically different, since they involve different numbers of variables. However, they are very closely related and we shall now discuss in detail the relation between them. Call the original problem (A) and the new problem (A′). If $\mathbf{x} = [x_1, x_2, x_3]$ is a feasible solution of (A), then, as we reasoned above, there must be nonnegative numbers x_4, x_5, x_6, and x_7 such that (5) holds. Hence, corresponding to each feasible solution $\mathbf{x} = [x_1, x_2, x_3]$ of (A) is a feasible solution $\mathbf{x}' = [x_1, x_2, x_3, x_4, x_5, x_6, x_7]$ of (A′). Conversely, starting with a feasible solution $\mathbf{x}'$ of (A′), by leaving off the last four components of $\mathbf{x}'$, we obtain a feasible solution of (A). Hence, there is a one-to-one correspondence between feasible solutions of (A) and feasible solutions of (A′). Moreover, it is clear that corresponding feasible solutions yield identical values of the objective functions z and z'. Consequently, under this correspondence of solutions, an optimal solution of one problem corresponds to an optimal solution of the other, and, if one has no optimal solution, then neither does the other. Finally, it is also clear that, if one of these problems has no feasible solution, then the other also has no feasible solution.

When a system of linear inequalities is converted in the manner of this example to a system of linear equations with nonnegative constant terms, the extra variables introduced are called *slack variables*. It should be evident now that, given any linear programming problem with nonnegativity restrictions we can, by the introduction of slack variables, formulate a corresponding problem in standard form. This corresponding problem will be referred to as the *related standard problem*. There is a one-to-one correspondence between the feasible solutions of the given problem and those of the related standard problem with the property that corresponding solutions yield equal values of the objective functions. Hence, to solve a given problem with nonnegativity restrictions, it is sufficient to solve its related standard problem.

EXERCISES

In each of Exercises 1 through 4, a linear programming problem with nonnegativity restrictions is stated. In each case, state an equivalent problem in standard form.

1. Maximize $z = 3x_1 - 2x_2 - x_3$ subject to

$$\begin{cases} 5x_1 - x_2 + 2x_3 \leqq 13, \\ 3x_1 + 2x_2 - x_3 \geqq -4, \\ x_1 - x_2 + x_3 \leqq 6, \\ x_j \geqq 0 \qquad (j = 1, 2, 3). \end{cases}$$

2. Maximize $z = 2x_1 + 6x_2$ subject to

$$\begin{cases} x_1 - 4x_2 \geqq -16, \\ x_1 + x_2 \leqq 9, \\ x_1 - x_2 \leqq 3, \\ x_1 \geqq 0, \qquad x_2 \geqq 0. \end{cases}$$

3. Minimize $z = -2x_1 + x_2$ subject to

$$\begin{cases} 2x_1 + 5x_2 \leqq 35, \\ 3x_1 + x_2 \leqq 20, \\ x_1 - 2x_2 \leqq 2, \\ x_1 \geqq 0, \qquad x_2 \geqq 0. \end{cases}$$

4. Minimize $z = 6x_1 + x_2 - 2x_3$ subject to

$$\begin{cases} 5x_1 - x_2 + x_3 \geqq 6, \\ 2x_1 + x_2 + 3x_3 \leqq 7, \\ -3x_1 + x_2 + 2x_3 \geqq 2, \\ x_j \geqq 0 \qquad (j = 1, 2, 3). \end{cases}$$

5. Sketch the two-dimensional polygon determined by the constraints in Exercise 2, and find the coordinates of each of its corner points. For each of these corner points, find the corresponding feasible solution of the related standard problem. Which of these solutions is optimal?
6. Follow the instructions in Exercise 5 for the problem stated in Exercise 3.
7. Prove that the problem stated in Exercise 4 has no feasible solutions at all.
8. For the problem stated in Exercise 1, either find a feasible solution of the related standard problem in which each slack variable is zero, or else prove that there is no such solution.
9. Prove that the problem of maximizing a function z subject to some set of

constraints is equivalent to the problem of minimizing $-z$ subject to the same constraints. Hence, it would be sufficient to study only maximizing problems (or only minimizing problems).

3-2. *BASIC FEASIBLE SOLUTIONS.*

As we have stated earlier (but have not yet justified), knowing how to solve the standard problem will enable us to solve any linear programming problem. Hence, we shall concentrate in this and the following two sections on the solution of the standard problem. We first define a special type of feasible solution for standard problems as follows:

DEFINITION 4. Consider the standard problem stated in Definition 3. A feasible solution $\mathbf{x} = [x_1, x_2, \ldots, x_n]$ of this problem is called a *basic feasible solution* if, and only if, $\mathbf{x}$ is a basic solution of the system of m equations in n unknowns contained in (2) (see Definition 24, Section 2–6).

Example 2. To illustrate this, consider the problem stated in Example 1, Chapter 1:

Minimize $z = -4x_1 + 3x_2$ subject to the constraints

$$\begin{cases} x_1 - 2x_2 \geqq -4, \\ 2x_1 + 3x_2 \leqq 13, \\ x_1 - x_2 \leqq 4, \\ x_1 \geqq 0, \quad x_2 \geqq 0. \end{cases}$$

The related standard problem is the following:

Minimize $z' = -4x_1 + 3x_2 + 0x_3 + 0x_4 + 0x_5$ subject to

$$(6) \qquad \begin{cases} -x_1 + 2x_2 + x_3 = 4, \\ 2x_1 + 3x_2 + x_4 = 13, \\ x_1 - x_2 + x_5 = 4, \\ x_j \geqq 0 \quad (j = 1, 2, 3, 4, 5). \end{cases}$$

One basic feasible solution of this problem is the vector $\mathbf{x} = [0, 0, 4, 13, 4]$. The student may find it instructive to try to find other basic feasible solutions before reading the rest of this section.

The importance of basic feasible solutions cannot be fully explained at this point, but it will become clearer as we progress. Geometrically speaking, basic feasible solutions correspond to "corner points" on the set of all feasible solutions, and by means of them we can obtain complete information about the problem. If we have a problem with at least one basic feasible solution, then the iterative process (simplex method) which we are now developing will lead us through a sequence of basic feasible solutions until we either reach an optimal solution or prove that there is no optimal solution. Hence, we have to consider the means by which we may obtain a new basic feasible solution from a given one. We discuss this problem in the remainder of this section and begin by looking at a numerical example.

Example 3. Consider again the standard problem stated in Example 2. Write the system of three equations in five unknowns in (6) in the vector form

$$x_1\mathbf{v}_1 + x_2\mathbf{v}_2 + x_3\mathbf{v}_3 + x_4\mathbf{v}_4 + x_5\mathbf{v}_5 = \mathbf{b}, \tag{7}$$

where

$$\mathbf{v}_1 = \begin{pmatrix} -1 \\ 2 \\ 1 \end{pmatrix}, \quad \mathbf{v}_2 = \begin{pmatrix} 2 \\ 3 \\ -1 \end{pmatrix}, \quad \mathbf{v}_3 = \begin{pmatrix} 1 \\ 0 \\ 0 \end{pmatrix}, \quad \mathbf{v}_4 = \begin{pmatrix} 0 \\ 1 \\ 0 \end{pmatrix}, \quad \mathbf{v}_5 = \begin{pmatrix} 0 \\ 0 \\ 1 \end{pmatrix}, \quad \mathbf{b} = \begin{pmatrix} 4 \\ 13 \\ 4 \end{pmatrix}.$$

Then the basic feasible solution $\mathbf{x} = [0, 0, 4, 13, 4]$ mentioned above has, as its corresponding basis, the vectors $\mathbf{v}_3$, $\mathbf{v}_4$, and $\mathbf{v}_5$, and we can display this information by means of the following tableau (see Section 2–6):

(8)

Basis	$\mathbf{b}$	$\mathbf{v}_1$	$\mathbf{v}_2$	$\mathbf{v}_3$	$\mathbf{v}_4$	$\mathbf{v}_5$
$\mathbf{v}_3$	4	−1	2	1	0	0
$\mathbf{v}_4$	13	2	3	0	1	0
$\mathbf{v}_5$	4	1	−1	0	0	1

Now suppose we wish to find a new basic feasible solution. Then we are looking for a new basic solution of system (7) in which the variables are all nonnegative. As we learned in Section 2–6, one way to find a new basic solution is to insert one of the nonbasis vectors into the basis. In this case, either $\mathbf{v}_1$ or $\mathbf{v}_2$ may be inserted into the basis in place of any one of the vectors $\mathbf{v}_3$, $\mathbf{v}_4$, $\mathbf{v}_5$ and a new basic solution of (7) will be obtained (see Theorem 13, Section 2–6). However, some of these basic solutions will not be feasible since they will have one or more negative components. For instance, if $\mathbf{v}_1$ is inserted in place of $\mathbf{v}_3$, the resulting basic solution of (7) is $[-4, 0, 0, 21, 8]$. Similarly, a nonfeasible basic solution is obtained if $\mathbf{v}_1$ is inserted in place of $\mathbf{v}_4$. But if $\mathbf{v}_1$ replaces $\mathbf{v}_5$, then the basic feasible solution $[4, 0, 8, 5, 0]$ is obtained.

The question is, how do we decide in advance what change of basis to make in order to obtain a new basic feasible solution without going through such a series of trial-and-error calculations? There are two decisions which have to be made in effecting a change of basis: First, we must decide which nonbasis vector shall be inserted into the basis, and, second, we must choose a basis vector to be removed from the basis. It turns out to be more convenient to discuss these decisions in the reverse order from that in which they are actually made in solving a problem. Hence, in this section we shall assume that the first decision has been made and shall concentrate on the second one. The second decision is determined by the desire that the new basic solution be *feasible*. Thus, in the preceding example, we arbitrarily selected $\mathbf{v}_1$ to enter the basis and then found that only if we selected $\mathbf{v}_5$ to leave the basis did we obtain a feasible solution.

Suppose now that we have a linear programming problem in standard form. We can write the constraints in the form

$$(9) \qquad \begin{cases} x_1\mathbf{v}_1 + x_2\mathbf{v}_2 + \cdots + x_n\mathbf{v}_n = \mathbf{b}, \\ x_j \geqq 0 \qquad (j = 1, 2, \ldots, n), \end{cases}$$

where $\mathbf{v}_1, \mathbf{v}_2, \ldots, \mathbf{v}_n$, and $\mathbf{b}$ are m-dimensional column vectors and the components of $\mathbf{b}$ are nonnegative. The objective function does not concern us at present. Suppose that we have found a basic feasible solution of our problem. This implies that $m \leqq n$ and that we have found a set of m linearly independent vectors among $\mathbf{v}_1, \mathbf{v}_2, \ldots, \mathbf{v}_n$. Now, if $m = n$, the situation is trivial. The problem has exactly one feasible solution (which is basic) since $\mathbf{b}$ can be expressed uniquely as a linear combination of $\mathbf{v}_1, \mathbf{v}_2, \ldots, \mathbf{v}_m$. This unique solution is of course optimal. Let us now consider the nontrivial case $m < n$. For convenience, we shall assume that the basis corresponding to our known basic feasible solution consists of the vectors $\mathbf{v}_1, \mathbf{v}_2, \ldots, \mathbf{v}_m$. (This is done merely to simplify the notation and will be done frequently in the sequel. Our statements are perfectly general in essential content, and the student should see that, by simply changing the notation, they apply to any basis selected from among $\mathbf{v}_1, \mathbf{v}_2, \ldots, \mathbf{v}_n$.) With this assumption, our basic feasible solution is an n-dimensional column vector $\mathbf{x}$, where

$$(10) \qquad \begin{cases} \mathbf{x} = [x_1, \ldots, x_m, 0, \ldots, 0] \qquad (n - m \text{ zeros}), \\ \mathbf{b} = x_1\mathbf{v}_1 + \cdots + x_m\mathbf{v}_m, \qquad \text{and} \\ x_j \geqq 0 \qquad (j = 1, \ldots, m). \end{cases}$$

Let us assume we have made the first decision as to which nonbasis vector we shall insert into the basis. Call this vector $\mathbf{v}_k$. This could be any vector not in the basis corresponding to our known basic feasible solution. We now wish to see which of the basis vectors can be replaced by $\mathbf{v}_k$ so that the resulting basic solution will be feasible.

First, we must express $\mathbf{v}_k$ as a linear combination of the basis vectors. Let us write

$$(11) \qquad \mathbf{v}_k = y_{1k}\mathbf{v}_1 + y_{2k}\mathbf{v}_2 + \cdots + y_{mk}\mathbf{v}_m = \sum_{i=1}^{m} y_{ik}\mathbf{v}_i,$$

where the use of double subscripts reflects the dependence of the coefficient of $\mathbf{v}_i$ upon both i and k. For instance in Example 3, the equation corresponding to (11) is

$$\mathbf{v}_1 = -\mathbf{v}_3 + 2\mathbf{v}_4 + \mathbf{v}_5$$

[see tableau (8)], assuming that $\mathbf{v}_1$ is the vector chosen to replace one of the basis vectors $\mathbf{v}_3$, $\mathbf{v}_4$, and $\mathbf{v}_5$. Of course, the notation in the example is different from that in the general discussion above, but the point is that, having decided which vector is to enter the basis, we must have available the expression of that vector as a linear combination of the basis vectors in order to decide which vector is to leave the basis. In a numerical problem, as indicated in Example 3, the coefficients in this linear combination can be read directly from the tableau displaying the known basic feasible solution.

Returning to our general discussion, we know from Eq. (11) and Theorem 13, Section 2–6, that a basic solution of the system of equations in constraints (9) will be obtained if $\mathbf{v}_k$ replaces any vector whose coefficient in (11) is nonzero. This basic solution, however, may or may not be feasible. Suppose $y_{rk} \neq 0$ in (11), where r is one of the integers $1, 2, \ldots, m$. We shall solve (11) for $\mathbf{v}_r$ and then substitute the resulting expression in Eq. (10). This will enable us to determine the components of the new basic solution obtained by inserting $\mathbf{v}_k$ for $\mathbf{v}_r$ and hence to determine conditions under which they will all be nonnegative. The student who has done Exercise 6, Section 2–6, will have already carried through calculations essentially the same as those which follow.

From Eq. (11), we obtain first

$$y_{rk}\mathbf{v}_r = \mathbf{v}_k - \sum_{\substack{i=1\\ i\neq r}}^{m} y_{ik}\mathbf{v}_i,$$

and hence

(12) $$\mathbf{v}_r = \frac{1}{y_{rk}}\mathbf{v}_k - \sum_{\substack{i=1\\ i\neq r}}^{m} \frac{y_{ik}}{y_{rk}}\mathbf{v}_i,$$

since $y_{rk} \neq 0$. (The notation $i \neq r$ accompanying the summations in these and future equations indicates that the term in the sum corresponding to $i = r$ is to be omitted.) The next step is to substitute the expression for $\mathbf{v}_r$ in (12) into Eq. (10). First, however, let us rewrite (10) as follows:

(13) $$\mathbf{b} = x_r\mathbf{v}_r + \sum_{\substack{i=1\\ i\neq r}}^{m} x_i\mathbf{v}_i.$$

Then, making our substitution from (12) into (13), we obtain

$$\begin{aligned}\mathbf{b} &= x_r\left(\frac{1}{y_{rk}}\mathbf{v}_k - \sum_{\substack{i=1\\ i\neq r}}^{m} \frac{y_{ik}}{y_{rk}}\mathbf{v}_i\right) + \sum_{\substack{i=1\\ i\neq r}}^{m} x_i\mathbf{v}_i\\ &= \frac{x_r}{y_{rk}}\mathbf{v}_k - \sum_{\substack{i=1\\ i\neq r}}^{m} \frac{x_r y_{ik}}{y_{rk}}\mathbf{v}_i + \sum_{\substack{i=1\\ i\neq r}}^{m} x_i\mathbf{v}_i,\end{aligned}$$

and, by combining the two summations into one,

(14) $$\mathbf{b} = \frac{x_r}{y_{rk}}\mathbf{v}_k + \sum_{\substack{i=1\\ i\neq r}}^{m}\left(x_i - \frac{x_r y_{ik}}{y_{rk}}\right)\mathbf{v}_i.$$

The components of the new basic solution are the coefficients appearing in (14). This basic solution will be feasible if, and only if, each of its components is nonnegative; i.e., if, and only if, we have

$$\text{(15)} \qquad \frac{x_r}{y_{rk}} \geqq 0, \qquad x_i - \frac{x_r y_{ik}}{y_{rk}} \geqq 0 \qquad (i = 1, \ldots, m;\ i \neq r).$$

Now, in the tableau, when we perform the row operations corresponding to the above calculations, y_{rk} is the pivot element. We shall consider the two possible cases according to the sign of y_{rk}. Suppose, first, that $y_{rk} < 0$. Then the first inequality in (15) holds if, and only if, $x_r = 0$. Now, if $x_r = 0$, the remaining inequalities in (15) become $x_i \geqq 0$ $(i = 1, \ldots, m; i \neq r)$, which hold because **x** is feasible. But, with $x_r = 0$, the right sides of Eq. (13) and (14) are identical, and so we have not obtained a different basic feasible solution. We have made a change of basis, but, since Eq. (13) expresses **b** as a linear combination of the $m - 1$ vectors $\mathbf{v}_i$ $(i = 1, \ldots, m; i \neq r)$ and these vectors remain in the basis after the change, the theorem on uniqueness of linear combinations of linearly independent vectors (Theorem 7, Section 2–4) guarantees that the expression for **b** in terms of the new basis will be the same as that in terms of the original basis. Thus, having chosen the vector $\mathbf{v}_k$ to enter the basis, we could choose to leave the basis a vector $\mathbf{v}_r$ for which the pivot element y_{rk} is negative only if the component x_r of **x** corresponding to $\mathbf{v}_r$ is zero, and even then we should merely reobtain our known solution **x**. Hence, it would appear useless to choose a negative pivot element, and, indeed, subsequent developments will show that we may as well always choose the vector to leave the basis as one for which the pivot element is positive.

Let us now consider the case in which we select a vector $\mathbf{v}_r$ to leave the basis so that the corresponding pivot element y_{rk} is positive. We wish to determine further restrictions on y_{rk} which will insure the feasibility of the resulting basic solution. Of course, we have to assume here that we have selected a vector $\mathbf{v}_k$ for which there is at least one positive y_{rk}. Should there be no such vector, then, as we shall show later, our problem is solved and no further change of basis is necessary. With $y_{rk} > 0$, the first inequality in (15) is satisfied. Hence, we turn our attention to the others. For each subscript i such that $y_{ik} \leqq 0$, the inequality

$$\text{(16)} \qquad x_i - \frac{x_r y_{ik}}{y_{rk}} \geqq 0$$

is easily seen to hold. Thus, it only remains to consider those subscripts i for which $y_{ik} > 0$. For such a value of i, (16) is equivalent to

$$\text{(17)} \qquad \frac{x_r}{y_{rk}} \leqq \frac{x_i}{y_{ik}}.$$

Thus, if r is chosen so that $y_{rk} > 0$, then inequalities (15) will be satisfied if, and only if, r is also chosen so that (17) holds for each i such that $y_{ik} > 0$. To insure a choice of r meeting these requirements, we must proceed as follows: Consider all of the ratios x_i/y_{ik} for which $y_{ik} > 0$. Choose r so that x_r/y_{rk} is the smallest of all these ratios. In case two or more ratios are tied for smallest, let r be the subscript corresponding to any one of the tied ratios. Having first chosen a vector $\mathbf{v}_k$ to enter the basis and then having selected r as just described, we replace $\mathbf{v}_r$ in the basis by $\mathbf{v}_k$ and the resulting basic solution will be feasible. We now illustrate the procedure with an example.

Example 4. Consider once more the basic feasible solution, displayed in tableau (8), of the standard problem stated in Example 2. Suppose now that we have decided to insert the vector $\mathbf{v}_2$ into the basis. To decide which basis vector can be removed, we must consider the ratios 4/2 and 13/3 which are, respectively, x_3/y_{32} and x_4/y_{42}. We do not consider the ratio x_5/y_{52}, since $y_{52} = -1$, which is negative. Of the two ratios 4/2 and 13/3, the smaller is $4/2 = x_3/y_{32}$. Hence, if $\mathbf{v}_2$ is chosen to enter the basis, $\mathbf{v}_3$ must be chosen to leave. The student should verify that the basic feasible solution which results when we make this change of basis is

$$\mathbf{x}' = [0, 2, 0, 7, 6].$$

Note that the ratios x_i/y_{ik} may easily be read from the tableau displaying the known basic feasible solution. The numerators and denominators appear, respectively, in the column labeled $\mathbf{b}$ and the column labeled $\mathbf{v}_k$.

EXERCISES

1. The following tableau displays a basic feasible solution of a linear programming problem in standard form. Obtain a new basic feasible solution by inserting the vector $\mathbf{v}_4$ into the basis.

Basis	$\mathbf{b}$	$\mathbf{v}_1$	$\mathbf{v}_2$	$\mathbf{v}_3$	$\mathbf{v}_4$	$\mathbf{v}_5$	$\mathbf{v}_6$
$\mathbf{v}_2$	2	1	1	0	4	0	−7
$\mathbf{v}_5$	6	3	0	0	9	1	6
$\mathbf{v}_3$	3	−2	0	1	5	0	2

2. Follow the instructions of Exercise 1, except insert $\mathbf{v}_6$ into the basis shown in the tableau.

3. Follow the instructions of Exercise 1, except insert $\mathbf{v}_1$ into the given basis.

4. Notice that a degenerate basic feasible solution was obtained in Exercise 3, but not in either of Exercises 1 and 2. Prove the following generalization of this: Given a linear programming problem in standard form and a nondegenerate basic feasible solution of the problem, if we insert a vector into the basis and obtain a new basic feasible solution, the new solution is degenerate if, and only if, there is a tie for smallest among two or more of the ratios x_i/y_{ik} which we consider in determining which vector is to leave the basis.

5. Consider the following tableau, which displays a degenerate basic feasible solution of some linear programming problem:

Basis	**b**	$\mathbf{v}_1$	$\mathbf{v}_2$	$\mathbf{v}_3$	$\mathbf{v}_4$	$\mathbf{v}_5$	$\mathbf{v}_6$	$\mathbf{v}_7$	$\mathbf{v}_8$	$\mathbf{v}_9$
$\mathbf{v}_4$	2	0	−2	0	1	4	0	1	0	−3
$\mathbf{v}_1$	0	1	8	0	0	0	0	−2	0	−4
$\mathbf{v}_3$	3	0	6	1	0	2	0	3	0	2
$\mathbf{v}_6$	4	0	5	0	0	3	1	1	0	4
$\mathbf{v}_8$	0	0	1	0	0	−1	0	−4	1	0

Which of the four nonbasis vectors can be inserted into the basis so as to obtain a *nondegenerate* basic feasible solution? Carry out the replacement, and obtain the nondegenerate solution.

6. Suppose that, as illustrated in the preceding exercise, we have a linear programming problem in standard form and a degenerate basic feasible solution of the problem. Suppose also that we choose a vector to enter the basis, and then determine the vector to leave by considering only the ratios x_i/y_{ik} for which $y_{ik} > 0$, as described in this section. Determine necessary and sufficient conditions for the resulting basic feasible solution to be nondegenerate, and prove that your answer is correct.

7. Refer to Exercise 5, Section 3–1. Prove that the corner-point solutions found there are basic by starting with one of them, say the one corresponding to the origin, and obtaining all the rest by making successive changes of basis.

8. Follow the procedure outlined in Exercise 7 with reference to Exercise 6, Section 3–1.

3-3. *IMPROVING THE VALUE OF THE OBJECTIVE FUNCTION.*

In the preceding section, we learned how to proceed from one basic feasible solution of a standard problem to another, but we did not take into account the values of the objective function. That is, whether the objective function increased in value or decreased in value was of no concern to us. In the simplex process, however, the changes of basis are always made so as to improve the value of the objective function. This means that, in a maximizing problem, the changes are made so as to increase the value of the objective function and, in a minimizing problem, they are made so as to decrease the value of the objective function (although it sometimes happens that the objective function does not change at all from one step to the next). As it turns out, it is the vector entering the basis which determines the change in value of the objective function. In this section, we shall discuss this point in detail and shall show how the entering vector should be chosen so that the desired improvement will be achieved.

Suppose, then, that we have a linear programming problem in standard form: Maximize (or minimize) $z = c_1x_1 + c_2x_2 + \cdots + c_nx_n$ subject to

$$\begin{cases} x_1\mathbf{v}_1 + x_2\mathbf{v}_2 + \cdots + x_n\mathbf{v}_n = \mathbf{b}, \\ x_j \geqq 0 \qquad (j = 1, 2, \ldots, n), \end{cases}$$

where $\mathbf{v}_1, \mathbf{v}_2, \ldots, \mathbf{v}_n$, and $\mathbf{b}$ are m-dimensional column vectors, $m < n$, and the components of $\mathbf{b}$ are nonnegative. Suppose also that we have found a basic feasible solution of this problem. As before, we shall assume for convenience that this solution has the form $\mathbf{x} = [x_1, \ldots, x_m, 0, \ldots, 0]$ ($n - m$ zeros), so that the associated basis consists of $\mathbf{v}_1, \mathbf{v}_2, \ldots, \mathbf{v}_m$.

Let z_0 be the value of the objective function associated with our known basic feasible solution $\mathbf{x}$. Then

$$z_0 = c_1x_1 + c_2x_2 + \cdots + c_mx_m.$$

If we insert a vector $\mathbf{v}_k$ into the basis and remove the proper vector, as explained in the preceding section, we shall obtain a basic feasible solution, say $\mathbf{x}'$. Let z_0' be the value of the objective function corresponding to $\mathbf{x}'$. Then $z_0' - z_0$ represents the change in value of the objective function, and it may be zero, positive, or negative. If we wish to be able to improve the value of the objective function, then we must at least be able to determine, in terms of the vector $\mathbf{v}_k$ chosen to enter the basis, the algebraic sign of $z_0' - z_0$. In a maximizing problem, we should choose as the entering vector one for which $z_0' - z_0 \geqq 0$, so that $z_0' \geqq z_0$. In a minimizing problem, we should insert a vector for which $z_0' - z_0 \leqq 0$, so that $z_0' \leqq z_0$.

Suppose, then, that we have chosen a vector $\mathbf{v}_k$ to enter the basis. We wish to compute $z_0' - z_0$ in terms of quantities associated with $\mathbf{v}_k$. As in the preceding section, we write

$$\mathbf{v}_k = \sum_{i=1}^{m} y_{ik}\mathbf{v}_i.$$

We shall assume that $y_{ik} > 0$ for at least one value of i. If there were no nonbasis vector $\mathbf{v}_k$ with at least one $y_{ik} > 0$, then, as we shall show later, our problem would be solved and there would be no need to determine any more basic feasible solutions. Let the basis vector $\mathbf{v}_r$, which $\mathbf{v}_k$ replaces, be chosen as explained in the previous section. That is, $\mathbf{v}_r$ is selected so that

$$\frac{x_r}{y_{rk}} = \min\left\{\frac{x_i}{y_{ik}} \,\middle|\, y_{ik} > 0\right\}.$$

Let us write the new basic feasible solution $\mathbf{x}'$ as $\mathbf{x}' = [x_1', x_2', \ldots, x_n']$. Then, from Eq. (14), we can read formulas for the components x_i' as follows:

$$(18) \qquad \begin{cases} x_i' = x_i - \dfrac{x_r y_{ik}}{y_{rk}}, \qquad i = 1, \ldots, m \qquad (i \neq r), \\ x_k' = \dfrac{x_r}{y_{rk}}, \\ x_j' = 0 \qquad \text{for all other subscripts } j. \end{cases}$$

Now, to compute z_0', we multiply each component x_i' of $\mathbf{x}'$ by its corresponding coefficient c_i and add the products:

(19) $$z_0' = \sum_{i=1}^{n} c_i x_i' = \sum_{\substack{i=1 \\ i \neq r}}^{m} c_i \left(x_i - \frac{x_r y_{ik}}{y_{rk}} \right) + c_k \frac{x_r}{y_{rk}}.$$

Notice that, in the first line of (18), the restriction $i \neq r$ is superfluous, since

$$x_r' = x_r - \frac{x_r y_{rk}}{y_{rk}} = x_r - x_r = 0.$$

Hence, the restriction $i \neq r$ appearing in (19) is also superfluous, and we may write

(20) $$z_0' = \sum_{i=1}^{m} c_i \left(x_i - \frac{x_r y_{ik}}{y_{rk}} \right) + c_k \frac{x_r}{y_{rk}}.$$

Hence, we have

(21) $$z_0' = \sum_{i=1}^{m} c_i x_i - \sum_{i=1}^{m} c_i \frac{x_r y_{ik}}{y_{rk}} + c_k \frac{x_r}{y_{rk}}.$$

Now the first sum in (21) is simply z_0, and there is a common factor of x_r/y_{rk} in each of the other terms. Hence, we have

(22) $$z_0' = z_0 + \frac{x_r}{y_{rk}} \left(c_k - \sum_{i=1}^{m} c_i y_{ik} \right).$$

For brevity, we let

(23) $$\theta_k = \frac{x_r}{y_{rk}} \quad \text{and} \quad z_k = \sum_{i=1}^{m} c_i y_{ik}.$$

Then (22) becomes

(24) $$z_0' = z_0 + \theta_k (c_k - z_k),$$

which we may also write as

(25) $$z_0' - z_0 = \theta_k (c_k - z_k).$$

Formula (25) tells us how to compute the change in value of the objective function in terms of the numbers θ_k and z_k associated with the vector $\mathbf{v}_k$ chosen to enter the basis. Notice that $\theta_k \geqq 0$, since $y_{rk} > 0$ and $x_r \geqq 0$. If $\theta_k > 0$, then $z_0' - z_0$ and $c_k - z_k$ have the same sign, or both are zero. If $\theta_k = 0$, then $z_0' = z_0$ regardless of the sign of $c_k - z_k$. From these observations, we can see that, if the entering vector $\mathbf{v}_k$ is chosen so that $c_k - z_k$ has the proper sign (positive in a maximizing problem, negative in a minimizing problem), then the value of the objective function will either improve or remain constant when the new basic feasible solution is obtained. If we wish to obtain the maximum improvement, we must compute $\theta_j(c_j - z_j)$ for every nonbasis vector for which $c_j - z_j$ has the proper sign and then choose as the entering vector one for which this quantity is a maximum in absolute value. However, in our description of the simplex process, we are not going to be any more explicit about the choice of the entering vector than to say that it must be a vector $\mathbf{v}_k$ for which $c_k - z_k$ has the proper sign. A simple and reasonable way to decide in computations done by hand is to choose $\mathbf{v}_k$ so that $c_k - z_k$ has the proper sign and is maximum in absolute value. Note, however, that maximizing $|c_k - z_k|$ does not necessarily maximize $\theta_k |c_k - z_k|$.

Before we give a numerical example to illustrate the foregoing ideas, a minor point should be mentioned. It turns out to be slightly more convenient computationally to work with $z_j - c_j$ than with $c_j - z_j$; the reason for this will be explained at the end of this section. Of course, these numbers are just negatives of each other, so that our selection rule for the entering vector $\mathbf{v}_k$ can be stated as follows: In a maximizing problem, choose $\mathbf{v}_k$ so that $z_k - c_k < 0$; in a minimizing problem, choose $\mathbf{v}_k$ so that $z_k - c_k > 0$. As an abbreviation, we shall say from now on that, if the algebraic sign of $z_k - c_k$ is negative in a maximizing problem, or positive in a minimizing problem, then $z_k - c_k$ has the *proper sign for improvement of the objective function.*

Example 5. Maximize $z = 2x_1 + x_2 - 3x_3 + 5x_4$ subject to

$$\begin{cases} 3x_1 - x_2 + x_3 + 2x_4 \leqq 8, \\ x_1 + x_2 + 4x_3 - x_4 \leqq 6, \\ 2x_1 + 3x_2 - x_3 + x_4 \leqq 10, \\ x_1 + x_3 + x_4 \leqq 7, \\ x_j \geqq 0 \quad (j = 1, 2, 3, 4). \end{cases}$$

The related standard problem is as follows:

Maximize $z = 2x_1 + x_2 - 3x_3 + 5x_4 + 0x_5 + 0x_6 + 0x_7 + 0x_8$ subject to

$$\begin{cases} 3x_1 - x_2 + x_3 + 2x_4 + x_5 = 8 \\ x_1 + x_2 + 4x_3 - x_4 + x_6 = 6 \\ 2x_1 + 3x_2 - x_3 + x_4 + x_7 = 10 \\ x_1 + x_3 + x_4 + x_8 = 7 \\ x_j \geqq 0 \quad (j = 1, 2, \ldots, 8). \end{cases}$$

(Because of the close relationship of the original problem and the related standard problem, no harm will result if we ignore the technical difference between the two objective functions and denote them each by z). In the following tableau we display, as before, a basic feasible solution of the standard problem as well as some additional information. The bottom row contains the numbers $z_j - c_j$ for each vector $\mathbf{v}_j$ and, in the column headed $\mathbf{b}$, the value of z corresponding to the basic feasible solution shown. The column headed *Obj* contains the objective function coefficients c_j corresponding to the basis vectors. For convenience of reference, all the coefficients in the objective function are written across the top of the tableau.

			2	1	−3	5	0	0	0	0
Basis	*Obj*	**b**	$\mathbf{v}_1$	$\mathbf{v}_2$	$\mathbf{v}_3$	$\mathbf{v}_4$	$\mathbf{v}_5$	$\mathbf{v}_6$	$\mathbf{v}_7$	$\mathbf{v}_8$
$\mathbf{v}_5$	0	8	3	−1	1	(2)	1	0	0	0
$\mathbf{v}_6$	0	6	1	1	4	−1	0	1	0	0
$\mathbf{v}_7$	0	10	2	3	−1	1	0	0	1	0
$\mathbf{v}_8$	0	7	1	0	1	1	0	0	0	1
$z_j - c_j$		0	−2	−1	3	−5	0	0	0	0

Using the definition of z_k given in (23), we see that z_k is computed from the tableau by adding the products of corresponding numbers in the *Obj* and $\mathbf{v}_k$ columns. For the particular solution displayed in the above tableau, each coefficient c_i corresponding to a basis vector is zero, so that each $z_j = 0$. Hence, in this case, $z_j - c_j = -c_j$. To improve this solution, we could insert into the basis any vector $\mathbf{v}_j$ for $c_j - z_j > 0\ (z_j - c_j < 0)$. Since $c_4 - z_4 = 5$ is the largest positive $c_j - z_j$, we choose $\mathbf{v}_4$ to enter the basis. The vector which must leave the basis is $\mathbf{v}_5$, determined as explained in the preceding section. We have

$$\theta_4 = \frac{x_5}{y_{54}} = \frac{8}{2} = 4.$$

Hence, the improvement in the objective function will be $\theta_4(c_4 - z_4) = 4 \cdot 5 = 20$. The student should verify that, had we chosen $\mathbf{v}_1$ or $\mathbf{v}_2$ to enter the basis, the improvement in z would have been, respectively, $\theta_1(c_1 - z_1) = \frac{8}{3} \cdot 2 = \frac{16}{3}$ and $\theta_2(c_2 - z_2) = \frac{10}{3} \cdot 1 = \frac{10}{3}$. Thus, in this case, our procedure has led to maximum improvement in z. The new basic feasible solution, obtained in the usual way, using the indicated pivot element, is displayed in the tableau below. The new values of $z_j - c_j$ are again computed by use of (23), but presently we shall discuss an alternative procedure for finding these numbers.

			2	1	−3	5	0	0	0	0
Basis	*Obj*	**b**	$\mathbf{v}_1$	$\mathbf{v}_2$	$\mathbf{v}_3$	$\mathbf{v}_4$	$\mathbf{v}_5$	$\mathbf{v}_6$	$\mathbf{v}_7$	$\mathbf{v}_8$
$\mathbf{v}_4$	5	4	$\frac{3}{2}$	$-\frac{1}{2}$	$\frac{1}{2}$	1	$\frac{1}{2}$	0	0	0
$\mathbf{v}_6$	0	10	$\frac{5}{2}$	$\frac{1}{2}$	$\frac{9}{2}$	0	$\frac{1}{2}$	1	0	0
$\mathbf{v}_7$	0	6	$\frac{1}{2}$	($\frac{7}{2}$)	$-\frac{3}{2}$	0	$-\frac{1}{2}$	0	1	0
$\mathbf{v}_8$	0	3	$-\frac{1}{2}$	$\frac{1}{2}$	$\frac{1}{2}$	0	$-\frac{1}{2}$	0	0	1
$z_j - c_j$		20	$\frac{11}{2}$	$-\frac{7}{2}$	$\frac{11}{2}$	0	$\frac{5}{2}$	0	0	0

The corresponding feasible solution of the standard problem is $\mathbf{x} = [0, 0, 0, 4, 0, 10, 6, 3]$ for which $z = 20$. To improve this solution, we must insert $\mathbf{v}_2$ into the basis. Using the indicated pivot element, we obtain the following result:

			2	1	−3	5	0	0	0	0
Basis	*Obj*	$\mathbf{b}$	$\mathbf{v}_1$	$\mathbf{v}_2$	$\mathbf{v}_3$	$\mathbf{v}_4$	$\mathbf{v}_5$	$\mathbf{v}_6$	$\mathbf{v}_7$	$\mathbf{v}_8$
$\mathbf{v}_4$	5	$\frac{34}{7}$	$\frac{11}{7}$	0	$\frac{2}{7}$	1	$\frac{3}{7}$	0	$\frac{1}{7}$	0
$\mathbf{v}_6$	0	$\frac{64}{7}$	$\frac{17}{7}$	0	$\frac{33}{7}$	0	$\frac{4}{7}$	1	$-\frac{1}{7}$	0
$\mathbf{v}_2$	1	$\frac{12}{7}$	$\frac{1}{7}$	1	$-\frac{3}{7}$	0	$-\frac{1}{7}$	0	$\frac{2}{7}$	0
$\mathbf{v}_8$	0	$\frac{15}{7}$	$-\frac{4}{7}$	0	$\frac{5}{7}$	0	$-\frac{3}{7}$	0	$-\frac{1}{7}$	1
$z_j - c_j$		26	6	0	4	0	2	0	1	0

The corresponding feasible solution of the *original* (nonstandard) problem is $\mathbf{x} = [0, 12/7, 0, 34/7]$, for which $z = 26$.

From this last tableau we see that $z_j - c_j \geqq 0$, and hence that $c_j - z_j \leqq 0$, for each j. Since there is no vector $\mathbf{v}_j$ for which $c_j - z_j > 0$, we cannot improve our basic feasible solution by introducing another vector into the basis. Hence, we are tempted to conclude that we have reached an optimal solution. As it turns out, this conclusion is correct, although at this point in our development we are certainly not justified in drawing it. How do we know there is not some other sequence of vector insertions and replacements which would lead us to a basic feasible solution with a larger value for z? Also how do we know that there is not some nonbasic feasible solution with a larger value for z? These questions will be answered in the next section.

We mentioned, in the preceding example, an alternative procedure for calculating the numbers $z_j - c_j$ at successive stages of the process. We shall now show that, from the tableau at one stage, with z_0 and the numbers $z_j - c_j$ in its last row, the last row of the new tableau can be obtained by a row transformation just as the other rows in the new tableau are obtained.

We continue to use the same notation and consider the same situation as described earlier in this section. Thus z_0, x_j, y_{ij}, and z_j are numbers associated with some particular basic feasible solution, and we are concerned with the transition to a new basic feasible solution by the replacement of one vector in the basis. Suppose $\mathbf{v}_k$ replaces $\mathbf{v}_r$ in the basis. We define θ_k by (23), and we use primes to indicate numbers associated with the new basic feasible solution. We have already calculated x'_j [see (18)] and z'_0 [see (24)]. We now need to calculate y'_{ij} and z'_j. We have, for each $j = 1, 2, \ldots, n$,

$$\mathbf{v}_j = \sum_{i=1}^{m} y_{ij}\mathbf{v}_i = y_{rj}\mathbf{v}_r + \sum_{\substack{i=1 \\ i \neq r}}^{m} y_{ij}\mathbf{v}_i, \tag{26}$$

and, in particular for $j = k$,

$$\mathbf{v}_k = y_{rk}\mathbf{v}_r + \sum_{\substack{i=1 \\ i \neq r}}^{m} y_{ik}\mathbf{v}_i. \tag{27}$$

Solving (27) for $\mathbf{v}_r$ yields

$$\mathbf{v}_r = \frac{1}{y_{rk}}\mathbf{v}_k - \sum_{\substack{i=1 \\ i \neq r}}^{m} \frac{y_{ik}}{y_{rk}}\mathbf{v}_i.$$

Substituting this for $\mathbf{v}_r$ in (26), we get

$$\mathbf{v}_j = y_{rj}\left(\frac{1}{y_{rk}}\mathbf{v}_k - \sum_{\substack{i=1\\i\neq r}}^{m} \frac{y_{ik}}{y_{rk}}\mathbf{v}_i\right) + \sum_{\substack{i=1\\i\neq r}}^{m} y_{ij}\mathbf{v}_i,$$

which, after combining summations, becomes

$$\mathbf{v}_j = \frac{y_{rj}}{y_{rk}}\mathbf{v}_k + \sum_{\substack{i=1\\i\neq r}}^{m}\left(y_{ij} - \frac{y_{rj}y_{ik}}{y_{rk}}\right)\mathbf{v}_i. \tag{28}$$

From (28), we see that, for each $j = 1, 2, \ldots, n$,

$$\begin{cases} y'_{ij} = y_{ij} - \dfrac{y_{rj}y_{ik}}{y_{rk}} & (i = 1, \ldots, m;\ i \neq r), \\ y'_{rj} = \dfrac{y_{rj}}{y_{rk}}. \end{cases} \tag{29}$$

Now, by definition,

$$z'_j = \sum_{\substack{i=1\\i\neq r}}^{m} c_i y'_{ij} + c_k y'_{rj}$$

and

$$(z_j - c_j)' = z'_j - c_j \qquad (j = 1, 2, \ldots, n).$$

Hence,

$$(z_j - c_j)' = \sum_{\substack{i=1\\i\neq r}}^{m} c_i\left(y_{ij} - \frac{y_{rj}y_{ik}}{y_{rk}}\right) + c_k\frac{y_{rj}}{y_{rk}} - c_j.$$

Notice, however, that the restriction $i \neq r$ on the summation is unnecessary since, if it were removed, the term introduced would be

$$c_r\left(y_{rj} - \frac{y_{rj}y_{rk}}{y_{rk}}\right) = c_r 0 = 0.$$

Hence, we can write

$$\begin{aligned}(z_j - c_j)' &= \sum_{i=1}^{m} c_i\left(y_{ij} - \frac{y_{rj}y_{ik}}{y_{rk}}\right) + c_k\frac{y_{rj}}{y_{rk}} - c_j \\ &= \sum_{i=1}^{m} c_i y_{ij} - c_j - \frac{y_{rj}}{y_{rk}}\left(\sum_{i=1}^{m} c_i y_{ik} - c_k\right)\end{aligned}$$

or

$$(z_j - c_j)' = (z_j - c_j) - \frac{y_{rj}}{y_{rk}}(z_k - c_k). \tag{30}$$

For convenience of reference, we rewrite here our formula (24) for z'_0:

$$z'_0 = z_0 - \frac{x_r}{y_{rk}}(z_k - c)_k. \tag{31}$$

Now consider the following "fragment" of the tableau corresponding to the solution $\mathbf{x} = [x_1, \ldots, x_m, 0, \ldots, 0]$ of our problem:

(32)

Basis	$\mathbf{b}$	$\cdots$	$\mathbf{v}_k$	$\cdots$	$\mathbf{v}_j$	$\cdots$
$\vdots$	$\vdots$		$\vdots$		$\vdots$	
$\mathbf{v}_i$	x_i	$\cdots$	y_{ik}	$\cdots$	y_{ij}	$\cdots$
$\vdots$	$\vdots$		$\vdots$		$\vdots$	
$\mathbf{v}_r$	x_r	$\cdots$	$\boxed{y_{rk}}$	$\cdots$	y_{rj}	$\cdots$
$\vdots$	$\vdots$		$\vdots$		$\vdots$	
	z_0	$\cdots$	$z_k - c_k$	$\cdots$	$z_j - c_j$	$\cdots$

Suppose we first divide the $\mathbf{v}_r$ row by y_{rk} and then add multiples of this row to the other rows (including the $z_j - c_j$ row) so that the elements of column $\mathbf{v}_k$ in the new tableau are zeros, except for the 1 in the y_{rk} position. The new tableau has the following appearance:

(33)

Basis	$\mathbf{b}$	$\cdots$	$\mathbf{v}_k$	$\cdots$	$\mathbf{v}_j$	$\cdots$
$\vdots$	$\vdots$		$\vdots$		$\vdots$	
$\mathbf{v}_i$	$x_i - \dfrac{x_r}{y_{rk}} y_{ik}$	$\cdots$	0	$\cdots$	$y_{ij} - \dfrac{y_{rj}}{y_{rk}} y_{ik}$	$\cdots$
$\vdots$	$\vdots$		$\vdots$		$\vdots$	
$\mathbf{v}_k$	$\dfrac{x_r}{y_{rk}}$	$\cdots$	1	$\cdots$	$\dfrac{y_{rj}}{y_{rk}}$	$\cdots$
$\vdots$	$\vdots$		$\vdots$		$\vdots$	
	$z_0 - \dfrac{x_r}{y_{rk}}(z_k - c_k)$	$\cdots$	0	$\cdots$	$(z_j - c_j) - \dfrac{y_{rj}}{y_{rk}}(z_k - c_k)$	$\cdots$

By comparison with (30) and (31), we see that the numbers in the last row of this tableau are z_0' and $(z_j - c_j)'$ $(j = 1, 2, \ldots, n)$. Hence, in proceeding from one basic feasible solution to another, these numbers may be computed by a simple row transformation rather than by direct application of the definition. We can also read from the above tableau our previously derived formulas for x_i' and y_{ij}'.

Finally, the reason for preferring to tabulate $z_j - c_j$ instead of $c_j - z_j$ can be seen. Suppose in (32) we replace each $z_j - c_j$ by $c_j - z_j$, but leave z_0 alone. If we then perform the row transformations, the elements of the last row in, respectively, columns $\mathbf{b}$, $\mathbf{v}_k$, and $\mathbf{v}_j$ of (33) become

$$z_0 - \frac{x_r}{y_{rk}}(c_k - z_k), \qquad 0, \qquad (c_j - z_j) - \frac{y_{rj}}{y_{rk}}(c_k - z_k).$$

Now, from (30), we see that

$$(c_j - z_j)' = (c_j - z_j) - \frac{y_{rj}}{y_{rk}}(c_k - z_k),$$

but

$$z_0' \neq z_0 - \frac{x_r}{y_{rk}}(c_k - z_k).$$

If we also replace z_0 by $-z_0$ in (32), then the element in row $m + 1$, column **b** of (33), becomes

$$-z_0 - \frac{x_r}{y_{rk}}(c_k - z_k) = -\left[z_0 + \frac{x_r}{y_{rk}}(c_k - z_k)\right] = -z_0'.$$

Thus, if we tabulate $c_j - z_j$, we must also tabulate $-z_0$, the negative of the value of the objective function. To avoid having to make this change of sign, we use $z_j - c_j$.

EXERCISES

1. For each of the following problems, first formulate the related standard problem. Note that, in each case, there is an obvious basic feasible solution. Set up the complete tableau displaying this initial basic feasible solution, and determine all vectors for which $z_j - c_j$ has the proper sign for improvement of the objective function. Choose for entry into the basis a vector for which $z_j - c_j$ is maximum in absolute value and has the proper sign for improvement of z. By making the appropriate row transformations, obtain the tableau corresponding to the new basic feasible solution.

(a) Maximize $z = 2x_1 + 4x_2 - x_3 + x_4$ subject to

$$\begin{cases} 5x_1 + 3x_2 - 2x_3 + x_4 \leqq 12, \\ 4x_1 + 2x_2 + 7x_4 \leqq 8, \\ x_1 + x_2 + 3x_3 + 3x_4 \leqq 3, \\ x_j \geqq 0 \quad (j = 1, 2, 3, 4). \end{cases}$$

(b) Minimize $z = 3x_1 + x_2 - 5x_3 - 2x_4$ subject to

$$\begin{cases} x_1 + 5x_2 + 2x_3 - x_4 \leqq 2, \\ 2x_1 - x_2 + 4x_3 + 3x_4 \leqq 5, \\ 6x_1 + 2x_2 + x_3 + 3x_4 \leqq 3, \\ x_j \geqq 0 \quad (j = 1, 2, 3, 4). \end{cases}$$

(c) Maximize $z = 4x_1 - 2x_2 - x_3 + 6x_4 - 2x_5$ subject to

$$\begin{cases} x_1 + 2x_2 - x_4 + x_5 \leqq 6, \\ x_1 - x_2 + x_3 + 2x_4 + 3x_5 \geqq 5, \\ x_1 - 4x_2 - x_4 + 2x_5 \geqq -2, \\ 2x_1 + 5x_2 + 4x_4 + 2x_5 \leqq 10, \\ x_j \geqq 0 \quad (j = 1, 2, 3, 4, 5). \end{cases}$$

(d) Minimize $z = x_1 + 2x_2 - 6x_3 + 8x_4 + 5x_5$ subject to

$$\begin{cases} 5x_1 + x_2 - 2x_3 + 8x_4 - 4x_5 \geqq 5, \\ 3x_1 \qquad + x_3 + 3x_4 + 2x_5 \leqq 12, \\ 4x_1 \qquad - x_3 + 2x_4 + x_5 \leqq 6, \\ x_j \geqq 0 \qquad (j = 1, 2, 3, 4, 5). \end{cases}$$

2. In each part of Exercise 1, determine the vector which must be inserted into the initial basis in order to obtain the maximum improvement in z.

3. Complete the following tableau. Then find a basic feasible solution giving maximum improvement of z, assuming that the tableau represents (a) a maximizing problem, (b) a minimizing problem. Assuming that the variables corresponding to zero coefficients of the objective function are slack variables, state the original problem in each case.

			4	−2	3	−3	1	0	0	0
Basis	*Obj*	**b**	$\mathbf{v}_1$	$\mathbf{v}_2$	$\mathbf{v}_3$	$\mathbf{v}_4$	$\mathbf{v}_5$	$\mathbf{v}_6$	$\mathbf{v}_7$	$\mathbf{v}_8$
$\mathbf{v}_6$		2	2	3	1	−1	6			
$\mathbf{v}_7$		1	2	1	−1	1	2			
$\mathbf{v}_8$		3	5	2	1	2	−1			
$z_j - c_j$										

4. The following incomplete tableau represents the *second* stage in the solution of a linear programming problem by the simplex method. All variables corresponding to zero coefficients of the objective function are slack variables. Complete the tableau. Then find the first and third tableau, and state the *original* problem, assuming it to be a maximizing problem.

								0	0	0
Basis	*Obj*	**b**	$\mathbf{v}_1$	$\mathbf{v}_2$	$\mathbf{v}_3$	$\mathbf{v}_4$	$\mathbf{v}_5$	$\mathbf{v}_6$	$\mathbf{v}_7$	$\mathbf{v}_8$
$\mathbf{v}_6$		9	13		1	−1	9			3
$\mathbf{v}_7$		4	−2		0	4	1			−1
$\mathbf{v}_2$		2	4		0	−1	1			1
$z_j - c_j$		8	15		2	−7	5			4

3-4. *TERMINATION OF THE SIMPLEX PROCESS.*

We have not yet completely described the simplex procedure, but it should be clear that, given a standard problem and a basic feasible solution of the problem, the process involves finding a sequence of basic feasible solutions. This is done by making a succession of changes of basis, only one basis vector at a time being replaced, in such a way that, as we go from one solution in the sequence to the next, the value of the objective function either is improved or remains constant. We learned in the preceding section that it is the choice of the vector entering the basis which governs the change in the value of the objective function. Once this choice has been made, the vector which leaves the basis must then be chosen, as explained in Section 3–2, so that the basic solution corresponding to the new basis will be feasible. We can continue to make changes of basis in this way as long as there are nonbasis vectors $\mathbf{v}_k$ for which $z_k - c_k$ has the proper sign for improvement of z and for which at least one y_{ik} is positive. The object of the process, of course, is either to determine an optimal solution or to prove that the problem has no optimal solution. Once we have achieved this, the process terminates.

This brings us to the three principal remaining questions concerning the simplex process as it applies to standard problems with known basic feasible solutions: First, how do we recognize an optimal solution? Second, how do we prove there is no optimal solution? Third, is the process guaranteed to work? (That is, if we start with a standard problem and a basic feasible solution of the problem and follow the rules of the simplex process, must we eventually either reach an optimal solution or prove that no optimal solution exists?) In this section we consider only the first two questions; the third is discussed in the following section.

Given a standard problem with a known basic feasible solution, it may or may not have an optimal solution. But if it does have an optimal solution, then at least one of its basic feasible solutions must be optimal. (This will follow from subsequent developments.) This is why we shall now consider the problem of determining conditions under which a basic feasible solution is optimal. Given a basic feasible solution, in order to determine whether or not it is optimal, we must be able to compare its associated value of z with the value of z associated with any other feasible solution. Let $\hat{\mathbf{x}}$ be a basic feasible solution of a standard problem, where the constraints, as usual, are written in the form of (9). Let $\bar{\mathbf{x}}$ be a feasible, but not necessarily basic, solution of the same problem. For convenience, assume as before that $\hat{\mathbf{x}} = [\hat{x}_1, \ldots, \hat{x}_m, 0, \ldots, 0]$, and let $\bar{\mathbf{x}} = [\bar{x}_1, \bar{x}_2, \ldots, \bar{x}_n]$. Let $\hat{z} = z(\hat{\mathbf{x}})$ and $\bar{z} = z(\bar{\mathbf{x}})$. The comparison mentioned above is made by means of a formula for $\hat{z} - \bar{z}$, which we now proceed to develop.

By definition, we have

$$\hat{z} - \bar{z} = \sum_{i=1}^{m} c_i \hat{x}_i - \sum_{j=1}^{n} c_j \bar{x}_j. \tag{34}$$

In order to simplify the expression on the right in (34), we make use of the relationship between the components of $\hat{\mathbf{x}}$ and those of $\bar{\mathbf{x}}$. This relationship can be seen in the following way: The sequence of elementary row transformations used to obtain the basic feasible solution $\hat{\mathbf{x}}$ has transformed our system of constraint equations into an equivalent system with the following augmented matrix:

$$\left(\begin{array}{cccccccc|c} 1 & 0 & \ldots & 0 & y_{1,m+1} & \ldots & y_{1n} & & \hat{x}_1 \\ 0 & 1 & \ldots & 0 & y_{2,m+1} & \ldots & y_{2n} & & \hat{x}_2 \\ 0 & 0 & \ldots & 0 & y_{3,m+1} & \ldots & y_{3n} & & \hat{x}_3 \\ \cdot & \cdot & & \cdot & \cdot & & \cdot & & \cdot \\ \cdot & \cdot & & \cdot & \cdot & & \cdot & & \cdot \\ \cdot & \cdot & & \cdot & \cdot & & \cdot & & \cdot \\ 0 & 0 & \ldots & 1 & y_{m,m+1} & \ldots & y_{mn} & & \hat{x}_m \end{array}\right)$$

The components of $\bar{\mathbf{x}}$ satisfy this system, since $\bar{\mathbf{x}}$ is a feasible solution; hence, we have

$$\bar{x}_i + \sum_{j=m+1}^{n} y_{ij}\bar{x}_j = \hat{x}_i \qquad (i = 1, \ldots, m). \tag{35}$$

Substituting this expression for $\hat{x}_i$ into Eq. (34), we obtain

$$\begin{aligned} \hat{z} - \bar{z} &= \sum_{i=1}^{m} c_i\left(\bar{x}_i + \sum_{j=m+1}^{n} y_{ij}\bar{x}_j\right) - \sum_{j=1}^{n} c_j\bar{x}_j \\ &= \sum_{i=1}^{m} c_i\bar{x}_i + \sum_{i=1}^{m}\left(\sum_{j=m+1}^{n} c_i y_{ij}\bar{x}_j\right) - \left(\sum_{i=1}^{m} c_i\bar{x}_i + \sum_{j=m+1}^{n} c_j\bar{x}_j\right) \\ &= \sum_{j=m+1}^{n}\left(\sum_{i=1}^{m} c_i y_{ij}\right)\bar{x}_j - \sum_{j=m+1}^{n} c_j\bar{x}_j \\ &= \sum_{j=m+1}^{n} z_j\bar{x}_j - \sum_{j=m+1}^{n} c_j\bar{x}_j = \sum_{j=m+1}^{n} (z_j - c_j)\bar{x}_j. \end{aligned}$$

Now $z_j - c_j = 0$ for each $j = 1, \ldots, m$ (why?). Hence, we can write

$$\hat{z} - \bar{z} = \sum_{j=1}^{n} (z_j - c_j)\bar{x}_j. \tag{36}$$

This is the desired formula for $\hat{z} - \bar{z}$. Note that it is valid no matter which vectors are in the basis, even though in deriving it we assumed the basis vectors to be $\mathbf{v}_1, \ldots, \mathbf{v}_m$.

From (36) we see that, if $\hat{\mathbf{x}}$ is a feasible solution for which $z_j - c_j \geqq 0$ for each $j = 1, 2, \ldots, n$, then $\hat{z} \geqq \bar{z}$ for each feasible solution $\bar{x}$. If our problem is a maximizing problem, such a solution $\hat{\mathbf{x}}$ would be optimal. Similarly in a minimizing problem, if $z_j - c_j \leqq 0$ for each $j = 1, 2, \ldots, n$, then $\hat{\mathbf{x}}$ is optimal. Thus we have proved the following theorem, which answers the first of our three questions:

THEOREM 1. In a standard linear programming problem, any basic feasible solution for which no $z_j - c_j$ has the proper sign for improvement of z is optimal.

An illustration of Theorem 1 is provided by Example 5 in the preceding section. Since that problem is a maximizing problem and we arrived, in the third tableau, at a basic feasible solution with each $z_j - c_j \geqq 0$, we have obtained an optimal solution. Our conclusions about the original problem are as follows: The maximum value of z subject to the given constraints is 26, and this maximum is attained at the point $\mathbf{x} = [0, \frac{12}{7}, 0, \frac{34}{7}]$.

Now suppose we have a standard problem with a known basic feasible solution and we are in the process of finding a sequence of basic feasible solutions with improved values of z. If we obtain a solution satisfying the hypotheses of Theorem 1, it is optimal, the process terminates, and we write down our conclusions about the original problem. But what if we never obtain such a solution? If we continue making changes of basis as long as there is at least one nonbasis vector $\mathbf{v}_k$ such that $z_k - c_k$ has the proper sign for improvement of z and $y_{ik} > 0$ for at least one value of i, then the only other occurrence which would force us to stop would be that we reach a basic feasible solution for which there is at least one nonbasis vector $\mathbf{v}_k$ such that $z_k - c_k$ has the proper sign for improvement of z and for which each such $\mathbf{v}_k$ has $y_{ik} \leqq 0$ for each i. Actually, however, we may be able to draw a conclusion about the problem before this stage is reached, as the next theorem explains.

THEOREM 2. Suppose we have a basic feasible solution of a standard problem and there is at least one vector $\mathbf{v}_k$ not in its associated basis such that $z_k - c_k$ has the proper sign for improvement of z and $y_{ik} \leqq 0$ for each i. Then, in the case of a maximizing problem, for each $M > 0$, feasible solutions $\mathbf{x}$ exist for which $z(\mathbf{x}) > M$. In the case of a minimizing problem, for each $M > 0$, feasible solutions $\mathbf{x}$ exist for which $z(\mathbf{x}) < -M$. In each case, consequently, there is no optimal solution.

This theorem answers the second of the questions raised above. Notice that, to conclude there is no optimal solution, it need not be the case that *every* vector $\mathbf{v}_k$ for which $z_k - c_k$ has the proper sign for improvement of z has each $y_{ik} \leqq 0$. If there is just *one* such vector, even though there might also be other vectors which could be inserted into the basis to obtain new basic feasible solutions with improved values of z, we can terminate the process and conclude that the problem has no optimal solution.

Proof of Theorem 2: Let $\hat{\mathbf{x}} = [\hat{x}_1, \ldots, \hat{x}_m, 0, \ldots, 0]$ be a basic feasible solution of a standard problem, and assume there is a vector $\mathbf{v}_k$, not in the basis associated with $\hat{\mathbf{x}}$, such that $y_{ik} \leqq 0$ for each $i = 1, \ldots, m$. For each nonnegative number θ, we can write

$$\begin{aligned} \mathbf{b} &= \sum_{i=1}^{m} \hat{x}_i \mathbf{v}_i - \theta \mathbf{v}_k + \theta \mathbf{v}_k \\ &= \sum_{i=1}^{m} \hat{x}_i \mathbf{v}_i - \theta \sum_{i=1}^{m} y_{ik} \mathbf{v}_i + \theta \mathbf{v}_k \end{aligned}$$

and hence

$$\mathbf{b} = \sum_{i=1}^{m} (\hat{x}_i - \theta y_{ik}) \mathbf{v}_i + \theta \mathbf{v}_k. \tag{37}$$

Since $y_{ik} \leqq 0$ for each $i = 1, \ldots, m$ and $\theta \geqq 0$, we see that $\hat{x}_i - \theta y_{ik} \geqq 0$. Hence, Eq. (37) tells us that the vector

$$\hat{\mathbf{x}}(\theta) = [\hat{x}_1 - \theta y_{1k}, \ldots, \hat{x}_m - \theta y_{mk}, 0, \ldots, \theta, \ldots, 0],$$

where θ is the kth component, is a feasible (though not necessarily basic) solution. Let us denote its associated value of z by z_θ. Then, by definition,

$$\begin{aligned} z_\theta = z[\hat{\mathbf{x}}(\theta)] &= \sum_{i=1}^{m} c_i(\hat{x}_i - \theta y_{ik}) + c_k\theta \\ &= \sum_{i=1}^{m} c_i \hat{x}_i - \theta \sum_{i=1}^{m} c_i y_{ik} + c_k\theta \\ &= \hat{z} - \theta z_k + \theta c_k = \hat{z} - \theta(z_k - c_k), \end{aligned}$$

where $\hat{z} = z(\hat{\mathbf{x}})$.

Now suppose our problem is a maximizing problem and that $z_k - c_k < 0$. Let M be any positive number, and let θ be a positive number satisfying

$$\theta > \frac{M - \hat{z}}{c_k - z_k}. \tag{38}$$

Then, since $c_k - z_k > 0$, we have

$$z_\theta = \hat{z} + \theta(c_k - z_k) > \hat{z} + \frac{M - \hat{z}}{c_k - z_k}(c_k - z_k) = \hat{z} + M - \hat{z} = M.$$

Thus, for each $M > 0$, each feasible solution $\hat{\mathbf{x}}(\theta)$ for which θ satisfies (38) is a feasible solution $\mathbf{x}$ such that $z(\mathbf{x}) > M$. The argument for the case of a minimizing problem is similar and is left as an exercise.

Let us now illustrate Theorem 2 with a simple numerical example:

Example 6. Maximize $z = x_1 + x_2$ subject to

$$\begin{cases} -2x_1 + x_2 \leqq 1, \\ x_1 - x_2 \leqq 1, \\ x_1 \geqq 0, \quad x_2 \geqq 0. \end{cases}$$

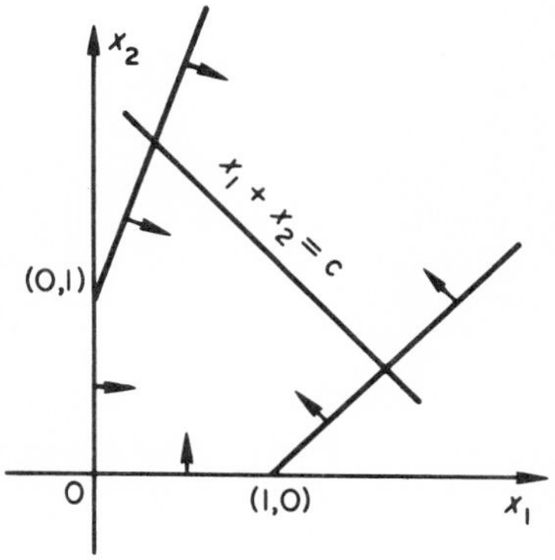

In the figure, we have sketched the set of feasible solutions and have shown a typical position of the line $x_1 + x_2 = c$. Clearly, increasing c moves this line away from the origin, and the problem has no optimal solution. Let us see how this shows up algebraically. The related standard problem is to maximize $z = x_1 + x_2$ subject to

$$\begin{cases} -2x_1 + x_2 + x_3 = 1 \\ x_1 - x_2 + x_4 = 1 \\ x_j \geqq 0 \quad (j = 1, 2, 3, 4). \end{cases}$$

The only two tableaux needed are shown below

			1	1	0	0
Basis	*Obj*	**b**	$\mathbf{v}_1$	$\mathbf{v}_2$	$\mathbf{v}_3$	$\mathbf{v}_4$
$\mathbf{v}_3$	0	1	−2	①	1	0
$\mathbf{v}_4$	0	1	1	−1	0	1
$z_j - c_j$		0	−1	−1	0	0
$\mathbf{v}_2$	1	1	−2	1	1	0
$\mathbf{v}_4$	0	2	−1	0	1	1
$z_j - c_j$		1	−3	0	1	0

For the second basic feasible solution $\mathbf{x} = [0, 1, 0, 2]$ we see that $z_1 - c_1 = -3 < 0$, while each coefficient of $\mathbf{v}_1$ relative to the basis is negative. Hence, by Theorem 2, the problem has no optimal solution. It is instructive to retrace the steps in the proof of Theorem 2 for this example. We have

$$\begin{aligned}\mathbf{b} &= \mathbf{v}_2 + 2\mathbf{v}_4 - \theta\mathbf{v}_1 + \theta\mathbf{v}_1 \\ &= \mathbf{v}_2 + 2\mathbf{v}_4 - \theta(-2\mathbf{v}_2 - \mathbf{v}_4) + \theta\mathbf{v}_1 \\ &= (1 + 2\theta)\mathbf{v}_2 + (2 + \theta)\mathbf{v}_4 + \theta\mathbf{v}_1\end{aligned}$$

for each θ. In particular, for $\theta \geqq 0$, we see that the vector

$$\mathbf{x}(\theta) = [\theta, 1 + 2\theta, 0, 2 + \theta]$$

is a feasible solution. Its corresponding value of z is given by

$$z_\theta = 1\theta + 1(1 + 2\theta) = 1 + 3\theta.$$

From this we can verify directly that, given any $M > 0$, we shall have $z_\theta > M$ if $\theta > (M - 1)/3$. Notice also that the Eqs. $x_1 = \theta$, $x_2 = 1 + 2\theta$, $\theta \geqq 0$ are parametric equations for the half-line (or ray) which forms the upper boundary of the set of all feasible solutions. This means that the set of solutions $[\theta, 1 + 2\theta]$ $(\theta \geqq 0)$ of the *original* problem corresponding to the family of solutions $\mathbf{x}(\theta)$ of the related standard problem is simply this half-line.

Next, consider the following example:

Example 7. Suppose that, in the course of applying the simplex method to a standard *minimizing* problem, we obtain the following tableau:

			−4	6	−1	3	3	0
Basis	*Obj*	**b**	$\mathbf{v}_1$	$\mathbf{v}_2$	$\mathbf{v}_3$	$\mathbf{v}_4$	$\mathbf{v}_5$	$\mathbf{v}_6$
$\mathbf{v}_4$	3	7	−1	2	0	1	1	0
$\mathbf{v}_6$	0	2	−4	3	0	0	2	1
$\mathbf{v}_3$	−1	4	0	5	1	0	−8	0
$z_j - c_j$		17	1	−5	0	0	8	0

Here again we see that the conditions of Theorem 2 are fulfilled with $\mathbf{v}_k = \mathbf{v}_1$, and consequently the problem has no optimal solution. Had we not noticed this, we should have chosen $\mathbf{v}_5$ to replace $\mathbf{v}_6$ in the basis, and, as the student may verify for himself, the next basic feasible solution would not have satisfied the conditions of Theorem 2. In one more step, however, we should again obtain a basic feasible solution to which Theorem 2 applies, this time with $\mathbf{v}_k = \mathbf{v}_6$. This example thus illustrates the point that, in order to avoid unnecessary steps, it is essential to check all nonbasis vectors $\mathbf{v}_j$ for which $z_j - c_j$ has the proper sign for improvement of z and make sure that the conditions of Theorem 2 are not satisfied, before proceeding with another change of basis.

To conclude this section, let us now summarize the rules of the simplex method as it applies to a standard linear programming problem with a known basic feasible solution. At each stage of the process we have a basic feasible solution, and we proceed as follows:

1. If no $z_j - c_j$ has the proper sign for improvement of z, we have found an optimal basic feasible solution. The process terminates. From the tableau, we can read the components of an optimal solution and the optimal value of z.

2. If there is some vector $\mathbf{v}_j$ for which $z_j - c_j$ has the proper sign for improvement of z, but each $y_{ij} \leqq 0$, the problem has no optimal solution. Again the process terminates. If desired, one can determine from the tableau a family of feasible solutions $\mathbf{x}(\theta)$ such that $z[\mathbf{x}(\theta)] \longrightarrow +\infty$ (in a maximizing problem) or $-\infty$ (in a minimizing problem) as $\theta \longrightarrow +\infty$.

3. If neither of the preceding two sets of conditions is satisfied, then there will be at least one vector for which $z_j - c_j$ has the proper sign for improvement of z and, for every such vector, there will be at least one positive y_{ij}. Choose any such vector for entry into the basis. Determine the vector to leave the basis as any one for which the ratio x_i/y_{ij} is minimum among all such ratios with positive denominators. Carry out the appropriate row transformations, and a new basic feasible solution will be obtained for which the value of z has either been improved or held constant.

EXERCISES

1. Solve each of the following problems by the simplex method. In each case it is possible to obtain the solution by making just one or two changes of basis.

(a) Maximize $z = 3x_1 + x_2 - 2x_3$ subject to

$$\begin{cases} x_1 - 2x_2 - x_3 \leqq 10, \\ 2x_1 + x_2 + 2x_3 \leqq 12, \\ x_1 - x_2 + x_3 \leqq 5, \\ x_j \geqq 0 \qquad (j = 1, 2, 3). \end{cases}$$

(b) Minimize $z = x_1 - 2x_2 - x_3$ subject to

$$\begin{cases} 3x_1 + x_2 - 4x_3 \leqq 4, \\ x_1 - x_2 - x_3 \leqq 10, \\ x_1 - 2x_2 + 6x_3 \leqq 9, \\ x_j \geqq 0 \quad (j = 1, 2, 3). \end{cases}$$

(c) Maximize $z = x_1 + 4x_2 + 2x_3 + x_4$ subject to

$$\begin{cases} 2x_1 + x_2 - x_3 - x_4 \leqq 6, \\ x_1 - x_2 + x_3 + x_4 \leqq 8, \\ x_1 + x_2 + 2x_3 - 2x_4 \leqq 12, \\ x_j \geqq 0 \quad (j = 1, 2, 3, 4). \end{cases}$$

(d) Minimize $z = 3x_1 - 2x_2 + x_3$ subject to

$$\begin{cases} x_1 - 2x_2 + x_3 \geqq -4, \\ x_1 + x_2 + x_3 \leqq 9, \\ 2x_1 - x_2 - x_3 \leqq 5, \\ x_j \geqq 0 \quad (j = 1, 2, 3). \end{cases}$$

(e) Maximize $z = 3x_1 - 2x_2 + x_3 + 5x_4 - x_5$ subject to

$$\begin{cases} 3x_1 + x_2 - 2x_4 + x_5 \leqq 4, \\ x_1 - x_3 + x_4 - x_5 \leqq 2, \\ 4x_1 - 2x_2 + x_3 + 3x_4 + 4x_5 \leqq 7, \\ x_j \geqq 0 \quad (j = 1, 2, 3, 4, 5). \end{cases}$$

2. Use the simplex method to verify that the following problem has no optimal solution; then follow the steps in the proof of Theorem 2 to find a family of feasible solutions $\mathbf{x}(\theta)$ such that $z[\mathbf{x}(\theta)] \to +\infty$ as $\theta \to +\infty$:
Maximize $z = 3x_1 + 2x_2 - x_3 + x_4$ subject to

$$\begin{cases} 2x_1 - 4x_2 - x_3 + x_4 \leqq 8, \\ x_1 + x_2 + 2x_3 - 3x_4 \leqq 10, \\ x_1 - x_2 - 4x_3 + x_4 \leqq 3, \\ x_j \geqq 0 \quad (j = 1, 2, 3, 4). \end{cases}$$

In particular, find a feasible solution for which $z > 1000$.

3. Solve the following problems:
(a) Maximize $z = 3x_1 + 4x_2 - x_3 + 2x_4$ subject to

$$\begin{cases} 3x_1 - x_2 + 2x_4 \leqq 2, \\ x_1 + 4x_2 + 2x_3 + x_4 \geqq 6, \\ x_1 + x_2 - x_4 \leqq 1, \\ x_j \geqq 0 \quad (j = 1, 2, 3, 4). \end{cases}$$

(b) Minimize $z = x_1 + 6x_2 + 5x_3 - 2x_4 + 8x_5$ subject to

$$\begin{cases} 2x_1 - x_2 + 2x_4 - 3x_5 \leqq 4, \\ 3x_1 + x_2 + x_4 + 2x_5 \leqq 6, \\ -x_1 + 2x_2 + x_3 + 2x_5 \geqq 2, \\ 2x_1 - x_3 + x_4 + x_5 \leqq 1, \\ x_j \geqq 0 \quad (j = 1, 2, 3, 4, 5). \end{cases}$$

Note: In each of these problems, in contrast to those of Exercise 1, a simple calculation must first be performed in order to obtain the initial basic feasible solution of the related standard problem. In the next section, we describe a general method for dealing with problems having no obvious initial basic feasible solutions.

4. Supply the missing details of the proof of Theorem 2 for the case of a minimizing problem.

5. The converse of Theorem 1 is not true. That is, it need not be the case that each optimal solution of a standard problem satisfies the hypotheses of Theorem 1. Prove, however, that each *nondegenerate* optimal basic feasible solution of a standard problem must satisfy the conditions of Theorem 1.

6. Suppose we have an optimal basic feasible solution $\hat{\mathbf{x}}$ of a standard linear programming problem which satisfies the conditions of Theorem 1 and, in addition, has the property that $z_j - c_j \neq 0$ for each nonbasis vector $\mathbf{v}_j$. Prove that $\hat{\mathbf{x}}$ is the *unique* optimal solution; i.e., if $\bar{\mathbf{x}}$ is any other feasible (but not necessarily basic) solution, then $z(\bar{\mathbf{x}}) \neq z(\hat{\mathbf{x}})$. [*Hint*: Use formula (36).]

Note: In the problems below it will be helpful to make a change of variables of the form $x_j = cx'_j$ before beginning the calculations.

7. Solve the problem formulated in Exercise 7, Chapter 1.

8. Solve the preceding problem if the capacity of the assembly department can be increased to 2400 hours per week. What is the value of this additional 600 hours in increased profits?

9. Solve the problem formulated in Exercise 9, Chapter 1. Note that one of the variables can be eliminated before beginning the calculations.

10. Solve the preceding problem if the selling price of product A is $20 per pound.

11. Solve the problem formulated in Exercise 10, Chapter 1.

3-5. *NONTERMINATION OF THE SIMPLEX PROCESS.**

In this section we consider the third of the questions raised in the preceding section, which we may now phrase as follows: If we start with a basic feasible solution of a standard linear programming problem and follow the

*The latter part of this section may be omitted without loss of continuity. It is suggested that the student read at least through the statement of Lemma 1 in order to get some idea of the problem of nontermination.

rules of the simplex process, must we eventually obtain a basic feasible solution to which either Theorem 1 or Theorem 2 applies? Before answering this question, let us take another look at the simplex process. At each stage, we have a basic feasible solution. If that solution satisfies neither the hypotheses of Theorem 1 nor those of Theorem 2, then the rules require us to make a change of basis in such a way that the value of the objective function is either improved or remains constant. Furthermore, we know that, under these conditions, such a change of basis is possible. Thus, starting with a basis B_1 corresponding to the initial basic feasible solution, we obtain, by following the simplex rules, a sequence $B_1, B_2, B_3, \ldots$ of bases of the vector space $\mathscr{V}_m$ spanned by the columns of the system of constraint equations. Each basis determines a unique basic feasible solution of the problem, though it may happen (in the case of degenerate solutions) that two or more different bases correspond to the same basic feasible solution. As soon as we reach (if we ever do) a basis B_k corresponding to a basic feasible solution to which either Theorem 1 or Theorem 2 applies, the sequence terminates, and we shall call B_k a *terminal basis* for the problem. This is a finite sequence. If a terminal basis never occurs, we have an *infinite* sequence of bases. Let us call any such sequence of bases (finite or infinite) associated with a given problem a *simplex sequence* for that problem. There will usually be more than one simplex sequence associated with a given problem, but a finite simplex sequence, and only a finite simplex sequence, will yield a solution of the problem. The simplex process itself may be thought of as the process of constructing a simplex sequence.

The question we are considering may now be put this way: Given a basis B_1 corresponding to a basic feasible solution of a standard problem, must each simplex sequence for the problem which starts with B_1 necessarily be a finite sequence? The answer to this question, unfortunately, is "No." Problems have been devised (see [2], Chapter 7, or [3], Chapter 6, for instance) for which it is possible to construct simplex sequences of the following type:

$$B_1, B_2, \ldots, B_k, B_{k+1}, \ldots, B_{k+r}, B_k, B_{k+1}, \ldots, B_{k+r}, B_k, \ldots.$$

That is, at some stage a basis is obtained which had been obtained at an earlier stage. Then the intervening sequence of bases is repeated indefinitely, yielding an infinite simplex sequence. A simplex sequence of this type is called a *cycle*. For each of the problems devised to illustrate this cycling behavior, however, *finite* simplex sequences also exist. That is, each of these problems can be solved by the simplex method if the sequence of bases is chosen properly. This raises the following question: Do there exist problems for which *every* simplex sequence is infinite? If the answer to this question were "Yes," then there could be some standard linear programming problems unsolvable by the simplex method. Fortunately, however, the answer is "No." In fact, we have the following result:

THEOREM 3. Given a standard linear programming problem and a basis B_1 corresponding to a basic feasible solution of the problem, there is a finite simplex sequence for the problem starting with B_1 and repeating no basis.

By definition, a finite simplex sequence terminates with a basis corresponding to a basic feasible solution to which either Theorem 1 or 2 applies. Hence, Theorem 3 says that any standard problem can be solved by the simplex process if an initial basic feasible solution can be found. The theorem does not tell us how to find a finite simplex sequence for a given problem, but normally this is not difficult. In every problem the student is likely to encounter, unless he seeks out one of the very few known examples constructed to prove that cycling can occur, every simplex sequence will be finite. Procedures are known which, if followed in constructing a simplex sequence, guarantee that no basis will be repeated in the sequence (see either of the references cited above). Since, for a given problem, the number of different bases is finite, any simplex sequence in which no basis is repeated is necessarily a finite sequence. Thus, the description and justification of an explicit procedure for avoiding repetition of bases would constitute a constructive proof of Theorem 3. In practice, however, knowledge of such an explicit procedure is not essential since cycling almost never occurs. Our proof, which occupies most of the remainder of this section, is not constructive but merely demonstrates the *existence* of a finite simplex sequence.

As we have seen, an infinite simplex sequence can occur only if some basis can occur twice (and hence infinitely many times) in the same sequence. Thus we are led to consider the conditions under which a basis can repeat. Let $B_1, B_2, B_3, \ldots$ be a simplex sequence for some standard problem, and let $z^{(1)}, z^{(2)}, z^{(3)}, \ldots$ be the corresponding sequence of values of the objective function z. For definiteness, suppose we are talking about a maximizing problem. Then we must have

$$z^{(1)} \leqq z^{(2)} \leqq z^{(3)} \leqq \cdots. \tag{39}$$

Now each basis B_i uniquely determines the corresponding number $z^{(i)}$. Hence, if a basis repeats so that $B_i = B_{i+r}$ for some pair of integers i and r, we must have $z^{(i)} = z^{(i+r)}$. But then, by (39), it must also be true that $z^{(i)} = z^{(i+1)} = \cdots = z^{(i+r-1)} = z^{(i+r)}$; i.e., z remains constant between any two occurrences of the same basis. Clearly, this is also true for minimizing problems. Under what conditions does z remain constant from one basis to the next? As we found in Section 3–3, if $z = z_0$ at one stage and $\mathbf{v}_k$ enters the basis, then $z = z_0 + \theta(c_k - z_k)$ at the next stage, where θ is the minimum of a certain set of ratios whose numerators are basic variables. Now, if $\mathbf{v}_k$ is selected to enter the basis, we must have $c_k - z_k \neq 0$. Hence, z remains constant if, and only if, $\theta = 0$, and this, in turn, can occur only if at least one of the basic variables is zero, i.e., the corresponding basic feasible solution is degenerate. Thus, if $B_i = B_{i+r}$, then the basic feasible solution corresponding to B_i must be degenerate and this same solution must correspond to each of the intervening bases $B_{i+1}, \ldots, B_{i+r-1}$. We cannot conclude from this discussion that the occurrence of a degenerate basic feasible solution necessarily means that repetition of a basis will be possible—this is not true. What can be inferred is that a simplex sequence for which each corresponding basic feasible solution is nondegenerate cannot repeat a basis and hence is necessarily finite. In particular, the following is true:

LEMMA 1. For a standard linear programming problem having at least one basic feasible solution and having no degenerate basic feasible solutions, no basis can appear twice in the same simplex sequence. Consequently, each simplex sequence is finite.

Thus the conclusion of Theorem 3 holds for problems having only nondegenerate basic feasible solutions. The idea behind the proof of Theorem 3 is that, even though a particular problem may have degenerate basic feasible solutions, there will be other problems "arbitrarily near," in some sense, to the given problem, which have only nondegenerate basic feasible solutions. To these nearby problems, Lemma 1 applies, and, from this, it will follow that the conclusion of Theorem 3 holds for the given problem as well.

Now let us make precise and then justify the above statement about the existence of nearby problems having no degenerate solutions. Consider a standard problem, which we shall refer to as problem P_0, having the following system of constraints:

$$(40) \qquad \begin{cases} x_1\mathbf{v}_1 + x_2\mathbf{v}_2 + \cdots + x_n\mathbf{v}_n = \mathbf{b}, \\ x_j \geqq 0 \qquad (j = 1, 2, \ldots, n), \end{cases}$$

where each $\mathbf{v}_j$ and $\mathbf{b}$ is an m-dimensional column vector. The problem P_0 may be either a maximizing or a minimizing problem. We assume that P_0 has at least one basic feasible solution, which may be either degenerate or nondegenerate. The vague statement under consideration is made precise as follows:

LEMMA 2. Let B_1 be the basis corresponding to some basic feasible solution of P_0. Then there exists an m-dimensional column vector $\mathbf{u}$ such that, for each ϵ satisfying $0 < \epsilon < 1$, the system of constraints

$$(41) \qquad \begin{cases} x_1\mathbf{v}_1 + x_2\mathbf{v}_2 + \cdots + x_n\mathbf{v}_n = \mathbf{b} + \epsilon\mathbf{u}, \\ x_j \geqq 0 \qquad (j = 1, 2, \ldots, n) \end{cases}$$

has a nondegenerate basic feasible solution with basis B_1 and has no degenerate basic feasible solutions at all.

It is easy to see what is going on here if one looks at one of the special cases $m = 2$ or $m = 3$ and thinks of vectors as directed line segments issuing from the origin. Let us consider the two-dimensional case $m = 2$. Suppose the basis B_1 corresponding to some basic feasible solution of P_0 consists of the vectors $\mathbf{v}_1$ and $\mathbf{v}_2$. In Fig. 10, we have pictured the situation as it might appear if B_1 corresponds to a nondegenerate basic feasible solution. If the

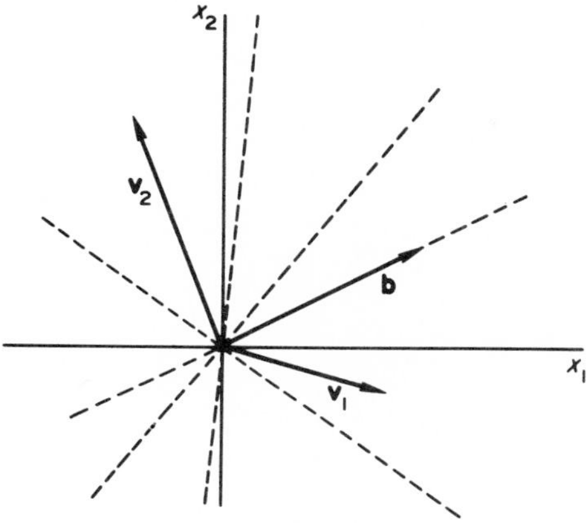

Figure 10

solution were degenerate, then **b** would have the same direction as either $\mathbf{v}_1$ or $\mathbf{v}_2$. The other lines through the origin in Fig. 10 represent the lines determined by the remaining vectors $\mathbf{v}_3, \mathbf{v}_4, \ldots, \mathbf{v}_n$. They are the geometrical representations of the one-dimensional subspaces of the column space of the constraint equations. In the situation pictured in Fig. 10, **b** lies in one of these subspaces and hence there is one degenerate basic feasible solution, unless **b** is a negative multiple of each vector $\mathbf{v}_j$ lying in the subspace determined by **b**. Since there are only a finite number of lines to avoid, it is

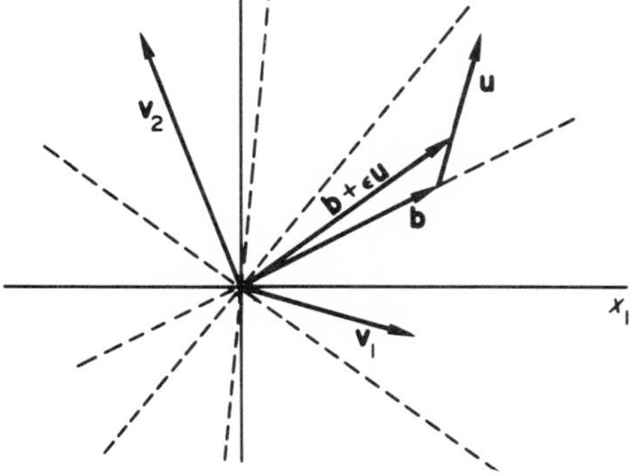

Figure 11

clear that a vector **u** can be found which is a positive linear combination of $\mathbf{v}_1$ and $\mathbf{v}_2$ (i.e., a linear combination $a_1\mathbf{v}_1 + a_2\mathbf{v}_2$ with $a_1 > 0$ and $a_2 > 0$) and which is short enough so that, when it is drawn from the terminal point of **b**, it does not meet any of these subspace lines except, of course, at its initial point (see Fig. 11). This means that, for each ϵ, $0 < \epsilon < 1$, the vector $\mathbf{b} + \epsilon\mathbf{u}$ does not lie in any of the one-dimensional subspaces determined by the vectors $\mathbf{v}_1, \mathbf{v}_2, \ldots, \mathbf{v}_n$ and hence that system (41) has no degenerate basic feasible solutions. Moreover, if $\mathbf{b} = \bar{x}_1\mathbf{v}_1 + \bar{x}_2\mathbf{v}_2$ ($\bar{x}_j \geqq 0$) and $\mathbf{u} = u_1\mathbf{v}_1 + u_2\mathbf{v}_2$ ($u_j > 0$), then $\mathbf{b} + \epsilon\mathbf{u} = y_1\mathbf{v}_1 + y_2\mathbf{v}_2$, where $y_j = \bar{x}_j + \epsilon u_j > 0$ for each $j = 1, 2$. Hence, system (41) has a nondegenerate basic feasible solution with basis B_1 for each ϵ, $0 < \epsilon < 1$. In the three-dimensional case, we could reason similarly, choosing the vector **u** as a positive linear combination of the vectors in the basis B_1 and short enough so that, when translated to the terminal end of **b**, it does not intersect (except possibly for its initial point) any of the planes through the origin corresponding to the two-dimensional subspaces of the column space of the constraint system. We now give the proof for the general case:

Proof of Lemma 2: Let the $(m - 1)$-dimensional subspaces of $\mathscr{V}_m$, determined by the various sets of $m - 1$ linearly independent vectors from among $\mathbf{v}_1, \mathbf{v}_2, \ldots, \mathbf{v}_n$, be denoted by $T_1, T_2, \ldots, T_k$. Now there must be some positive linear combination of the vectors in the basis B_1 which does not lie in any of the subspaces $T_1, T_2, \ldots, T_k$. (This follows from the facts that the set of all positive linear combinations of the vectors in B_1 is an m-dimensional set, whereas the union of the subspaces $T_1, T_2, \ldots, T_k$ is only $(m - 1)$-dimensional.) Let **v** be any such vector. Then, for each $\lambda > 0$, $\lambda\mathbf{v}$ is a positive linear combination of the vectors in B_1 and does not lie in any of the subspaces $T_1, T_2, \ldots, T_k$. We assert that, for some $\lambda_0 > 0$, each of the vectors $\mathbf{b} + \epsilon(\lambda_0\mathbf{v})$, $0 < \epsilon < 1$, does not lie in any of the subspaces $T_1, T_2, \ldots, T_k$. To justify this assertion, consider any one of the subspaces T_i. There is at most one number λ such that $\lambda \neq 0$ and $\mathbf{b} + \lambda\mathbf{v}$ lies in T_i. For, if there were two such numbers λ_1 and λ_2, then the vector $(\mathbf{b} + \lambda_1\mathbf{v}) - (\mathbf{b} + \lambda_2\mathbf{v}) = (\lambda_1 - \lambda_2)\mathbf{v}$ would lie in T_i. But then, since $\lambda_1 \neq \lambda_2$, **v** would lie in T_i, contradicting our choice of **v**. Let λ_0 be the smallest positive number such that $\mathbf{b} + \lambda_0\mathbf{v}$ lies in at least one of the subspaces $T_1, T_2, \ldots, T_k$. If, for each $\lambda > 0$, $\mathbf{b} + \lambda\mathbf{v}$ does not lie in any T_i, then let $\lambda_0 = 1$. Then, if $0 < \epsilon < 1$, the vector $\mathbf{b} + \epsilon(\lambda_0\mathbf{v})$ lies in none of these subspaces. Let $\mathbf{u} = \lambda_0\mathbf{v}$. Then, for each ϵ, $0 < \epsilon < 1$, system (41) has no degenerate basic feasible solutions. (In fact, disregarding the nonnegativity restrictions, there are no degenerate basic solutions at all for $0 < \epsilon < 1$.) Finally, since **b** is a linear combination with nonnegative coefficients and $\epsilon\mathbf{u} = \epsilon\lambda_0\mathbf{v}$ is a linear combination with positive coefficients of the vectors in the basis B_1, it follows that $\mathbf{b} + \epsilon\mathbf{u}$ $(0 < \epsilon < 1)$ is a linear combination with positive coefficients of these vectors; i.e., system (41) has a nondegenerate basic feasible solution with basis B_1. This completes the proof of Lemma 2.

Proof of Theorem 3: Consider the standard problem P_0 with constraints given by (40). Let B_1 be a basis corresponding to some basic feasible solution of P_0. Let $\mathbf{u}$ be a vector having the properties stated in the conclusion of Theorem 2. For each ϵ, $0 < \epsilon < 1$, let P_ϵ denote the problem whose objective function is the same as that of P_0 and whose constraints are given by (41). Each problem P_ϵ has a basic feasible solution with basis B_1 and has no degenerate basic feasible solutions. Hence, by Lemma 1, there is a finite simplex sequence without repetitions for each problem P_ϵ. Since no repetitions occur in these simplex sequences, the number of bases in each sequence cannot exceed the total number of different bases obtainable from $\mathbf{v}_1, \ldots, \mathbf{v}_n$ and, hence, there are only a finite number of finite sequences of bases with no repetitions. Now let us consider the sequence of problems $P_{1/2}, P_{1/3}, P_{1/4}, \ldots$. For each of these, there is a corresponding finite simplex sequence, and, since there are but a finite number of such sequences, at least one of them must occur infinitely many times. Hence, there is one particular sequence of bases, say $B_1, B_2, \ldots, B_k$ which is a simplex sequence for each of a sequence of problems $P_{\epsilon_1}, P_{\epsilon_2}, \ldots$, where $\lim_{n\to\infty} \epsilon_n = 0$.

We wish to show that this sequence $B_1, B_2, \ldots, B_k$ is also a simplex sequence for the original problem P_0. We know that B_1 corresponds to a basic feasible solution of P_0. In addition, we must show that (i) the entering and departing vectors at each stage are chosen in accordance with rule 3 of the preceding section and (ii) B_k is a terminal basis for P_0. First, note that, in any tableau associated with a problem P_ϵ, the numbers y_{ij} and $z_j - c_j$ depend only on the basis vectors at that stage and the objective function coefficients—not on ϵ. The only numbers dependent upon ϵ are the coefficients of $\mathbf{b} + \epsilon\mathbf{u}$ relative to the basis and, consequently, the value of z. Hence, the entering vector at each stage is one for which $z_j - c_j$ has the proper sign, since $B_1, B_2, \ldots, B_k$ is a simplex sequence for each P_{ϵ_i} $(i = 1, 2, \ldots)$. Now let us consider the vector which leaves the basis in the transformation from B_i to B_{i+1}. For convenience, let the vectors in B_i be $\mathbf{v}_1, \mathbf{v}_2, \ldots, \mathbf{v}_m$. For each $j = 1, 2, \ldots$, let $x_1(\epsilon_j), x_2(\epsilon_j), \ldots, x_m(\epsilon_j)$ be the positive numbers such that

$$(42) \qquad x_1(\epsilon_j)\mathbf{v}_1 + x_2(\epsilon_j)\mathbf{v}_2 + \cdots + x_m(\epsilon_j)\mathbf{v}_m = \mathbf{b} + \epsilon_j\mathbf{u}.$$

Let $\mathbf{b} = b_1\mathbf{v}_1 + b_2\mathbf{v}_2 + \cdots + b_m\mathbf{v}_m$, $\mathbf{u} = u_1\mathbf{v}_1 + u_2\mathbf{v}_2 + \cdots + u_m\mathbf{v}_m$. Then

(43) $\mathbf{b} + \epsilon_j \mathbf{u} = (b_1 + \epsilon_j u_1)\mathbf{v}_1 + (b_2 + \epsilon_j u_2)\mathbf{v}_2 + \cdots + (b_m + \epsilon_j u_m)\mathbf{v}_m.$

From (42) and (43), it follows that

$$b_r + \epsilon_j u_r = x_r(\epsilon_j) \tag{44}$$

for each $r = 1, 2, \ldots, m$ and each $j = 1, 2, \ldots$. Hence, we must have $b_r \geqq 0$ for each $r = 1, 2, \ldots, m$. For, if some $b_r < 0$, then $b_r + \epsilon_j u_r < 0$ for large enough j, because $\lim_{j\to\infty} \epsilon_j u_r = 0$. But this contradicts the fact that $x_r(\epsilon_j) > 0$. This shows that each basis B_i corresponds to a basic *feasible* solution of P_0. It follows that the vector selected to leave the basis at each stage is a vector $\mathbf{v}_r$ for which b_r/y_{rj} is minimum with $y_{rj} > 0$. For y_{rj} is independent of ϵ, so that we could not have $y_{rj} \leqq 0$ and, if the ratio were not minimum, we should not obtain a feasible solution. Thus, (i) is established. Finally, whether or not a basis is terminal depends only upon the numbers $z_j - c_j$ and y_{ij} associated with that basis. Now B_k is a terminal basis for each of the problems P_{ϵ_i} $(i = 1, 2, \ldots)$. Hence, it is also a terminal basis for P_0. This proves (ii), and hence completes the proof of Theorem 3.

3-6. *THE TWO-PHASE PROCESS.*

The results of the previous sections tell us that any standard linear programming problem for which we can find an initial basic feasible solution can be solved by the simplex method. All of the problems which have occurred in examples and exercises so far have been arranged so that it is easy to find this initial basic feasible solution. But many problems are not so arranged and, in fact, there is no reason why a standard linear programming problem should have any basic feasible solutions at all. One method which has been devised to deal with such problems is a modification of the simplex method, known as the *two-phase process*. This section is devoted to a description of this process and to the statement and proof of two "termination" theorems analogous to Theorems 1 and 2 of Section 3–4. In the following section we use Theorem 3 to prove that the two-phase process can always be terminated in a finite number of steps.

We begin our discussion by considering the following example:

Example 8. Maximize $z = 2x_1 - x_2 + x_3$ subject to

$$\begin{cases} x_1 + x_2 - 3x_3 \leqq 8, \\ 4x_1 - x_2 + x_3 \geqq 2, \\ 2x_1 + 3x_2 - x_3 \geqq 4, \\ x_j \geqq 0 \qquad (j = 1, 2, 3). \end{cases}$$

The related standard problem, which we shall call P_0, is stated as follows:

Maximize $z = 2x_1 - x_2 + x_3$ subject to

$$\begin{cases} x_1 + \ x_2 - 3x_3 + x_4 & = 8, \\ 4x_1 - \ x_2 + \ x_3 \qquad - x_5 & = 2, \\ 2x_1 + 3x_2 - \ x_3 \qquad\qquad - x_6 & = 4, \\ x_j \geqq 0 \qquad (j = 1, 2, \ldots, 6). \end{cases}$$

There is no obvious basic feasible solution of P_0, since the slack variables x_5 and x_6 have coefficients of -1 rather than $+1$. To attempt to discover a basic feasible solution, we first consider the following problem, which we shall call P_1:

Maximize $z^* = 0x_1 + \cdots + 0x_6 - x_7 - x_8$ subject to

$$\begin{cases} x_1 + \ x_2 - 3x_3 + x_4 & = 8, \\ 4x_1 - \ x_2 + \ x_3 \qquad - x_5 \qquad + x_7 & = 2, \\ 2x_1 + 3x_2 - \ x_3 \qquad\qquad - x_6 \qquad + x_8 & = 4, \\ x_j \geqq 0 \qquad (j = 1, 2, \ldots, 8). \end{cases}$$

Before doing any numerical calculations, let us see why consideration of this problem might be expected to achieve the desired result. First of all, P_1 does have an obvious basic feasible solution in which $x_4 = 8$, $x_7 = 2$, $x_8 = 4$, and all other variables are zero. Now $z^* \leqq 0$ for each feasible solution of this problem. Hence, there is an optimal basic feasible solution, and the maximum value of z^* (call it z^*_{max}) cannot exceed zero. Suppose that $z^*_{\text{max}} < 0$. Then P_0 has no feasible solution. For, if $\mathbf{x} = [x_1, \ldots, x_6]$ were a feasible solution of P_0, then $\mathbf{x}^* = [x_1, \ldots, x_6, 0, 0]$ would be a feasible solution of P_1. But $z^*(\mathbf{x}^*) = 0$, contrary to our assumption that $z^*_{\text{max}} < 0$. Next, suppose we have found an optimal basic feasible solution $\mathbf{x}^* = [x_1, x_2, \ldots, x_8]$ of P_1 and that $z^*_{\text{max}} = z^*(\mathbf{x}^*) = 0$. Then we must have $x_7 = x_8 = 0$, but this does not necessarily mean that the vectors corresponding to x_1 and x_8 do not appear in the basis at this stage. If they do not, then $\mathbf{x} = [x_1, x_2, \ldots, x_6]$ is a basic feasible solution of P_0 and we can proceed to solve P_0 by the usual simplex method. This would be phase 2 of the two-phase process in this case. If either of the vectors corresponding to x_7 and x_8 appears in the basis associated with $\mathbf{x}^*$, the discussion of the ensuing operations becomes more complicated. We postpone such discussion until later in this section.

Let us now proceed with the actual solution of our problem. The simplex calculations for the solution of P_1 appear in (45). An optimal solution of this problem is $\mathbf{x}^* = [\frac{5}{7}, \frac{6}{7}, 0, \frac{45}{7}, 0, 0, 0, 0,]$ and $z^*_{\text{max}} = 0$. Since $\mathbf{v}_7$ and $\mathbf{v}_8$ have both been eliminated from the basis, we have discovered a basic feasible solution of the problem P_0, namely, $\mathbf{x} = [\frac{5}{7}, \frac{6}{7}, 0, \frac{45}{7}, 0, 0]$. Starting with this solution, we use the simplex process to solve P_0. This is phase 2; the calculations appear in (46). It turns out that P_0, and hence also the original problem, have no optimal solutions because the second solution displayed in (46) satisfies the conditions of Theorem 2.

(45)

			0	0	0	0	0	0	−1	−1
Basis	*Obj*	**b**	$\mathbf{v}_1$	$\mathbf{v}_2$	$\mathbf{v}_3$	$\mathbf{v}_4$	$\mathbf{v}_5$	$\mathbf{v}_6$	$\mathbf{v}_7$	$\mathbf{v}_8$
$\mathbf{v}_4$	0	8	1	1	−3	1	0	0	0	0
$\mathbf{v}_7$	−1	2	(4)	−1	1	0	−1	0	1	0
$\mathbf{v}_8$	−1	4	2	3	−1	0	0	−1	0	1
$z_j - c_j$		−6	−6	−2	0	0	1	1	0	0
$\mathbf{v}_4$	0	$\frac{15}{2}$	0	$\frac{5}{4}$	$-\frac{13}{4}$	1	$\frac{1}{4}$	0	$-\frac{1}{4}$	0
$\mathbf{v}_1$	0	$\frac{1}{2}$	1	$-\frac{1}{4}$	$\frac{1}{4}$	0	$-\frac{1}{4}$	0	$\frac{1}{4}$	0
$\mathbf{v}_8$	−1	3	0	($\frac{7}{2}$)	$-\frac{3}{2}$	0	$\frac{1}{2}$	−1	$-\frac{1}{2}$	1
$z_j - c_j$		−3	0	$-\frac{7}{2}$	$\frac{3}{2}$	0	$-\frac{1}{2}$	1	$\frac{3}{2}$	0
$\mathbf{v}_4$	0	$\frac{45}{7}$	0	0	$-\frac{19}{7}$	1	$\frac{1}{14}$	$\frac{5}{14}$	$-\frac{1}{14}$	$-\frac{5}{14}$
$\mathbf{v}_1$	0	$\frac{5}{7}$	1	0	$\frac{1}{7}$	0	$-\frac{3}{14}$	$-\frac{1}{14}$	$\frac{3}{14}$	$\frac{1}{14}$
$\mathbf{v}_2$	0	$\frac{6}{7}$	0	1	$-\frac{3}{7}$	0	$\frac{1}{7}$	$-\frac{2}{7}$	$-\frac{1}{7}$	$\frac{2}{7}$
$z_j - c_j$		0	0	0	0	0	0	0	1	1

(46)

			2	−1	1	0	0	0
Basis	*Obj*	**b**	$\mathbf{v}_1$	$\mathbf{v}_2$	$\mathbf{v}_3$	$\mathbf{v}_4$	$\mathbf{v}_5$	$\mathbf{v}_6$
$\mathbf{v}_4$	0	$\frac{45}{7}$	0	0	$-\frac{19}{7}$	1	$\frac{1}{14}$	$\frac{5}{14}$
$\mathbf{v}_1$	2	$\frac{5}{7}$	1	0	($\frac{1}{7}$)	0	$-\frac{3}{14}$	$-\frac{1}{14}$
$\mathbf{v}_2$	−1	$\frac{6}{7}$	0	1	$-\frac{3}{7}$	0	$\frac{1}{7}$	$-\frac{2}{7}$
$z_j - c_j$		$\frac{4}{7}$	0	0	$-\frac{2}{7}$	0	$-\frac{4}{7}$	$\frac{1}{7}$
$\mathbf{v}_4$	0	20	19	0	0	1	−4	−1
$\mathbf{v}_3$	1	5	7	0	1	0	$-\frac{3}{2}$	$-\frac{1}{2}$
$\mathbf{v}_2$	−1	3	3	1	0	0	$-\frac{1}{2}$	$-\frac{1}{2}$
$z_j - c_j$		2	2	0	0	0	−1	0

We now discuss the two-phase process in general terms. We start with a problem in standard form, which we shall call P_0:

Maximize (or minimize) $z = c_1x_1 + c_2x_2 + \cdots + c_nx_n$ subject to

$$\begin{cases} x_1\mathbf{v}_1 + x_2\mathbf{v}_2 + \cdots + x_n\mathbf{v}_n = \mathbf{b}, \\ x_j \geqq 0 \qquad (j = 1, 2, \ldots, n), \end{cases}$$

where $\mathbf{b}$ and each $\mathbf{v}_i$ are m-dimensional column vectors and each component of $\mathbf{b}$ is nonnegative. If among the vectors $\mathbf{v}_1, \mathbf{v}_2, \ldots, \mathbf{v}_n$ we find the unit vectors $\mathbf{e}_1^m, \mathbf{e}_2^m, \ldots, \mathbf{e}_m^m$, then P_0 has an obvious basic feasible solution and we can proceed by the usual simplex method. Hence, let us assume that not all of these unit vectors appear among $\mathbf{v}_1, \mathbf{v}_2, \ldots, \mathbf{v}_n$. Let $\mathbf{a}_1, \ldots, \mathbf{a}_p$ be those unit vectors $\mathbf{e}_i^m$ which do not appear, and let P_1 denote the following problem:

Maximize $z^* = 0x_1 + 0x_2 + \cdots + 0x_n - x_{n+1} - x_{n+2} - \cdots - x_{n+p}$ (or minimize $z^* = 0x_1 + 0x_2 + \cdots + 0x_n + x_{n+1} + x_{n+2} + \cdots + x_{n+p}$) subject to

$$\begin{cases} x_1\mathbf{v}_1 + x_2\mathbf{v}_2 + \cdots + x_n\mathbf{v}_n + x_{n+1}\mathbf{a}_1 + x_{n+2}\mathbf{a}_2 + \cdots + x_{n+p}\mathbf{a}_p = \mathbf{b}, \\ x_j \geqq 0 \qquad (j = 1, 2, \ldots, n+p) \end{cases}$$

This is a standard problem with an obvious initial basic feasible solution. The vectors $\mathbf{a}_1, \ldots, \mathbf{a}_p$ are called *artificial vectors*, and the corresponding variables $x_{n+1}, \ldots, x_{n+p}$ are called *artificial variables*. Note that, in a maximizing problem, we have $z^* \leqq 0$ and, in a minimizing problem, we have $z^* \geqq 0$ for each feasible solution. It follows that P_1 must have an optimal solution. In phase 1 we obtain a sequence of basic feasible solutions of P_1 by following the usual simplex rules for selecting the entering and departing vectors. But, whereas the usual simplex process terminates only when a solution to which Theorem 1 or Theorem 2 applies is obtained, the phase 1 process may terminate at an earlier stage. To be precise, phase 1 terminates as soon as one of the following occurs:

Case 1. A basic feasible solution of P_1 is obtained in which all of the basic vectors are nonartificial. (Necessarily, $z^* = 0$ for such a solution, and the solution is optimal for P_1.)

Case 2. A basic feasible solution of P_1 is obtained for which $z^* = 0$, but at least one of its basis vectors is artificial. (Such a solution is optimal, even though the criterion of Theorem 1 may not be satisfied.)

Case 3. A basic feasible solution of P_1 is obtained for which no $z_j - c_j$ corresponding to a nonartificial vector $\mathbf{v}_j$ has the proper sign for improvement of z^*, but $z^* \neq 0$. (We shall prove later that such a solution is optimal for P_1.)

By Theorem 3, the termination of phase 1 in a finite number of steps can be assured. Then phase 2 begins; its nature depends upon the way in which phase 1 terminates. We must consider each of the possibilities just listed.

Case 1. Since no artificial vectors are in the basis, we have in effect obtained a basic feasible solution of the original problem P_0. Each feasible solution of P_1, of course, is an $(n + p)$-dimensional column vector, while solutions of P_0 are n-dimensional column vectors. But, if we have a feasible solution of P_1 such that each component corresponding to an artificial vector is zero, as must be the case if $z^* = 0$, then, by simply discarding these p zero components, we obtain an n-dimensional column vector which is a feasible solution of P_0. Having found, then, a basic feasible solution of P_0, we proceed to solve P_0 by the usual simplex method. This constitutes phase 2 in this case. The first tableau in phase 2 is obtained from the last one in phase 1 by eliminating the columns corresponding to artificial vectors, inserting the coefficients $c_1, c_2, \ldots, c_n$ from the original objective function z, and recomputing the numbers $z_j - c_j$ using these coefficients. Example 8 is an illustration of case 1.

Case 2. This is the most complicated of the three cases to discuss. For convenience of notation, let the artificial vectors still in the basis be $\mathbf{a}_1, \ldots, \mathbf{a}_s$. Since $z^* = 0$, we must have $x_{n+1} = \cdots = x_{n+s} = 0$ in this basic feasible solution of P_1. Hence, this solution yields (by discarding the zeros corresponding to artificial variables) a feasible solution of P_0. However, since we have not obtained a basis composed entirely of nonartifical vectors, we do not know at this point whether P_0 has any basic feasible solutions or not. In some cases we might be able to continue making changes of basis and eliminate some or all of the artificial vectors from the basis. There is nothing logically wrong with this procedure, but it could be a useless waste of effort. Instead, we proceed with phase 2 which, in this case, consists of the application of a modified version of the simplex method to the following problem, which we shall call P_2:

Maximize (or minimize) $z^{**} = c_1x_1 + c_2x_2 + \cdots + c_nx_n + 0x_{n+1} + \cdots + 0x_{n+s}$ subject to

$$\begin{cases} x_1\mathbf{v}_1 + x_2\mathbf{v}_2 + \cdots + x_n\mathbf{v}_n + x_{n+1}\mathbf{a}_1 + \cdots + x_{n+s}\mathbf{a}_s = \mathbf{b}, \\ x_j \geqq 0 \qquad (j = 1, 2, \ldots, n+s). \end{cases}$$

The first tableau for P_2 is obtained from the last tableau for P_1 by eliminating all columns corresponding to artificial vectors not in the terminal basis for P_1, reassigning the original coefficients $c_1, c_2, \ldots, c_n$ to the nonartificial variables, assigning zero coefficients to the artificial variables, and recomputing the numbers $z_j - c_j$ accordingly. Note that any feasible solution of P_2 for which each artificial variable is zero yields, by discarding these zeros, a feasible solution of P_0 such that $z = z^{**}$. For this reason, we modify the simplex rules in phase 2 so that all artificial variables are zero in each basic feasible solution obtained. Notice that the initial basic feasible solution of P_2 necessarily has this property, since $z^* = 0$ for the terminal solution of P_1. Another way in which the phase 2 process differs from the usual simplex process is that, once an artificial vector has left the basis, the corresponding column is eliminated from the tableau and that vector never again enters the basis.

(47)

			c_1		c_k		c_j		c_n	0		0
Basis	*Obj*	**b**	$\mathbf{v}_1$	$\cdots$	$\mathbf{v}_k$	$\cdots$	$\mathbf{v}_j$	$\cdots$	$\mathbf{v}_n$	$\mathbf{a}_1$	$\cdots$	$\mathbf{a}_t$
$\mathbf{v}_1$	c_1	$\hat{x}_1$	1	$\cdots$	0	$\cdots$	y_{1j}	$\cdots$	y_{1n}	0	$\cdots$	0
$\mathbf{v}_2$	c_2	$\hat{x}_2$	0	$\cdots$	0	$\cdots$	y_{2j}	$\cdots$	y_{2n}	0	$\cdots$	0
$\vdots$	$\vdots$	$\vdots$	$\vdots$	$\ddots$	$\vdots$	$\ddots$	$\vdots$	$\ddots$	$\vdots$	$\vdots$	$\ddots$	$\vdots$
$\mathbf{v}_k$	c_k	$\hat{x}_k$	0	$\cdots$	1	$\cdots$	y_{kj}	$\cdots$	y_{kn}	0	$\cdots$	0
$\mathbf{a}_1$	0	0	0	$\cdots$	0	$\cdots$	$y_{k+1,j}$	$\cdots$	$y_{k+1,n}$	1	$\cdots$	0
$\mathbf{a}_2$	0	0	0	$\cdots$	0	$\cdots$	$y_{k+2,j}$	$\cdots$	$y_{k+2,n}$	0	$\cdots$	0
$\vdots$	$\vdots$	$\vdots$	$\vdots$	$\ddots$	$\vdots$	$\ddots$	$\vdots$	$\ddots$	$\vdots$	$\vdots$	$\ddots$	$\vdots$
$\mathbf{a}_t$	0	0	0	$\cdots$	0	$\cdots$	$y_{k+t,j}$	$\cdots$	$y_{k+t,n}$	0	$\cdots$	1
$z_j - c_j$		$\hat{z}$	0	$\cdots$	0	$\cdots$	$z_j - c_j$	$\cdots$	$z_n - c_n$	0	$\cdots$	0

To describe precisely the procedure in phase 2, let us now consider a typical stage at which there is at least one artificial vector in the basis and each artificial variable is zero. For convenience of notation, let the basis vectors be $\mathbf{v}_1, \ldots, \mathbf{v}_k, \mathbf{a}_1, \ldots, \mathbf{a}_t$, where $t = m - k$. Let the basic feasible solution of P_2 at this stage be $\hat{\mathbf{x}} = [\hat{x}_1, \ldots, \hat{x}_k, 0, \ldots, 0]$ ($n + s$ components). Tableau (47) is the tableau corresponding to this stage as it would appear under these conditions. Such segregation of the rows corresponding to artificial vectors and those corresponding to nonartificial vectors into two groups of adjacent rows is purely for convenience and is not likely to occur in practice. This must be borne in mind in applying the following results to particular problems. For instance, a statement concerning the numbers $y_{k+i,j}$ ($i = 1, \ldots, t$) is to be interpreted as a statement about the coefficients of the artificial vectors in the expression of $\mathbf{v}_j$ as a linear combination of the basis vectors. It will be necessary to consider several cases. The first two are termination theorems analogous to Theorems 1 and 2.

Case 2a. (THEOREM 4) A basic feasible solution of P_2 in which each artificial variable is zero and which has the property that no $z_j - c_j$ corresponding to a nonartificial vector has the proper sign for improvement of z^{**} yields, by discarding the zeros corresponding to artificial variables, an optimal solution of P_0.

Proof: Suppose the solution $\hat{\mathbf{x}} = [\hat{x}_1, \ldots, \hat{x}_k, 0, \ldots, 0]$ ($n + s$ components) of P_2 corresponding to tableau (47) satisfies the hypotheses of this theorem. We must prove that the vector $\hat{\mathbf{x}}' = [\hat{x}_1, \ldots, \hat{x}_k, 0, \ldots, 0]$ (n

components) is an optimal solution of P_0. Consider the following problem, which we shall call P_2', obtained from P_2 by simply discarding the variables corresponding to those artificial vectors (if any) which have already been removed from the basis:

Maximize (or minimize) $z' = c_1x_1 + c_2x_2 + \cdots + c_nx_n + 0x_{n+1} + \cdots + 0x_{n+t}$ subject to

$$\begin{cases} x_1\mathbf{v}_1 + x_2\mathbf{v}_2 + \cdots + x_n\mathbf{v}_n + x_{n+1}\mathbf{a}_1 + \cdots + x_{n+t}\mathbf{a}_{n+t} = \mathbf{b}, \\ x_j \geqq 0 \qquad (j = 1, 2, \ldots, n+t). \end{cases}$$

Let $\hat{\mathbf{x}}'' = [\hat{x}_1, \ldots, \hat{x}_k, 0, \ldots, 0]$ ($n + t$ components). This is a basic feasible solution of P_2' and, by Theorem 1, it is optimal. Also, $z'(\hat{\mathbf{x}}'') = z(\hat{\mathbf{x}}')$. Suppose $\hat{\mathbf{x}}'$ is not an optimal solution of P_0. At this point, let us assume that P_0 is a maximizing problem. The rest of the argument is entirely similar for a minimizing problem. If $\hat{\mathbf{x}}'$ is not optimal, then, there must be a feasible solution $\bar{\mathbf{x}} = [\bar{x}_1, \bar{x}_2, \ldots, \bar{x}_n]$ of P_0 for which $z(\bar{\mathbf{x}}) > z(\hat{\mathbf{x}}')$. Let $\bar{\mathbf{x}}' = [\bar{x}_1, \bar{x}_2, \ldots, \bar{x}_n, 0, \ldots, 0]$ ($n + t$ components). Then $\bar{\mathbf{x}}'$ is a feasible solution of P_2'. But we have

$$z'(\bar{\mathbf{x}}') = z(\bar{\mathbf{x}}) > z(\hat{\mathbf{x}}') = z'(\hat{\mathbf{x}}''),$$

which contradicts the fact that $\hat{\mathbf{x}}''$ is an optimal solution of P_2'.

Case 2b. (THEOREM 5) Suppose the basic feasible solution of P_2 shown in tableau (47) has the property that, for some nonartificial vector $\mathbf{v}_j$, $z_j - c_j$ has the proper sign for improvement of z^{**}, $y_{k+i,j} = 0$ for each $i = 1, \ldots, t$, and each $y_{ij} \leqq 0$, $i = 1, \ldots, k$. Then the original problem P_0 has no optimal solution.

Proof: The argument is essentially the same as that given in the proof of Theorem 2. For each $\theta > 0$, we can write

$$\mathbf{b} = \sum_{i=1}^{k} \hat{x}_i\mathbf{v}_i - \theta\mathbf{v}_j + \theta\mathbf{v}_j, \tag{48}$$

since each artificial variable is zero. Also, since each $y_{k+i,j} = 0$, we have

$$\mathbf{v}_j = \sum_{i=1}^{k} y_{ij}\mathbf{v}_i. \tag{49}$$

Hence, substituting the expression from (49) for the first appearance of $\mathbf{v}_j$ in (48) we obtain,

$$\begin{aligned} \mathbf{b} &= \sum_{i=1}^{k} \hat{x}_i\mathbf{v}_i - \theta \sum_{i=1}^{k} y_{ij}\mathbf{v}_i + \theta\mathbf{v}_j \\ &= \sum_{i=1}^{k} (\hat{x}_i - \theta y_{ij})\mathbf{v}_i + \theta\mathbf{v}_j. \end{aligned}$$

Let $\hat{\mathbf{x}}(\theta) = [\hat{x}_1 - \theta y_{1j}, \ldots, \hat{x}_k - \theta y_{kj}, 0, \ldots, \theta, \ldots, 0]$, where there are n

components of which θ is the jth. Then $\hat{\mathbf{x}}(\theta)$ is a feasible solution of P_0, and we have

$$\begin{aligned} z[\hat{\mathbf{x}}(\theta)] &= \sum_{i=1}^{k} c_i(\hat{x}_i - \theta y_{ij}) + \theta c_j \\ &= \sum_{i=1}^{k} c_i \hat{x}_i + \theta\left(c_j - \sum_{i=1}^{k} c_i y_{ij}\right) \\ &= z(\hat{\mathbf{x}}) + \theta(c_j - z_j). \end{aligned}$$

In a maximizing problem $c_j - z_j > 0$, so that $z[\hat{\mathbf{x}}(\theta)] \longrightarrow +\infty$ as $\theta \longrightarrow +\infty$. In a minimizing problem $c_j - z_j < 0$, so that $z[\hat{\mathbf{x}}(\theta)] \longrightarrow -\infty$ as $\theta \longrightarrow +\infty$. In either case P_0 has no optimal solution.

As soon as we obtain a basic feasible solution of P_2 satisfying the conditions of either Theorem 4 or Theorem 5, phase 2 terminates. The iterative procedure of phase 2 can only be explained by considering a basic feasible solution of P_2 to which neither Theorem 4 nor Theorem 5 applies. For such a basic feasible solution, the following must hold:

Case 2c. There is at least one nonartificial vector $\mathbf{v}_j$ for which $z_j - c_j$ has the proper sign for improvement of z^{**}, but no such $\mathbf{v}_j$ satisfies the conditions of Theorem 5.

Imagine now that Tableau (47) represents a basic feasible solution of P_2 meeting the requirements of case 2c. Then we make a change of basis in the following way: Select for entry into the basis a (nonartificial) vector $\mathbf{v}_j$ for which $z_j - c_j$ has the proper sign for improvement of z^{**}. Select a vector to leave the basis by considering the usual set of ratios with positive denominators and choosing any vector corresponding to the minimum such ratio, except as follows:

(i) If there is a tie involving both artificial and nonartificial vectors, select an artificial vector to leave the basis. (This could only happen if there is some nonartificial variable x_i in the solution which is zero, while $y_{ij} > 0$.)

(ii) If *each* $y_{k+i,j} \leqq 0$ and *some* $y_{k+i,j} < 0$, select an artifical vector $\mathbf{a}_i$ for which $y_{k+i,j} < 0$ to leave the basis. (The pivot element $y_{k+i,j}$ will be negative in this case, but, since the corresponding component of the basic feasible solution is zero, the components of this basic feasible solution will not be affected by this change of basis. If this rule were not followed, i.e., if a nonartificial vector were removed from the basis, then possibly one or more of the artificial variables in the new solution would be positive. Example 11 will illustrate this point.)

If the vector selected to leave the basis by these rules is artificial, then eliminate the corresponding column from the tableau. Clearly, these selection rules guarantee that all artificial variables in each basic feasible solution found in phase 2 (case 2) will be zero. Thus we always have a feasible solution of P_0 obtainable by simply discarding the artificial variables. If, at some stage in phase 2, the basis contains only nonartificial vectors, then the corresponding feasible solution of P_0 is basic and the solution of the problem proceeds by the usual simplex method.

Before discussing case 3, let us look at some examples illustrating case 2.

Example 9. Consider the following problem, already in standard form: (P_0) Maximize $z = x_1 + 2x_2 - x_3 + 3x_4 + 2x_5$ subject to

$$\begin{cases} x_1 - x_2 + 6x_3 + 10x_4 - 6x_5 - 8x_6 + 5x_7 = 3, \\ 3x_1 - 2x_2 + 13x_3 + 26x_4 - 11x_5 - 15x_6 + 13x_7 = 10, \\ 4x_1 - 2x_2 + 15x_3 + 33x_4 - 11x_5 - 16x_6 + 17x_7 = 14, \\ x_1 + 2x_2 - 11x_3 - x_4 + 12x_5 + 18x_6 + x_7 = 6, \\ x_1 + x_2 - 7x_3 + 9x_5 + 9x_6 - 4x_7 = 5, \\ x_j \geqq 0 \quad (j = 1, 2, \ldots, 7). \end{cases}$$

The phase 1 problem is as follows:

(P_1) Maximize $z^* = -x_8 - x_9 - x_{10} - x_{11} - x_{12}$ subject to

$$\begin{cases} x_1 - x_2 + 6x_3 + 10x_4 - 6x_5 - 8x_6 + 5x_7 + x_8 = 3, \\ 3x_1 - 2x_2 + 13x_3 + 26x_4 - 11x_5 - 15x_6 + 13x_7 + x_9 = 10, \\ 4x_1 - 2x_2 + 15x_3 + 33x_4 - 11x_5 - 16x_6 + 17x_7 + x_{10} = 14, \\ x_1 + 2x_2 - 11x_3 - x_4 + 12x_5 + 18x_6 + x_7 + x_{11} = 6, \\ x_1 + x_2 - 7x_3 + 9x_5 + 9x_6 - 4x_7 + x_{12} = 5, \\ x_j \geqq 0 \quad (j = 1, 2, \ldots, 12). \end{cases}$$

The solution of P_1 appears in (50). At the third stage, we obtain a basic feasible solution meeting the conditions of case 2. Hence, we next apply the modified simplex process to the problem P_2: Maximize $z = x_1 + 2x_2 - x_3 + 3x_4 + 2x_5$ subject to the same constraints as in P_1, except that x_8 and x_9 are omitted. Tableaux (51) show the phase 2 calculations. The first tableau in (51) is the same as the last one in (50), except that the coefficients of z have replaced the coefficients of z^* and the values of $z_j - c_j$ have been recomputed. After $\mathbf{v}_3$ has been selected to enter the basis, the selection rules tell us that $\mathbf{a}_3$ must leave. At the second stage, we obtain a basic feasible solution which satisfies the conditions of case 2a. Hence, the corresponding solution of P_0, $\mathbf{x} = [4, 1, 0, 0, 0, 0, 0]$, is optimal, and $z_{\max} = 6$.

It should be pointed out that in this example, as in most problems, the sequence of basis changes is not uniquely determined. The sequence used here was contrived to avoid computation with complicated fractions. In general, it is not possible to avoid such computation, and so the incoming vectors are usually chosen as those for which $|z_j - c_j|$ is maximum or for

(50)

			0	0	0	0	0	0	0	−1	−1	−1	−1	−1
Basis	*Obj*	**b**	$\mathbf{v}_1$	$\mathbf{v}_2$	$\mathbf{v}_3$	$\mathbf{v}_4$	$\mathbf{v}_5$	$\mathbf{v}_6$	$\mathbf{v}_7$	$\mathbf{a}_1$	$\mathbf{a}_2$	$\mathbf{a}_3$	$\mathbf{a}_4$	$\mathbf{a}_5$
$\mathbf{a}_1$	−1	3	(1)	−1	6	10	−6	−8	5	1	0	0	0	0
$\mathbf{a}_2$	−1	10	3	−2	13	26	−11	−15	13	0	1	0	0	0
$\mathbf{a}_3$	−1	14	4	−2	15	33	−11	−16	17	0	0	1	0	0
$\mathbf{a}_4$	−1	6	1	2	−11	−1	12	18	1	0	0	0	1	0
$\mathbf{a}_5$	−1	5	1	1	−7	0	9	9	−4	0	0	0	0	1
$z_j - c_j$		−38	−10	2	−16	−68	7	12	−32	0	0	0	0	0
$\mathbf{v}_1$	0	3	1	−1	6	10	−6	−8	5	1	0	0	0	0
$\mathbf{a}_2$	−1	1	0	(1)	−5	−4	7	9	−2	−3	1	0	0	0
$\mathbf{a}_3$	−1	2	0	2	−9	−7	13	16	−3	−4	0	1	0	0
$\mathbf{a}_4$	−1	3	0	3	−17	−11	18	26	−4	−1	0	0	1	0
$\mathbf{a}_5$	−1	2	0	2	−13	−10	15	17	−9	−1	0	0	0	1
$z_j - c_j$		−8	0	−8	44	32	−53	−68	18	10	0	0	0	0
$\mathbf{v}_1$	0	4	1	0	1	6	1	1	3	−2	1	0	0	0
$\mathbf{v}_2$	0	1	0	1	−5	−4	7	9	−2	−3	1	0	0	0
$\mathbf{a}_3$	−1	0	0	0	1	1	−1	−2	1	2	−2	1	0	0
$\mathbf{a}_4$	−1	0	0	0	−2	1	−3	−1	2	8	−3	0	1	0
$\mathbf{a}_5$	−1	0	0	0	−3	−2	1	−1	−5	5	−2	0	0	1
$z_j - c_j$		0	0	0	4	0	3	4	2	−14	8	0	0	0

(51)

			1	2	—1	3	2	0	0	0	0	0
Basis	*Obj*	**b**	$\mathbf{v}_1$	$\mathbf{v}_2$	$\mathbf{v}_3$	$\mathbf{v}_4$	$\mathbf{v}_5$	$\mathbf{v}_6$	$\mathbf{v}_7$	$\mathbf{a}_3$	$\mathbf{a}_4$	$\mathbf{a}_5$
$\mathbf{v}_1$	1	4	1	0	1	6	1	1	3	0	0	0
$\mathbf{v}_2$	2	1	0	1	−5	−4	7	9	−2	0	0	0
$\mathbf{a}_3$	0	0	0	0	(1)	1	−1	−2	1	1	0	0
$\mathbf{a}_4$	0	0	0	0	−2	1	−3	−1	2	0	1	0
$\mathbf{a}_5$	0	0	0	0	−3	−2	1	−1	−5	0	0	1
$z_j - c_j$		6	0	0	−8	−5	13	19	−1	0	0	0
$\mathbf{v}_1$	1	4	1	0	0	5	2	3	2		0	0
$\mathbf{v}_2$	2	1	0	1	0	1	2	−1	3		0	0
$\mathbf{v}_3$	−1	0	0	0	1	1	−1	−2	1		0	0
$\mathbf{a}_4$	0	0	0	0	0	3	−5	−5	4		1	0
$\mathbf{a}_5$	0	0	0	0	0	1	−2	−7	−2		0	1
$z_j - c_j$		6	0	0	0	3	5	3	7		0	0

which z (or z^*) is improved the most at each stage. The student may verify that, as it happens, z^* is improved as much as possible at each stage of phase 1 in this example.

The next three examples are not complete solutions of problems, but only fragments of solutions illustrating various situations that can arise in case 2. In each case assume that the given tableau occurs in phase 2 of the solution of a standard maximizing problem. As usual, $\mathbf{a}_j$ denotes an artificial vector and $\mathbf{v}_j$ a nonartificial vector.

Example 10.

			5	1	—2	4	2	2	0	0	0	0	0	0
Basis	*Obj*	**b**	$\mathbf{v}_1$	$\mathbf{v}_2$	$\mathbf{v}_3$	$\mathbf{v}_4$	$\mathbf{v}_5$	$\mathbf{v}_6$	$\mathbf{v}_7$	$\mathbf{v}_8$	$\mathbf{a}_1$	$\mathbf{a}_2$	$\mathbf{a}_3$	$\mathbf{a}_4$
$\mathbf{v}_5$	2	8	0	1	0	−1	1	5	1	−3	0	0	0	0
$\mathbf{v}_1$	5	1	1	1	0	−2	0	2	2	−5	0	0	0	0
$\mathbf{v}_3$	−2	7	0	6	1	−12	0	13	10	−19	0	0	0	0
$\mathbf{a}_1$	0	0	0	(1)	0	−3	0	2	1	−3	1	0	0	0
$\mathbf{a}_2$	0	0	0	0	0	2	0	−1	1	0	0	1	0	0
$\mathbf{a}_3$	0	0	0	−2	0	6	0	0	0	6	0	0	1	0
$\mathbf{a}_4$	0	0	0	3	0	−9	0	6	2	−9	0	0	0	1
$z_j - c_j$		7	0	−6	0	8	0	−8	—8	7	0	0	0	0

First we observe that the process does not terminate at this stage; i.e., neither the conditions of case 2a nor those of case 2b are satisfied. We have a choice of three vectors to enter the basis: $\mathbf{v}_2$ (in place of $\mathbf{a}_1$ or $\mathbf{a}_4$), $\mathbf{v}_6$ (in place of $\mathbf{a}_1$ or $\mathbf{a}_4$), and $\mathbf{v}_7$ (in place of $\mathbf{a}_1$, $\mathbf{a}_2$, or $\mathbf{a}_4$). We choose to insert $\mathbf{v}_2$ in place of $\mathbf{a}_1$ and obtain the following tableau:

			5	1	−2	4	2	2	0	0	0	0	0	0
Basis	*Obj*	$\mathbf{b}$	$\mathbf{v}_1$	$\mathbf{v}_2$	$\mathbf{v}_3$	$\mathbf{v}_4$	$\mathbf{v}_5$	$\mathbf{v}_6$	$\mathbf{v}_7$	$\mathbf{v}_8$	$\mathbf{a}_1$	$\mathbf{a}_2$	$\mathbf{a}_3$	$\mathbf{a}_4$
$\mathbf{v}_5$	2	8	0	0	0	2	1	3	0	0	−1	0	0	0
$\mathbf{v}_1$	5	1	1	0	0	1	0	0	1	−2	−1	0	0	0
$\mathbf{v}_3$	−2	7	0	0	1	6	0	1	4	−1	−6	0	0	0
$\mathbf{v}_2$	1	0	0	1	0	−3	0	2	1	−3	1	0	0	0
$\mathbf{a}_2$	0	0	0	0	0	2	0	−1	1	0	0	1	0	0
$\mathbf{a}_3$	0	0	0	0	0	0	0	4	2	0	2	0	1	0
$\mathbf{a}_4$	0	0	0	0	0	0	0	0	−1	0	−3	0	0	1
$z_j - c_j$		7	0	0	0	−10	0	4	−2	−11	6	0	0	0

From this tableau, considering the column corresponding to $\mathbf{v}_8$, we see that the conditions of case 2b are satisfied. Hence, the process terminates, and we conclude that the original standard problem has no optimal solutions.

Example 11.

			5	1	−3	4	2	2	0	0	0	0	0
Basis	*Obj*	$\mathbf{b}$	$\mathbf{v}_1$	$\mathbf{v}_2$	$\mathbf{v}_3$	$\mathbf{v}_4$	$\mathbf{v}_5$	$\mathbf{v}_6$	$\mathbf{v}_7$	$\mathbf{v}_8$	$\mathbf{a}_1$	$\mathbf{a}_2$	$\mathbf{a}_3$
$\mathbf{v}_5$	2	8	0	0	0	2	1	3	0	2	0	0	0
$\mathbf{v}_1$	5	1	1	0	0	1	0	0	1	2	0	0	0
$\mathbf{v}_3$	−3	7	0	0	1	6	0	1	4	−1	0	0	0
$\mathbf{v}_2$	1	3	0	1	0	−3	0	2	1	−3	0	0	0
$\mathbf{a}_1$	0	0	0	0	0	(−1)	0	−1	0	1	1	0	0
$\mathbf{a}_2$	0	0	0	0	0	−2	0	4	0	1	0	1	0
$\mathbf{a}_3$	0	0	0	0	0	−3	0	0	0	2	0	0	1
$z_j - c_j$		3	0	0	0	−16	0	3	−6	14	0	0	0

This is a case 2c (nonterminating) situation, and either $\mathbf{v}_4$ or $\mathbf{v}_7$ may be chosen to enter the basis. Suppose we choose $\mathbf{v}_4$. Then we have the situation described in (ii) under case 2c. According to the usual simplex rules, the vector which leaves the basis would be $\mathbf{v}_1$. However, if this were done, the artificial variables in the next basic feasible solution would be positive. In order to keep them zero, we may choose any one of the vectors $\mathbf{a}_1$, $\mathbf{a}_2$, $\mathbf{a}_3$ to leave the basis. For convenience, we choose $\mathbf{a}_1$ and obtain the following tableau:

			5	1	−3	4	2	2	0	0	0	0
Basis	*Obj*	**b**	$\mathbf{v}_1$	$\mathbf{v}_2$	$\mathbf{v}_3$	$\mathbf{v}_4$	$\mathbf{v}_5$	$\mathbf{v}_6$	$\mathbf{v}_7$	$\mathbf{v}_8$	$\mathbf{a}_2$	$\mathbf{a}_3$
$\mathbf{v}_5$	2	8	0	0	0	0	1	1	0	4	0	0
$\mathbf{v}_1$	5	1	1	0	0	0	0	−1	(1)	3	0	0
$\mathbf{v}_3$	−3	7	0	0	1	0	0	−5	4	5	0	0
$\mathbf{v}_2$	1	3	0	1	0	0	0	5	1	−6	0	0
$\mathbf{v}_4$	4	0	0	0	0	1	0	1	0	−1	0	0
$\mathbf{a}_2$	0	0	0	0	0	0	0	6	0	−1	1	0
$\mathbf{a}_3$	0	0	0	0	0	0	0	3	0	−1	0	1
$z_j - c_j$		3	0	0	0	0	0	19	−6	−2	0	0

Next we can insert either $\mathbf{v}_7$ or $\mathbf{v}_8$ into the basis. We choose $\mathbf{v}_7$. This time the ordinary simplex rule of minimum ratio applies in selecting the vector to leave the basis, and this vector is found to be $\mathbf{v}_1$. Making this change of basis, we obtain the following tableau:

			5	1	−3	4	2	2	0	0	0	0
Basis	*Obj*	**b**	$\mathbf{v}_1$	$\mathbf{v}_2$	$\mathbf{v}_3$	$\mathbf{v}_4$	$\mathbf{v}_5$	$\mathbf{v}_6$	$\mathbf{v}_7$	$\mathbf{v}_8$	$\mathbf{a}_2$	$\mathbf{a}_3$
$\mathbf{v}_5$	2	8	0	0	0	0	1	1	0	4	0	0
$\mathbf{v}_7$	0	1	1	0	0	0	0	−1	1	3	0	0
$\mathbf{v}_3$	−3	3	−4	0	1	0	0	−1	0	−7	0	0
$\mathbf{v}_2$	1	2	−1	1	0	0	0	6	0	−9	0	0
$\mathbf{v}_4$	4	0	0	0	0	1	0	1	0	−1	0	0
$\mathbf{a}_2$	0	0	0	0	0	0	0	6	0	−1	1	0
$\mathbf{a}_3$	0	0	0	0	0	0	0	3	0	−1	0	1
$z_j - c_j$		9	6	0	0	0	0	13	0	16	0	0

The optimality criterion, case 2a, tells us that we have reached an optimal solution. Thus, for the original standard problem, $z_{\max} = 9$ at $\mathbf{x} = [0, 2, 3, 0, 8, 0, 1, 0]$.

Example 12.

			5	1	−3	4	2	2	0	0	0	0	0
Basis	*Obj*	**b**	$\mathbf{v}_1$	$\mathbf{v}_2$	$\mathbf{v}_3$	$\mathbf{v}_4$	$\mathbf{v}_5$	$\mathbf{v}_6$	$\mathbf{v}_7$	$\mathbf{v}_8$	$\mathbf{a}_1$	$\mathbf{a}_2$	$\mathbf{a}_3$
$\mathbf{v}_5$	2	8	0	0	0	2	1	3	0	2	0	0	0
$\mathbf{v}_1$	5	0	1	0	0	1	0	0	−1	2	0	0	0
$\mathbf{v}_3$	−3	4	0	0	1	6	0	1	4	−1	0	0	0
$\mathbf{v}_2$	1	3	0	1	0	−3	0	2	1	−3	0	0	0
$\mathbf{a}_1$	0	0	0	0	0	(1)	0	−1	0	1	1	0	0
$\mathbf{a}_2$	0	0	0	0	0	2	0	4	0	1	0	1	0
$\mathbf{a}_3$	0	0	0	0	0	0	0	0	0	2	0	0	1
$z_j - c_j$		7	0	0	0	−16	0	3	−16	14	0	0	0

Suppose we choose $\mathbf{v}_4$ to enter the basis. Then, in determining the vector which leaves, we find a tie for minimum ratio involving $\mathbf{v}_1$, $\mathbf{a}_1$, and $\mathbf{a}_2$. According to case 2c, part (i), either $\mathbf{a}_1$ or $\mathbf{a}_2$ should be selected to leave. We choose $\mathbf{a}_1$ and obtain the following tableau:

			5	1	−3	4	2	2	0	0	0	0
Basis	*Obj*	**b**	$\mathbf{v}_1$	$\mathbf{v}_2$	$\mathbf{v}_3$	$\mathbf{v}_4$	$\mathbf{v}_5$	$\mathbf{v}_6$	$\mathbf{v}_7$	$\mathbf{v}_8$	$\mathbf{a}_2$	$\mathbf{a}_3$
$\mathbf{v}_5$	2	8	0	0	0	0	1	5	0	0	0	0
$\mathbf{v}_1$	5	0	1	0	0	0	0	1	−1	1	0	0
$\mathbf{v}_3$	−3	4	0	0	1	0	0	7	4	−7	0	0
$\mathbf{v}_2$	1	3	0	1	0	0	0	−1	1	0	0	0
$\mathbf{v}_4$	4	0	0	0	0	1	0	−1	0	1	0	0
$\mathbf{a}_2$	0	0	0	0	0	0	0	(6)	0	−1	1	0
$\mathbf{a}_3$	0	0	0	0	0	0	0	0	0	2	0	1
$z_j - c_j$		7	0	0	0	0	0	−13	−16	30	0	0

Next we choose $\mathbf{v}_6$ to enter the basis and again have a tie for minimum ratio between $\mathbf{v}_1$ and $\mathbf{a}_2$. Selecting $\mathbf{a}_2$ to leave, we obtain the next tableau:

			5	1	−3	4	2	2	0	0	0
Basis	*Obj*	**b**	$\mathbf{v}_1$	$\mathbf{v}_2$	$\mathbf{v}_3$	$\mathbf{v}_4$	$\mathbf{v}_5$	$\mathbf{v}_6$	$\mathbf{v}_7$	$\mathbf{v}_8$	$\mathbf{a}_3$
$\mathbf{v}_5$	2	8	0	0	0	0	1	0	0	$\frac{5}{6}$	0
$\mathbf{v}_1$	5	0	1	0	0	0	0	0	−1	$\frac{7}{6}$	0
$\mathbf{v}_3$	−3	4	0	0	1	0	0	0	(4)	$-\frac{35}{6}$	0
$\mathbf{v}_2$	1	3	0	1	0	0	0	0	1	$-\frac{1}{6}$	0
$\mathbf{v}_4$	4	0	0	0	0	1	0	0	0	$\frac{5}{6}$	0
$\mathbf{v}_6$	2	0	0	0	0	0	0	1	0	$-\frac{1}{6}$	0
$\mathbf{a}_3$	0	0	0	0	0	0	0	0	0	2	1
$z_j - c_j$		7	0	0	0	0	0	0	−16	$\frac{167}{6}$	0

The next step is to insert $\mathbf{v}_7$ in place of $\mathbf{v}_3$. By computing the $z_j - c_j$ row first (adding four times the third row to the last row in this tableau), we find that the optimality criterion, $z_j - c_j \geqq 0$ for each j, will be satisfied at the next stage. Hence, to determine $z_{\max}$ and an optimal solution, it is not necessary to compute the entire tableau, but only the **b** column. Doing this, we find that $z_{\max} = 7 + (4 \cdot 4) = 23$ and an optimal solution is $\mathbf{x} = [1, 2, 0, 0, 8, 0, 1, 0]$.

To complete our description of the two-phase process, we now consider the third way in which phase 1 can terminate:

Case 3. Since $z^* \neq 0$, there must be at least one artificial vector in the basis. For convenience, suppose that the artificial vectors still in the basis are $\mathbf{a}_1, \ldots, \mathbf{a}_r$. Let P_1' denote the following problem:

Maximize $z^{*\prime} = 0x_1 + \cdots + 0x_n - x_{n+1} - \cdots - x_{n+r}$ (or minimize

$z^{*\prime} = 0x_1 + \cdots + 0x_n + x_{n+1} + \cdots + x_{n+r})$ subject to

$$\begin{cases} x_1\mathbf{v}_1 + x_2\mathbf{v}_2 + \cdots + x_n\mathbf{v}_n + x_{n+1}\mathbf{a}_1 + \cdots + x_{n+r}\mathbf{a}_r = \mathbf{b}, \\ x_j \geqq 0 \qquad (j = 1, 2, \ldots, n + r). \end{cases}$$

Let $\hat{\mathbf{x}}$ be the terminal solution of P_1. By discarding the zero components of $\hat{\mathbf{x}}$ corresponding to the artificial vectors which have left the basis, we obtain a basic feasible solution $\hat{\mathbf{x}}'$ of P_1'. By Theorem 1, $\hat{\mathbf{x}}'$ is an optimal solution of P_1', and we have $z^*(\hat{\mathbf{x}}') = z^*(\hat{x}) \neq 0$. Now suppose that P_0 has a feasible solution $\mathbf{x} = [x_1, x_2, \ldots, x_n]$. Then $\mathbf{x}' = [x_1, x_2, \ldots, x_n, 0, \ldots, 0]$ ($n + r$ components) is a feasible solution of P_1'. But $z^{*\prime}(\mathbf{x}') = 0$, contrary to the fact that the optimal value $z^{*\prime}(\hat{\mathbf{x}}')$ of $z^{*\prime}$ is positive in the case of a minimizing problem and negative in the case of a maximizing problem. Thus, if a basic feasible solution of P_1 is obtained which satisfies the conditions of case 3, the process terminates and we conclude that P_0 has no feasible solutions at all. The next example illustrates this case.

Example 13. The following problem was solved graphically in Chapter 1: Minimize $z = 2x_1 - 3x_2$ subject to

$$\begin{cases} x_1 - 2x_2 \leqq -4, \\ x_1 + x_2 \leqq 5, \\ x_1 - x_2 \geqq 2, \\ x_1 \geqq 0, \qquad x_2 \geqq 0. \end{cases}$$

Let us now solve it by the two-phase method. The constraints for the related standard problem P_0 are

$$\begin{cases} -x_1 + 2x_2 - x_3 = 4, \\ x_1 + x_2 + x_4 = 5, \\ x_1 - x_2 - x_5 = 2, \\ x_j \geqq 0 \qquad (j = 1, \ldots, 5). \end{cases}$$

Hence we need two artificial vectors to complete our initial basis. The phase 1 problem P_1 is the following:

Minimize $z^* = x_6 + x_7$ subject to

$$\begin{cases} -x_1 + 2x_2 - x_3 + x_6 = 4, \\ x_1 + x_2 + x_4 = 5, \\ x_1 - x_2 - x_5 + x_7 = 2, \\ x_j \geqq 0 \qquad (j = 1, 2, \ldots, 7). \end{cases}$$

The phase 1 calculations follow.

Basis	Obj	b	$\mathbf{v}_1$	$\mathbf{v}_2$	$\mathbf{v}_3$	$\mathbf{v}_4$	$\mathbf{v}_5$	$\mathbf{a}_1$	$\mathbf{a}_2$
			0	0	0	0	0	1	1
$\mathbf{a}_1$	1	4	-1	2	-1	0	0	1	0
$\mathbf{v}_4$	0	5	1	1	0	1	0	0	0
$\mathbf{a}_2$	1	2	1	-1	0	0	-1	0	1
$z_j - c_j$		6	0	1	-1	0	-1	0	0
$\mathbf{v}_2$	1	2	$-\frac{1}{2}$	1	$-\frac{1}{2}$	0	0	$\frac{1}{2}$	0
$\mathbf{v}_4$	0	7	$\frac{3}{2}$	0	$\frac{1}{2}$	1	0	$-\frac{1}{2}$	0
$\mathbf{a}_2$	1	4	$\frac{1}{2}$	0	$-\frac{1}{2}$	0	-1	$\frac{1}{2}$	1
$z_j - c_j$		4	$\frac{1}{2}$	0	$-\frac{1}{2}$	0	-1	$-\frac{1}{2}$	0
$\mathbf{v}_2$	0	$\frac{13}{3}$	0	1	$-\frac{1}{3}$	$\frac{1}{3}$	0	$\frac{1}{3}$	0
$\mathbf{v}_1$	0	$\frac{14}{3}$	1	0	$\frac{1}{3}$	$\frac{2}{3}$	0	$-\frac{1}{3}$	0
$\mathbf{a}_2$	1	$\frac{5}{3}$	0	0	$-\frac{2}{3}$	$-\frac{1}{3}$	-1	$\frac{2}{3}$	1
$z_j - c_j$		$\frac{5}{3}$	0	0	$-\frac{2}{3}$	$-\frac{1}{3}$	-1	$-\frac{1}{3}$	0

In the third tableau, we find the basic feasible solution $\mathbf{x} = [\frac{14}{3}, \frac{13}{3}, 0, 0, 0, 0, \frac{5}{3}]$ of P_1 which satisfies the conditions of case 3. Hence, P_0 has no feasible solutions, and consequently the original problem has none either.

EXERCISES

1. Solve each of the following problems by the two-phase method, stating clearly your conclusion about the *original* problem in each case. For each problem, a number of iterations (total for phase 1 and 2) is given which is sufficient to solve the problem. The number actually needed by the student may vary slightly from this, because different sequences of bases are possible.

(a) Maximize $z = x_1 + x_2 - x_3 + 2x_4$ subject to

$$\begin{cases} x_1 - x_2 - x_3 - 2x_4 \geqq 2, \\ x_1 + x_2 + x_4 \leqq 8, \\ x_1 + 2x_2 - x_3 \leqq 4, \\ x_j \geqq 0 \quad (j = 1, 2, 3, 4) \end{cases} \quad \text{(3 iterations).}$$

(b) Minimize $z = 4x_1 - x_2 + 2x_3 - 2x_4$ subject to

$$\begin{cases} 2x_1 + x_2 + x_3 + x_4 \leqq 10, \\ x_1 - 2x_2 - x_3 + x_4 \geqq 4, \\ x_1 + x_2 + 3x_3 - x_4 \geqq 4, \\ x_j \geqq 0 \quad (j = 1, 2, 3, 4) \end{cases} \quad \text{(4 iterations).}$$

(c) Maximize $z = 3x_1 - x_2 + x_3 + 2x_4 + x_5$ subject to

$$\begin{cases} x_1 + x_2 + 3x_3 - x_4 + x_5 \leqq 12, \\ 2x_1 - x_2 - x_3 + x_4 - x_5 \geqq 2, \\ x_1 + x_2 + 2x_3 + x_4 + 3x_5 \geqq 10, \\ x_1 + 2x_2 - x_3 - x_4 + x_5 \leqq 6, \\ x_j \geqq 0 \quad (j = 1, 2, 3, 4, 5) \quad \text{(3 iterations)}. \end{cases}$$

(d) Minimize $z = x_1 - 4x_2 - x_3 + 6x_4 + 2x_5$ subject to

$$\begin{cases} x_1 + x_2 - 4x_3 + 2x_4 + x_5 \geqq 0, \\ -2x_1 + 3x_2 + 5x_3 - x_4 + x_5 \leqq 8, \\ x_1 - x_2 - 2x_3 + 3x_4 - x_5 \geqq 4, \\ x_1 + 2x_2 + x_3 - x_4 - 2x_5 \leqq -1, \\ x_j \geqq 0 \quad (j = 1, 2, 3, 4, 5) \quad \text{(4 iterations)}. \end{cases}$$

2. In Example 4, Chapter 1, we stated the transportation problem. This exercise uses the notation of that example. In the diagram given here, the number appearing in the row labeled W_i and the column labeled R_j is the cost c_{ij} of shipping one unit from W_i to R_j. The numbers to the right of the tableau indicate the amounts stored in each warehouse, while those underneath indicate the amounts required at the retail outlets. Formulate the problem as a linear programming problem, and solve it by the two-phase method. Note that, since the total supply equals the total demand, each of the inequalities in (4) and (5) of Example 4 must actually be an equality. A total of seven iterations is sufficient. In the next chapter a more efficient way of solving transportation problems will be explained.

	R_1	R_2	
W_1	9	1	18
W_2	6	2	11
W_3	2	8	6
	20	15	

3. Solve the problem of Example 2, Chapter 1, by the two-phase method. Five changes of basis are sufficient.

4. Assume that each of the following incomplete tableaux occurs at the beginning of phase 2 in the solution of a standard maximizing problem P_0, where phase 1 has terminated (as in case 2) with artificial vectors still in the basis. In each case, fill in the missing numbers in the tableau, complete the solution of the problem, and state your conclusion concerning problem P_0.

(a)

			3	2	−1	4	1	1		
Basis	*Obj*	**b**	$\mathbf{v}_1$	$\mathbf{v}_2$	$\mathbf{v}_3$	$\mathbf{v}_4$	$\mathbf{v}_5$	$\mathbf{v}_6$	$\mathbf{a}_2$	$\mathbf{a}_4$
$\mathbf{v}_3$		6		2		1	0	−2		
$\mathbf{a}_2$				3		0	−2	1		
$\mathbf{v}_1$		12		1		−2	1	0		
$\mathbf{a}_4$				1		−1	1	2		
$z_j - c_j$										

(b)

			2	1	1	−1	3	2	−1		
Basis	*Obj*	**b**	$\mathbf{v}_1$	$\mathbf{v}_2$	$\mathbf{v}_3$	$\mathbf{v}_4$	$\mathbf{v}_5$	$\mathbf{v}_6$	$\mathbf{v}_7$	$\mathbf{a}_3$	$\mathbf{a}_5$
$\mathbf{v}_5$		2			4	1		−1	−2		
$\mathbf{v}_2$		3			2	1		5	2		
$\mathbf{a}_3$					1	0		2	0		
$\mathbf{v}_1$		5			1	−4		1	1		
$\mathbf{a}_5$					1	0		3	0		
$z_j - c_j$											

(c)

			3	1	−1	2	2	4	1	
Basis	*Obj*	**b**	$\mathbf{v}_1$	$\mathbf{v}_2$	$\mathbf{v}_3$	$\mathbf{v}_4$	$\mathbf{v}_5$	$\mathbf{v}_6$	$\mathbf{v}_7$	$\mathbf{a}_3$
$\mathbf{v}_5$		4			1			−1	3	
$\mathbf{v}_2$		6			1			2	−1	
$\mathbf{a}_3$					−1			1	1	
$\mathbf{v}_1$		2			−5			1	2	
$\mathbf{v}_4$		2			2			2	−4	
$z_j - c_j$										

(d)

			3	2	−1	4	4	2	−2	1			
Basis	*Obj*	**b**	$\mathbf{v}_1$	$\mathbf{v}_2$	$\mathbf{v}_3$	$\mathbf{v}_4$	$\mathbf{v}_5$	$\mathbf{v}_6$	$\mathbf{v}_7$	$\mathbf{v}_8$	$\mathbf{a}_1$	$\mathbf{a}_3$	$\mathbf{a}_5$
$\mathbf{a}_1$			2		0		0	2		−1			
$\mathbf{v}_4$		10	1		1		−2	1		2			
$\mathbf{a}_3$			−3		−2		0	−1		1			
$\mathbf{v}_2$		7	1		1		3	1		−3			
$\mathbf{a}_5$			3		−1		0	3		2			
$\mathbf{v}_7$		2	−1		4		1	−1		1			
$z_j - c_j$													

(e)

			2	8	−1	5	0	2	3		
Basis	*Obj*	**b**	$\mathbf{v}_1$	$\mathbf{v}_2$	$\mathbf{v}_3$	$\mathbf{v}_4$	$\mathbf{v}_5$	$\mathbf{v}_6$	$\mathbf{v}_7$	$\mathbf{a}_1$	$\mathbf{a}_4$
$\mathbf{a}_1$			3	1		−1	4		−1		
$\mathbf{v}_3$		3	1	2		−6	2		1		
$\mathbf{v}_6$		8	4	1		−1	3		4		
$\mathbf{a}_4$			4	3		−3	1		−2		
$z_j - c_j$											

5. Solve the problem formulated in Exercise 8, Chapter 1.

3-7. *NONTERMINATION OF THE TWO-PHASE PROCESS.**

Since the procedure for making changes of basis in the two-phase process differs in some respects from that of the ordinary simplex method, we need to consider the possibility of nontermination of the process. Only the second phase need concern us here, since, as we have already observed, Theorem 3 guarantees that the first phase can be terminated in a finite number of steps.

If the first phase terminates in the manner described in case 1, then the usual simplex method is employed in phase 2 and again Theorem 3 guarantees the possibility of termination in a finite number of steps. If the first phase terminates in the manner described in case 3, there is no phase 2. Hence, the only case which requires discussion is that in which the first phase terminates in the manner described in case 2.

Suppose now that this occurs. Theorem 3, of course, guarantees that the second phase problem P_2 can be solved in a finite number of steps *if* the simplex rules of Section 3–4 are followed. The whole difficulty, and the reason for this discussion, is that we do *not* necessarily follow these rules in case 2.

First, let us note that, if we ever obtain a basis in phase 2 which is free of artificial vectors, Theorem 3 guarantees that, in a finite number of additional steps, we can reach a conclusion. Now, if we eliminate an artificial vector at each stage, then we are certain eventually either to eliminate all artificial vectors or to obtain a solution satisfying the conditions of either Theorem 4 or Theorem 5. Hence, replacing an artificial vector in the basis by a non-artificial one at each stage guarantees termination of the second phase in a finite number of steps. Unfortunately, it may not always be possible to do this, but we shall now show that in a finite number of steps, beginning at any stage at which an artificial vector cannot be eliminated, it is possible either to remove another artificial vector from the basis or to terminate the process without removing an artificial vector. This is sufficient to prove that the second phase can always be terminated in a finite number of steps.

For convenience of description, we refer to tableau (47) which displays a typical stage in the second phase. Suppose that, at the stage represented by this tableau, the process has not terminated and it is not possible to replace any one of the artificial vectors in the basis by a nonartificial vector. Then it must be the case that, for each vector $\mathbf{v}_j$ such that $z_j - c_j$ has the proper sign for improvement of z, we have $y_{k+1,j} = y_{k+2,j} = \cdots = y_{k+t,j} = 0$.

Temporarily discard from the tableau all nonbasis vectors $\mathbf{v}_j$ for which some $y_{k+i,j} \neq 0$. The resulting tableau can be thought of as representing a problem P_2^* which differs from P_2 only in that certain variables have been

*This section may be omitted without loss of continuity if the reader is willing to take for granted that the two-phase method can always be terminated in a finite number of steps.

omitted. To each basic feasible solution of P_2^*, there corresponds in an obvious way a basic feasible solution of P_2. By Theorem 3, there is a finite simplex sequence for P_2^*. Since rows $k + 1, k + 2, \ldots, k + t$ contain only zeros (except in columns $n + 1, n + 2, \ldots, n + t$), these rows are not changed by the simplex operations and, at each stage, a nonartificial vector replaces another nonartificial vector in the basis.

Now return to the initial tableau for P_2^*, reinstate the discarded columns, and perform the same sequence of row transformations upon the entire tableau. Each vector $\mathbf{v}_j$ which enters a basis in this process is one for which each $y_{k+i,j} = 0$. Hence, the selections of incoming and outgoing vectors do not violate the rules prescribed in case 2c.

Now there are two possibilities to consider. First, if the terminal solution for P_2^* is one to which Theorem 2 applies, then the corresponding solution of P_2 is one which meets the conditions of Theorem 5. Thus, P_2 (and, hence, the original problem P_0) has no optimal solution, and the second phase has terminated without removal of another artificial vector.

The second possibility is that the terminal solution of P_2^* is one to which Theorem 1 applies. For the corresponding solution of P_2, then, each $z_j - c_j$ corresponding to a nondiscarded vector $\mathbf{v}_j$ does not have the proper sign for improvement of z. This may or may not also be true of the other vectors. If it is, the process has terminated without another artificial vector being removed. If it is not, then there is at least one vector $\mathbf{v}_r$, discarded in forming P_2^*, such that $z_r - c_r$ has the proper sign for improvement of z. This vector $\mathbf{v}_r$ has the property that, at the stage corresponding to the terminal solution of P_2^*, at least one $y_{k+i,r}$ is nonzero, since the row operations performed in constructing the finite sequence of bases for P_2^* do not involve rows $k + 1, k + 2, \ldots, k + t$ at all. Such a vector $\mathbf{v}_r$ must be selected to enter the basis and, by case 2c(i), it will replace an artificial vector. This completes the proof that the second phase can always be terminated in a finite number of steps.

3-8. *PROBLEMS WITHOUT NONNEGATIVITY RESTRICTIONS.*

We now know how to solve any linear programming problem in which the variables are required to be nonnegative. Slack variables are employed to form the related standard problem. This standard problem is then solved by the ordinary simplex method or, if no initial basic feasible solution is evident, by the two-phase process. In this brief section we show that, given a linear programming problem in which not all of the variables are required to be nonnegative, it is possible to form a related problem with nonnegativity restrictions, whose solution yields the solution of the original problem. We shall then be able to solve any linear programming problem whatsoever.

We consider first an example:

Example 14. (This problem occurs in Exercise 1(a), Chapter 1.)
Maximize $z = 3x_1 + x_2$ subject to

$$\begin{cases} x_1 - 3x_2 \geqq -3, \\ 2x_1 + 3x_2 \geqq -6, \\ 2x_1 + x_2 \leqq 8, \\ 4x_1 - x_2 \leqq 16. \end{cases}$$

Note that neither x_1 nor x_2 is required to be nonnegative. Call this problem P. The device used to form the related problem with nonnegativity restrictions is based upon the following easily proved property of real numbers: Each real number can be expressed as the difference of two nonnegative numbers. For example, $6 = 6 - 0$ and $-4 = 2 - 6$. Of course there is nothing unique about such expressions, but that does not matter for our purposes. We make the change of variables $x_1 = y_1 - y_2$, $x_2 = y_3 - y_4$ and formulate the following problem P^*:

Maximize $z^* = 3(y_1 - y_2) + (y_3 - y_4) = 3y_1 - 3y_2 + y_3 - y_4$ subject to

$$\begin{cases} y_1 - y_2 - 3y_3 + 3y_4 \geqq -3, \\ 2y_1 - 2y_2 + 3y_3 - 3y_4 \geqq -6, \\ 2y_1 - 2y_2 + y_3 - y_4 \leqq 8, \\ 4y_1 - 4y_2 - y_3 + y_4 \leqq 16, \\ y_j \geqq 0 \quad (j = 1, 2, 3, 4). \end{cases}$$

Since P^* has nonnegativity restrictions, we know how to solve it. Before doing so, however, let us discuss the relationship between the two problems. Each feasible solution $\mathbf{x}$ of P determines infinitely many feasible solutions $\mathbf{y}$ of P^* such that $z^*(\mathbf{y}) = z(\mathbf{x})$. Each feasible solution $\mathbf{y}$ of P^*, on the other hand, determines through the equations $x_1 = y_1 - y_2$ and $x_2 = y_3 - y_4$ exactly one feasible solution $\mathbf{x}$ of P, and again $z(\mathbf{x}) = z^*(\mathbf{y})$. Now suppose P^* has an optimal feasible solution $\mathbf{y}$. Then the corresponding feasible solution $\mathbf{x}$ of P is also optimal. Otherwise, there would be a feasible solution $\hat{\mathbf{x}}$ of P for which $z(\hat{\mathbf{x}}) > z(\mathbf{x})$. But then our correspondence of solutions would yield a solution $\hat{\mathbf{y}}$ of P^* for which $z^*(\hat{\mathbf{y}}) = z(\hat{\mathbf{x}}) > z(\mathbf{x}) = z^*(\mathbf{y})$, contradicting the optimality of $\mathbf{y}$. Similar reasoning shows that, if P^* has no optimal solution, neither does P. Hence, the solution of P^* will yield the solution of P. The solution of P^* by the ordinary simplex method requires only three iterations, which appear in (52). We see that $z^*_{\max} = 12$ and the optimal solution of P^* is $\mathbf{y} = [4, 0, 0, 0]$. Hence, the optimal solution of P is $\mathbf{x} = [4 - 0, 0 - 0] = [4, 0]$ and $z_{\max} = 12$.

(52)

			3	−3	1	−1	0	0	0	0
Basis	*Obj*	**b**	$\mathbf{v}_1$	$\mathbf{v}_2$	$\mathbf{v}_3$	$\mathbf{v}_4$	$\mathbf{v}_5$	$\mathbf{v}_6$	$\mathbf{v}_7$	$\mathbf{v}_8$
$\mathbf{v}_5$	0	3	−1	1	3	−3	1	0	0	0
$\mathbf{v}_6$	0	6	−2	2	−3	3	0	1	0	0
$\mathbf{v}_7$	0	8	(2)	−2	1	−1	0	0	1	0
$\mathbf{v}_8$	0	16	4	−4	−1	1	0	0	0	1
$z_j - c_j$		0	−3	3	−1	1	0	0	0	0
$\mathbf{v}_5$	0	7	0	0	$\frac{7}{2}$	$-\frac{7}{2}$	1	0	$\frac{1}{2}$	0
$\mathbf{v}_6$	0	14	0	0	−2	2	0	1	1	0
$\mathbf{v}_1$	3	4	1	−1	$\frac{1}{2}$	$-\frac{1}{2}$	0	0	$\frac{1}{2}$	0
$\mathbf{v}_8$	0	0	0	0	−3	(3)	0	0	−2	1
$z_j - c_j$		12	0	0	$\frac{1}{2}$	$-\frac{1}{2}$	0	0	$\frac{3}{2}$	0
$\mathbf{v}_5$	0	7								
$\mathbf{v}_6$	0	14								
$\mathbf{v}_1$	3	4								
$\mathbf{v}_4$	−1	0								
$z_j - c_j$		12	0	0	0	0	0	0	$\frac{7}{6}$	$\frac{1}{6}$

The general procedure suggested by this example may be described as follows: Let P denote a linear programming problem stated in terms of variables $x_1, \ldots, x_n$, not all of which are required to be nonnegative. Make the substitution $x_j = y_{2j-1} - y_{2j}$ for each appearance of x_j in the statement of problem P, and add the requirement $y_i \geqq 0$ $(i = 1, 2, \ldots; 2_n)$. Call the resulting problem P^*. Corresponding to each feasible solution of one of these problems, there is at least one feasible solution of the other for which the objective functions are equal in value. Hence, if P^* has no feasible solutions, neither does P. If an optimal solution of P^* is found, we obtain from it by our equations $x_j = y_{2j-1} - y_{2j}$ an optimal solution of P. If P^* has no optimal solution, the same is true of P.

This procedure can be used to solve any linear programming problem. In practice, however, certain shortcuts can frequently be employed. For example, if some variables x_j are required to be nonnegative in the original problem, no substitution need be made for such variables. To illustrate, consider the following example:

Example 15. Maximize $z = 2x_1 - x_2 + x_3$ subject to

$$\begin{cases} x_1 + 3x_2 - x_3 \leqq 20, \\ 2x_1 - x_2 + x_3 \leqq 12, \\ x_1 - 4x_2 - 4x_3 \geqq 2, \\ x_1 \geqq 0. \end{cases}$$

This could be solved by making the substitutions $x_1 = y_1$, $x_2 = y_2 - y_3$, $x_3 = y_4 - y_5$. The related problem would be as follows:

Maximize $z^* = 2y_1 - y_2 + y_3 + y_4 - y_5$ subject to

$$\begin{cases} y_1 + 3y_2 - 3y_3 - y_4 + y_5 \leqq 20, \\ 2y_1 - y_2 + y_3 + y_4 - y_5 \leqq 12, \\ y_1 - 4y_2 + 4y_3 - 4y_4 + 4y_5 \geqq 2, \\ y_j \geqq 0 \quad (j = 1, \ldots, 5). \end{cases}$$

Another type of substitution which can sometimes be used to advantage is illustrated in the following example:

Example 16. Maximize $z = 4x_1 + x_2 + 3x_3$ subject to

$$\begin{cases} 2x_1 - x_2 + x_3 \leqq 12, \\ x_1 + 4x_2 - 2x_3 \leqq 15, \\ x_1 + x_2 + x_3 \leqq 15, \\ x_1 \geqq 2, \quad x_2 \leqq 6, \quad x_3 \geqq 4. \end{cases}$$

Call this problem P. The similarity of the last three inequalities to non-negativity restrictions suggests the following substitutions: $y_1 = x_1 - 2$, $y_2 = 6 - x_2$, $y_3 = x_3 - 4$. This leads to the formulation of the following problem P^*:

Maximize $z^* = 4(y_1 + 2) + (6 - y_2) + 3(y_3 + 4) = 4y_1 - y_2 + 3y_3 + 26$ subject to

$$\begin{cases} 2(y_1 + 2) - (6 - y_2) + (y_3 + 4) \leqq 12, \\ (y_1 + 2) + 4(6 - y_2) - 2(y_3 + 4) \leqq 15, \\ (y_1 + 2) + (6 - y_2) + (y_3 + 4) \leqq 15, \\ y_j \geqq 0 \quad (j = 1, 2, 3). \end{cases}$$

Dropping the constant term in z^*, we obtain problem P^{**}:

Maximize $z^{**} = 4y_1 - y_2 + 3y_3$ subject to

$$\begin{cases} 2y_1 + y_2 + y_3 \leqq 10, \\ y_1 - 4y_2 - 2y_3 \leqq -3, \\ y_1 - y_2 + y_3 \leqq 3, \\ y_j \geqq 0 \quad (j = 1, 2, 3). \end{cases}$$

We leave it to the student to verify that $z^{**}_{\max} = 16$ for $\mathbf{y} = [0, \frac{7}{2}, \frac{13}{2}]$. Consequently, $z_{\max} = 16 + 26 = 42$ for $\mathbf{x} = [2, \frac{5}{2}, \frac{21}{2}]$. We also leave it to the student to convince himself of the correctness of this conclusion by considering the relationship between problems P and P^{**}. Note that this problem could also have been solved by the previously described method of substituting $x_1 = y_1 - y_2$, $x_2 = y_3 - y_4$, and $x_3 = y_5 - y_6$, but that this would have been more cumbersome.

EXERCISES

Solve each of the following problems by use of the methods explained in this section:

1. Maximize $z = 2x_1 + x_2 + x_3$ subject to

$$\begin{cases} 3x_1 + 2x_2 - x_3 \leqq 6, \\ x_1 + x_2 + x_3 \leqq 4, \\ 2x_1 - x_2 + 2x_3 \leqq 4. \end{cases}$$

2. Maximize $z = 3x_1 + x_2 + 4x_3$ subject to

$$\begin{cases} x_1 + x_2 - 2x_3 \leqq 6, \\ x_1 + 2x_2 + x_3 \leqq 12, \\ 2x_1 - x_2 - x_3 \geqq 2, \\ 0 \leqq x_1 \leqq 2, \qquad -1 \leqq x_2 \leqq 1, \qquad 2 \leqq x_3 \leqq 5. \end{cases}$$

3. Minimize $z = x_1 + x_2 + 2x_3$ subject to

$$\begin{cases} 2x_1 - x_2 + x_3 \geqq 1, \\ x_1 + 2x_2 + 2x_3 \geqq 3, \\ x_1 + x_2 + x_3 \leqq 12. \end{cases}$$

4. Minimize $z = x_1 - x_2 + 2x_3 + x_4$ subject to

$$\begin{cases} x_1 + x_2 - x_3 + x_4 \leqq 12, \\ x_1 + x_2 + x_3 - x_4 \geqq 2, \\ x_1 - x_2 - x_3 + x_4 \geqq 3, \\ x_4 \geqq 0. \end{cases}$$

5. Complete the solution begun in Example 16.

3-9. *GEOMETRIC INTERPRETATIONS.*

In Chapter 1 we introduced the subject of linear programming with a geometric treatment of two-variable problems. Now, having described algebraic techniques for solving linear programming problems involving any number of variables, we conclude this chapter by turning again to geometric considerations. This time our purpose is to show that the simplex method can truly be regarded as a generalization of the geometric process we described in Chapter 1.

It will be necessary to define certain geometric concepts such as line and plane in the vector space $\mathscr{V}_n$ of n-dimensional column vectors, and of course these definitions must be consistent with our knowledge of the special cases $n = 2$ and $n = 3$. Let us consider first the matter of lines. In Fig. 12 we have shown two points P_1 and P_2 in the plane and their corresponding position vectors $\mathbf{v}_1 = \overrightarrow{OP_1}$ and $\mathbf{v}_2 = \overrightarrow{OP_2}$. Clearly, a point P lies on the straight line through P_1 and P_2 if, and only if, there is a scalar λ such that $\overrightarrow{OP} = \overrightarrow{OP_1} + \overrightarrow{P_1P} = \overrightarrow{OP_1} + \lambda\overrightarrow{P_1P_2} = \overrightarrow{OP_1} + \lambda(\overrightarrow{OP_2} - \overrightarrow{OP_1}) = (1 - \lambda)\overrightarrow{OP_1} + \lambda\overrightarrow{OP_2}$. Since we can interpret vectors in $\mathscr{V}_2$ as either arrows or tips of arrows (points), we can think of the line through P_1 and P_2 as a collection of vectors,

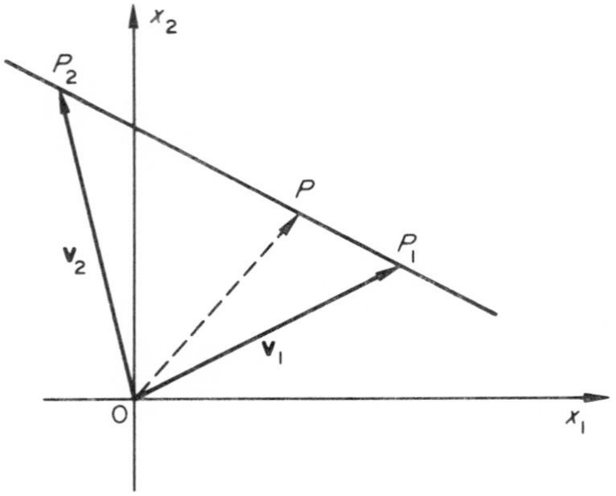

Figure 12

namely, the collection of all vectors of the form $(1 - \lambda)\mathbf{v}_1 + \lambda\mathbf{v}_2$, λ real. For $\lambda = 0$ we obtain $\mathbf{v}_1$ (or P_1), for $\lambda = 1$ we obtain $\mathbf{v}_2$ (or P_2), and for $0 < \lambda < 1$ the corresponding point lies on the segment between P_1 and P_2. These considerations lead us to formulate the following general definition:

DEFINITION 5. Let $\mathbf{v}_1$ and $\mathbf{v}_2$ be two different vectors in a vector space $\mathscr{V}$. Then the *line determined by* $\mathbf{v}_1$ *and* $\mathbf{v}_2$ is defined to be the collection of all vectors $\mathbf{v}$ of the form

$$\mathbf{v} = (1 - \lambda)\mathbf{v}_1 + \lambda\mathbf{v}_2 \tag{53}$$

for λ real. The *line segment joining* $\mathbf{v}_1$ *and* $\mathbf{v}_2$, denoted by $L[\mathbf{v}_1, \mathbf{v}_2]$, is defined to be the collection of all vectors $\mathbf{v}$ of the form (53) for which $0 \leqq \lambda \leqq 1$. The *open line segment joining* $\mathbf{v}_1$ *and* $\mathbf{v}_2$ is the collection of all vectors $\mathbf{v}$ of the form (53) for which $0 < \lambda < 1$.

Example 17. Let $\mathbf{v}_1 = [-3, 0, 2, 6]$, $\mathbf{v}_2 = [4, 1, -1, 2]$. Then $L[\mathbf{v}_1, \mathbf{v}_2]$ is the subset of $\mathscr{V}_4$ consisting of all vectors $\mathbf{v}$ expressible in the form

$$\begin{aligned}\mathbf{v} &= (1 - \lambda)\mathbf{v}_1 + \lambda\mathbf{v}_2 = (1 - \lambda)[-3, 0, 2, 6] + \lambda[4, 1, -1, 2] \\ &= [-3 + 7\lambda, \lambda, 2 - 3\lambda, 6 - 4\lambda]\end{aligned}$$

for $0 \leqq \lambda \leqq 1$.

If $\mathbf{x} = [x_1, x_2, x_3]$ and $\mathbf{y} = [y_1, y_2, y_3]$ are thought of as directed line segments, their scalar product (or dot product) $\mathbf{x} \cdot \mathbf{y}$ can be defined as the product of their lengths and the cosine of their included angle. It can then be proved that $\mathbf{x} \cdot \mathbf{y} = x_1y_1 + x_2y_2 + x_3y_3$. This last equation motivates the following definition:

DEFINITION 6. If $\mathbf{x} = [x_1, x_2, \ldots, x_n]$ and $\mathbf{y} = [y_1, y_2, \ldots, y_n]$ are vectors in $\mathscr{V}_n$, we define their *scalar product* $\mathbf{x} \cdot \mathbf{y}$ by the equation

$$\mathbf{x} \cdot \mathbf{y} = \sum_{j=1}^{n} x_j y_j.$$

The vectors $\mathbf{x}$ and $\mathbf{y}$ are said to be *perpendicular* (also *orthogonal* or *normal*) to each other if, and only if, $\mathbf{x} \cdot \mathbf{y} = 0$.

Example 18. If $\mathbf{v}_1$ and $\mathbf{v}_2$ are the vectors of Example 17, then $\mathbf{v}_1 \cdot \mathbf{v}_2 = -3 \cdot 4 + 0 \cdot 1 + 2 \cdot -1 + 6 \cdot 2 = -2$. Hence, $\mathbf{v}_1$ and $\mathbf{v}_2$ are not perpendicular.

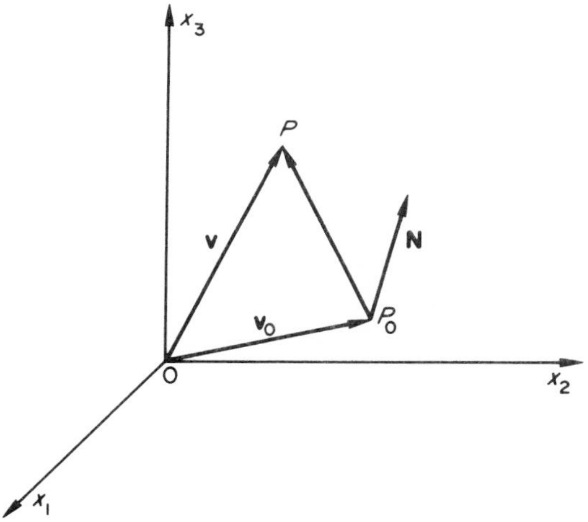

Figure 13

In three-dimensional space, given a point P_0 and a nonzero vector $\mathbf{N}$, the plane through P_0 with normal $\mathbf{N}$ is the locus of all points P such that $\overrightarrow{P_0P} \cdot \mathbf{N} = 0$. Since (see Fig. 13) $\overrightarrow{P_0P} = \mathbf{v} - \mathbf{v}_0$, this plane may be thought of as the collection of all vectors $\mathbf{v}$ such that $\mathbf{N} \cdot \mathbf{v} = k$, where k is the constant $\mathbf{N} \cdot \mathbf{v}_0$. This suggests the following definition:

DEFINITION 7. Given a nonzero vector $\mathbf{N} = [a_1, a_2, \ldots, a_n]$ in $\mathscr{V}_n$ and a real number k, the collection of all vectors $\mathbf{x} = [x_1, x_2, \ldots, x_n]$ in $\mathscr{V}_n$ for which

$$\mathbf{N} \cdot \mathbf{x} = a_1x_1 + a_2x_2 + \cdots + a_nx_n = k$$

is called an $(n - 1)$-*dimensional hyperplane*. Each nonzero scalar multiple of $\mathbf{N}$ is called a *normal* for the hyperplane.

Each $(n - 1)$-dimensional hyperplane divides the rest of $\mathscr{V}_n$ into two parts, namely, the collection of all vectors $\mathbf{x}$ for which $\mathbf{N} \cdot \mathbf{x} < k$ and the collection of all vectors $\mathbf{x}$ for which $\mathbf{N} \cdot \mathbf{x} > k$. The next definition gives a name to the set which results when we form the union of one of these sets with the hyperplane itself:

DEFINITION 8. If $\mathbf{N} \cdot \mathbf{x} = k$ is the equation of an $(n - 1)$-dimensional hyperplane in $\mathscr{V}_n$, then each of the sets $\{\mathbf{x} \mid \mathbf{N} \cdot \mathbf{x} \leqq k\}$ and $\{\mathbf{x} \mid \mathbf{N} \cdot \mathbf{x} \geqq k\}$ is called a *closed half-space* in $\mathscr{V}_n$.

For the case $n = 2$, hyperplanes become lines and closed half-spaces are what we called closed half-planes in Chapter 1. Note that, by Definition 1, the set of all vectors satisfying any particular constraint in a linear programming problem is either a hyperplane or a closed half-space. Hence, the set of all feasible solutions of a linear programming problem is the intersection, or common part, of these hyperplanes and closed half-spaces. We shall presently prove that such a set has the property of *convexity*, defined as follows:

DEFINITION 9. A set S in a vector space $\mathscr{V}$ is said to be *convex* if, and only if, for each pair of distinct vectors $\mathbf{v}_1$ and $\mathbf{v}_2$ in S, the line segment $L[\mathbf{v}_1, \mathbf{v}_2]$ is contained in S. Also, if S is empty or contains only one vector, we shall agree to call S convex.

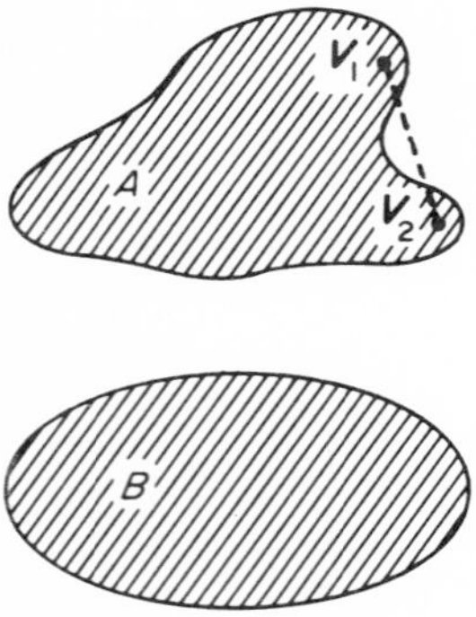

Figure 14

Example 19. Of the sets A and B shown in Fig. 14, only B is convex. The pair of points $\mathbf{v}_1$ and $\mathbf{v}_2$ shown in A have the property that $L[\mathbf{v}_1, \mathbf{v}_2]$ is not contained in A.

Example 20. In any nontrivial vector space, the set of all nonzero vectors is not convex. For, if $\mathbf{v} \neq 0$, then $L[\mathbf{v}, -\mathbf{v}]$ contains the zero vector.

THEOREM 6. The intersection of any collection of convex sets is convex.

Proof: Let C be the intersection (common part) of some collection $\mathscr{A}$ of convex sets. If C either is empty or contains only one vector, C is convex. Suppose, however, that C contains more than one vector. Let $\mathbf{v}_1$ and $\mathbf{v}_2$ be any two different vectors in C. Then $\mathbf{v}_1$ and $\mathbf{v}_2$ each belongs to each set in the collection $\mathscr{A}$, and each of these sets is convex. Hence, $L[\mathbf{v}_1, \mathbf{v}_2]$ is contained in each set in the collection $\mathscr{A}$ and, consequently, is contained in C. Therefore C is convex.

THEOREM 7. Hyperplanes and closed half-spaces are convex sets.

Proof: Consider a closed half-space S determined by an inequality of the form

$$\mathbf{N} \cdot \mathbf{x} \leqq k. \tag{54}$$

To prove that S is convex we must show that $L[\mathbf{u}, \mathbf{v}]$ is contained in S for each pair of vectors $\mathbf{u}$ and $\mathbf{v}$ in S. This requires proof that, if $\mathbf{x}$ belongs to $L[\mathbf{u}, \mathbf{v}]$, then $\mathbf{x}$ satisfies (54). Now, if $\mathbf{x}$ belongs to $L[\mathbf{u}, \mathbf{v}]$, then $\mathbf{x}$ can be written in the form

$$\mathbf{x} = (1 - \lambda)\mathbf{u} + \lambda\mathbf{v}$$

for some λ, $0 \leqq \lambda \leqq 1$. Then we have

$$\mathbf{N} \cdot \mathbf{x} = (1 - \lambda)\mathbf{N} \cdot \mathbf{u} + \lambda\mathbf{N} \cdot \mathbf{v}.$$

Since $\mathbf{N} \cdot \mathbf{u} \leqq k$, $\mathbf{N} \cdot \mathbf{v} \leqq k$, $1 - \lambda \geqq 0$, and $\lambda \geqq 0$, it follows that

$$\mathbf{N} \cdot \mathbf{x} \leqq (1 - \lambda)k + \lambda k = k,$$

which completes the proof that the closed half-space defined by (54) is convex. A similar argument can be used if the relation "$\leqq$" in (54) is replaced by "$\geqq$" or "$=$".

Combining the results of Theorems 6 and 7 with the fact previously noted that each constraint in a linear programming problem defines either a hyperplane or a closed half-space, we easily obtain the following corollary:

COROLLARY 1. The set of all feasible solutions of a linear programming problem is convex.

Since a convex set has either no points, exactly one point, or infinitely many points (all points on some line segment), we have another corollary:

COROLLARY 2. Each linear programming problem has either no feasible solutions, exactly one feasible solution, or infinitely many feasible solutions.

The possibilities listed in Corollary 2 were all illustrated by two-variable examples in Chapter 1.

In our geometric treatment of two-variable problems, we noticed the importance of the corner points of the set of all feasible solutions: If an optimal solution exists, there must be at least one corner point which is optimal. Thus, one method of solving a two-variable problem, assuming it is known to have an optimal solution, would be to locate all the corner points and compute z at each. The largest of this finite set of numbers would be the maximum value of z, and the smallest would be the minimum value of z.

In our study of the simplex method, we found a similar situation with regard to basic feasible solutions: For a problem with at least one basic feasible solution, either there is an optimal basic feasible solution or else there is no optimal solution at all. This suggests that basic feasible solutions correspond in some way to corner points. We shall now show that this is indeed the case.

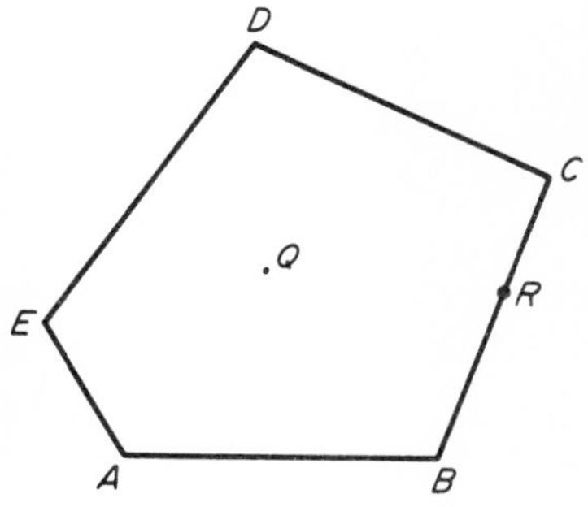

Figure 15

First, of course, it is necessary to say exactly what is meant by a corner point of a set. In a two-dimensional polygonal region, such as the one pictured in Fig. 15, each noncorner point, such as Q or R, has the property that it lies in the *open* line segment joining some pair of points of the region. For instance, R lies in $L(B, C)$. The corner points (A, B, C, D, E in the figure) do not have this property. The points on the edge of a circular disk also do not have this property. Since we do not wish to call such points "corners," the word "extreme" is substituted and we make the following definition:

DEFINITION 10. Let C be a convex set in a vector space. A vector $\mathbf{x}$ is called an *extreme point* of C if, and only if, there do not exist vectors $\mathbf{v}_1$ and $\mathbf{v}_2$ in C such that $\mathbf{x}$ lies in the open line segment $L(\mathbf{v}_1, \mathbf{v}_2)$.

The correspondence between basic feasible solutions and extreme points is established by the following theorem:

THEOREM 8. Suppose we have a standard linear programming problem with constraints

$$(55) \qquad \begin{cases} x_1\mathbf{v}_1 + x_2\mathbf{v}_2 + \cdots + x_n\mathbf{v}_n = \mathbf{b}, \\ x_j \geqq 0 \qquad (j = 1, 2, \ldots, n), \end{cases}$$

where each $\mathbf{v}_i$ and $\mathbf{b}$ are m-dimensional column vectors, $m < n$, and the rank of the coefficient matrix of the system of constraint equations is m. Let C be the subset of $\mathscr{V}_n$ consisting of all feasible solutions of the problem, i.e., all vectors $\mathbf{x} = [x_1, x_2, \ldots, x_n]$ satisfying (55). Then a vector $\mathbf{x}$ is a basic feasible solution if, and only if, $\mathbf{x}$ is an extreme point of C.

Proof: Suppose, first, that $\mathbf{x}$ is a basic feasible solution of the given problem. We must show that $\mathbf{x}$ is an extreme point of C. This will be done by proving that, if $\mathbf{x}'$ and $\mathbf{x}''$ are vectors in C such that $\mathbf{x}$ lies on $L[\mathbf{x}', \mathbf{x}'']$, then either $\mathbf{x} = \mathbf{x}'$ or $\mathbf{x} = \mathbf{x}''$. For convenience of notation, assume that $\mathbf{x} = [x_1, \ldots, x_m, 0, \ldots, 0]$. Let $\mathbf{x}' = [x_1', x_2', \ldots, x_n']$ and $\mathbf{x}'' = [x_1'', x_2'', \ldots, x_n'']$ be two different vectors in C such that $\mathbf{x}$ lies on $L[\mathbf{x}', \mathbf{x}'']$. Then there is some λ, $0 \leqq \lambda \leqq 1$, such that

$$(56) \qquad \mathbf{x} = (1 - \lambda)\mathbf{x}' + \lambda\mathbf{x}''.$$

From (56) it follows, by equating components, that

$$(57) \qquad x_i = (1 - \lambda)x_i' + \lambda x_i'' \qquad (i = 1, \ldots, m)$$

and

$$(58) \qquad 0 = (1 - \lambda)x_j' + \lambda x_j'' \qquad (j = m + 1, \ldots, n).$$

Suppose $0 < \lambda < 1$. Then, since $x_j' \geqq 0$ and $x_j'' \geqq 0$, (58) implies that $x_j' = x_j'' = 0$ for each $j = m + 1, \ldots, n$. Hence, we have

$$(59) \quad \mathbf{b} = x_1\mathbf{v}_1 + \cdots + x_m\mathbf{v}_m = x_1'\mathbf{v}_1 + \cdots + x_m'\mathbf{v}_m = x_1''\mathbf{v}_1 + \cdots + x_m''\mathbf{v}_m.$$

But (59) and Theorem 11, Section 2–5, imply that $x_i = x_i' = x_i''$ for each $i = 1, \ldots, m$ and hence that $\mathbf{x} = \mathbf{x}' = \mathbf{x}''$, contradicting the assumption that $\mathbf{x}' \neq \mathbf{x}''$. Hence, we must have either $\lambda = 0$ or $\lambda = 1$, and the proof that $\mathbf{x}$ is an extreme point is complete.

Now suppose that $\mathbf{x} = [x_1, x_2, \ldots, x_n]$ is an extreme point of C. We must show that $\mathbf{x}$ is a basic feasible solution. Since $\mathbf{x}$ is a feasible solution, we know that $x_j \geqq 0$ for each $j = 1, 2, \ldots, n$. If each $x_j = 0$, then $\mathbf{x}$ is basic and the associated basis could be any set of m linearly independent vectors chosen from $\mathbf{v}_1, \mathbf{v}_2, \ldots, \mathbf{v}_n$. Since the rank of the coefficient matrix in (55) is m, at least one such basis exists.

Now suppose that at least one of the components of $\mathbf{x}$ is positive. We shall first show by contradiction that the set of vectors associated with positive components of $\mathbf{x}$ is linearly independent. For convenience, let the positive components of $\mathbf{x}$ be $x_1, \ldots, x_k$ $(1 \leqq k \leqq n)$, so that we have $\mathbf{x} = [x_1, \ldots, x_k, 0, \ldots, 0]$. If the vectors $\mathbf{v}_1, \ldots, \mathbf{v}_k$ are linearly dependent, as we now suppose, there exist numbers $t_1, \ldots, t_k$, not all zero, such that

(60) $$t_1\mathbf{v}_1 + t_2\mathbf{v}_2 + \cdots + t_k\mathbf{v}_k = \mathbf{0}.$$

Let M be a positive number so large that

(61) $$\frac{|t_i|}{M} < x_i \qquad (i = 1, \ldots, k),$$

and put $t_i' = t_i/M$. Multiplying both sides of (60) by $1/M$, we obtain

(62) $$t_1'\mathbf{v}_1 + t_2'\mathbf{v}_2 + \cdots + t_k'\mathbf{v}_k = \mathbf{0}.$$

We also have

(63) $$x_1\mathbf{v}_1 + x_2\mathbf{v}_2 + \cdots + x_k\mathbf{v}_k = \mathbf{b}.$$

Successively subtracting (62) from (63) and adding (62) and (63) gives the two equations

(64) $$\begin{aligned} (x_1 - t_1')\mathbf{v}_1 + (x_2 - t_2')\mathbf{v}_2 + \cdots + (x_k - t_k')\mathbf{v}_k &= \mathbf{b}, \\ (x_1 + t_1')\mathbf{v}_1 + (x_2 + t_2')\mathbf{v}_2 + \cdots + (x_k + t_k')\mathbf{v}_k &= \mathbf{b}. \end{aligned}$$

Because of (61), we have

(65) $$x_j - t_j' > 0 \quad \text{and} \quad x_j + t_j' > 0 \qquad (j = 1, 2, \ldots, k).$$

Thus, (64) and (65) imply that the vectors $\mathbf{x}'$ and $\mathbf{x}''$, where

$$\begin{aligned} \mathbf{x}' &= [x_1 - t_1', \ldots, x_k - t_k', 0, \ldots, 0], \\ \mathbf{x}'' &= [x_1 + t_1', \ldots, x_k + t_k', 0, \ldots, 0], \end{aligned}$$

are feasible solutions. But we have

$$\mathbf{x} = \tfrac{1}{2}\mathbf{x}' + \tfrac{1}{2}\mathbf{x}'',$$

which implies that $\mathbf{x}$ is on the open segment $L(\mathbf{x}', \mathbf{x}'')$ and contradicts the assumption that $\mathbf{x}$ is an extreme point. Therefore the vectors $\mathbf{v}_1, \mathbf{v}_2, \ldots, \mathbf{v}_k$ are linearly independent.

This implies that $1 \leqq k \leqq m$. If $k = m$, we are through, since the vectors $\mathbf{v}_1, \ldots, \mathbf{v}_m$ then form a basis for $\mathscr{V}_m$. Suppose, however, that $k < m$. Then, in order to prove that $\mathbf{x}$ is a basic solution, we must show that a set of $m - k$ vectors can be chosen from the vectors $\mathbf{v}_{k+1}, \ldots, \mathbf{v}_n$ so that, when it is adjoined to the set of vectors $\mathbf{v}_1, \ldots, \mathbf{v}_k$, a set of m linearly independent vectors results. But this is a consequence of Theorem 12, Chapter 2. Hence the proof is complete.

Suppose now that we have a standard linear programming problem and that the hypotheses of Theorem 8 are satisfied. Let the objective function be given by $z = c_1x_1 + c_2x_2 + \cdots + c_nx_n$. By Definition 7, for each number k, the collection of all vectors $\mathbf{x}$ in $\mathscr{V}_m$ for which $z = k$ is an $(n - 1)$-dimensional hyperplane. Thus, solving the problem by the simplex method can be thought of geometrically as the process of "moving" a hyperplane across the set C of feasible solutions, stopping as it passes through certain extreme points, and continuing until either an optimal extreme point or one which indicates that there are no optimal solutions is reached.

In some two-dimensional problems, such as Example 6, Chapter 1, when we move the line corresponding to the objective function across the set of feasible solutions in the direction which improves z, it eventually passes simultaneously through two of the corner points. Hence, it then contains the line segment joining these two corners, and z has the same value at each point of this segment. In three dimensions, if the plane corresponding to the objective function passes through three corner points, then it contains the triangular region determined by these three points. Hence, z has the same value at each point of this triangular region. To discuss the generalization of this to n dimensions, it is convenient first to make the following definition:

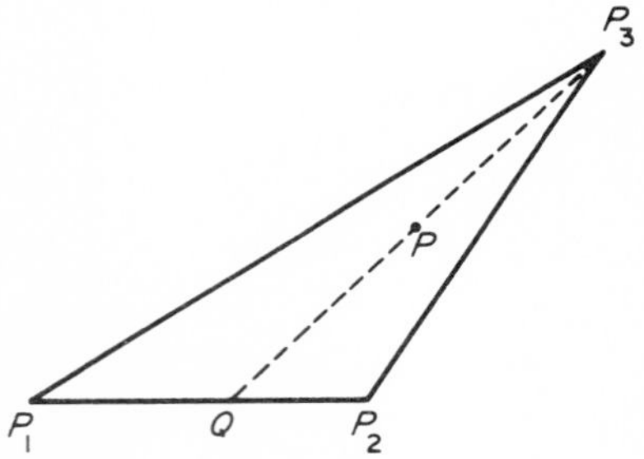

Figure 16

DEFINITION 11. A *convex combination* of a finite set of vectors is a linear combination of these vectors in which each coefficient is nonnegative and the sum of the coefficients is 1.

Thus, $t_1\mathbf{v}_1 + t_2\mathbf{v}_2 + \cdots + t_n\mathbf{v}_n$ is a convex combination of $\mathbf{v}_1, \mathbf{v}_2, \ldots, \mathbf{v}_n$ if, and only if, each $t_i \geqq 0$ and $t_1 + t_2 + \cdots + t_n = 1$. Comparing Definitions 5 and 11, we see that a line segment $L[\mathbf{v}_1, \mathbf{v}_2]$ may be described as the set of all convex combinations of $\mathbf{v}_1$ and $\mathbf{v}_2$. As a further geometric illustration of convex combinations, consider the triangle $P_1P_2P_3$ in Fig. 16. Let $\mathbf{v}_i$ be the position vector $\overrightarrow{OP_i}$ $(i = 1, 2, 3)$. Let P be a point on or inside the triangle. Let $\mathbf{v} = \overrightarrow{OP}$, $\mathbf{u} = \overrightarrow{OQ}$, where Q is the point of intersection of line P_3P (possibly extended) with P_1P_2. Then $\mathbf{v}$ is on $L[\mathbf{v}_3, \mathbf{u}]$, and $\mathbf{u}$ is on $L[\mathbf{v}_1, \mathbf{v}_2]$. Hence, there are numbers α and β such that

(66) $$\mathbf{v} = (1 - \alpha)\mathbf{v}_3 + \alpha\mathbf{u}, \qquad \mathbf{u} = (1 - \beta)\mathbf{v}_1 + \beta\mathbf{v}_2.$$

Substituting from the second of these equations into the first, we find that

$$\mathbf{v} = \alpha(1 - \beta)\mathbf{v}_1 + \alpha\beta\mathbf{v}_2 + (1 - \alpha)\mathbf{v}_3. \tag{67}$$

The sum of the coefficients on the right in (67) is easily found to be 1, and each is nonnegative. Thus, the position vector of each point inside or on the triangle is a convex combination of $\mathbf{v}_1$, $\mathbf{v}_2$, and $\mathbf{v}_3$. Conversely, it can be shown that each convex combination of $\mathbf{v}_1$, $\mathbf{v}_2$, and $\mathbf{v}_3$ can be written in the form (67). Hence, defining $\mathbf{u}$ and $\mathbf{v}$ by (66), we deduce that each convex combination of $\mathbf{v}_1$, $\mathbf{v}_2$, and $\mathbf{v}_3$ represents a point inside or on the triangle. Thus, this triangular convex set may be thought of as the set of all convex combinations of its vertices.

Returning now to the question under discussion, we state and prove a theorem which gives the desired generalization to n dimensions:

THEOREM 9. Given a finite number of feasible solutions of a linear programming problem, each convex combination of them is also a feasible solution. Furthermore, if $z = z_0$, say, at each of the given feasible solutions, then $z = z_0$ also at each convex combination of these feasible solutions.

The first part of the theorem is a consequence of the following more general result:

THEOREM 10. Let C be a convex set in any vector space, and let $\mathbf{v}_1, \ldots, \mathbf{v}_n$ be vectors belonging to C. Then each convex combination of these vectors also belongs to C.

By taking the set C of Theorem 10 to be the set of all feasible solutions of a linear programming problem, we obtain the first conclusion of Theorem 9. We now prove Theorem 10.

Proof of Theorem 10: The argument uses induction on n. For $n = 1$, the theorem merely says trivially that, if $\mathbf{v}_1$ belongs to C, then $\mathbf{v}_1$ belongs to C. For $n = 2$, the result follows immediately from the definition of convexity, since the collection of all convex combinations of $\mathbf{v}_1$ and $\mathbf{v}_2$ is the line segment $L[\mathbf{v}_1, \mathbf{v}_2]$. Now suppose the conclusion holds for $n = k$, where k is some integer $k \geqq 2$. We must deduce from this that it holds also for $n = k + 1$. Let $\mathbf{v}_1, \mathbf{v}_2, \ldots, \mathbf{v}_k, \mathbf{v}_{k+1}$ be vectors in C, and let $\mathbf{v}$ be a convex combination of these vectors. Then we have

$$\mathbf{v} = t_1\mathbf{v}_1 + t_2\mathbf{v}_2 + \cdots + t_k\mathbf{v}_k + t_{k+1}\mathbf{v}_{k+1}, \tag{68}$$

where each $t_i \geqq 0$ and $t_1 + t_2 + \cdots + t_k + t_{k+1} = 1$. We must show that $\mathbf{v}$ belongs to C. If $t_{k+1} = 1$, then $\mathbf{v} = \mathbf{v}_{k+1}$, which belongs to C. Suppose then that $t_{k+1} < 1$, and put $\alpha = t_1 + \cdots + t_k = 1 - t_{k+1}$. Then $\alpha > 0$, and we can write

$$\mathbf{v} = \alpha\left(\frac{t_1}{\alpha}\mathbf{v}_1 + \frac{t_2}{\alpha}\mathbf{v}_2 + \cdots + \frac{t_k}{\alpha}\mathbf{v}_k\right) + t_{k+1}\mathbf{v}_{k+1}. \tag{69}$$

The vector, call it $\mathbf{u}$, of which α is the coefficient in (69), is a convex combination of $\mathbf{v}_1, \ldots, \mathbf{v}_k$, because

$$\frac{t_1}{\alpha} + \cdots + \frac{t_k}{\alpha} = \frac{t_1 + \cdots + t_k}{\alpha} = \frac{\alpha}{\alpha} = 1$$

and each of the numbers t_i/α is nonnegative. Since we are assuming the conclusion holds for $n = k$, it follows that $\mathbf{u}$ belongs to C. But, since $\alpha + t_{k+1} = 1$, (69) implies that $\mathbf{v}$ lies on the line segment $L[\mathbf{u}, \mathbf{v}_{k+1}]$ and hence belongs to C. This completes the proof of Theorem 10.

Now consider the second conclusion of Theorem 9. Let $\mathbf{x}^{(1)}, \mathbf{x}^{(2)}, \ldots, \mathbf{x}^{(r)}$ be feasible solutions of a linear programming problem with objective function $z = c_1x_1 + c_2x_2 + \cdots + c_nx_n$. Suppose $z(\mathbf{x}^{(i)}) = z_0$ for each $i = 1, \ldots, r$, where z_0 is some fixed number. Let $\bar{\mathbf{x}} = t_1\mathbf{x}^{(1)} + t_2\mathbf{x}^{(2)} + \cdots + t_r\mathbf{x}^{(r)}$ be a convex combination of $\mathbf{x}^{(1)}, \mathbf{x}^{(2)}, \ldots, \mathbf{x}^{(r)}$. We wish to show that $z(\bar{\mathbf{x}}) = z_0$. Let $\mathbf{x}^{(i)} = [x_{1i}, \ldots, x_{ni}]$ for each $i = 1, 2, \ldots, r$. Then $\bar{\mathbf{x}} = [\bar{x}_1, \bar{x}_2, \ldots, \bar{x}_n]$, where

$$\bar{x}_j = \sum_{i=1}^{r} t_i x_{ji}$$

for each $j = 1, 2, \ldots, n$. Hence, we have

$$\begin{aligned} z(\bar{\mathbf{x}}) &= \sum_{j=1}^{n} c_j\bar{x}_j = \sum_{j=1}^{n} c_j\left(\sum_{i=1}^{r} t_i x_{ji}\right) = \sum_{i=1}^{r} t_i\left(\sum_{j=1}^{n} c_j x_{ji}\right) \\ &= \sum_{i=1}^{r} t_i z(\mathbf{x}^{(i)}) = z_0 \sum_{i=1}^{r} t_i = z_0, \end{aligned}$$

which completes the proof of Theorem 9.

Now suppose we have two or more basic feasible solutions $\mathbf{x}^{(1)}, \ldots, \mathbf{x}^{(r)}$ of a standard problem and that each of these solutions is optimal. Geometrically speaking, the "objective hyperplane" has been moved across the convex set C of feasible solutions to its optimal position, where it happens to contain two or more extreme points of C. Theorem 9 then tells us that all convex combinations of $\mathbf{x}^{(1)}, \ldots, \mathbf{x}^{(r)}$ are optimal solutions also.

We now wish to consider the question of how one might determine algebraically more than one optimal solution. Suppose we have a standard problem which is solvable by the ordinary simplex method and we obtain a basic feasible solution $\mathbf{x}^{(1)}$ which satisfies the criterion for optimality given in Theorem 1, Section 3–4. According to Exercise 6, Section 3–4, if $z_j - c_j \neq 0$ for each nonbasis vector $\mathbf{v}_j$, then $\mathbf{x}^{(1)}$ is the *only* optimal solution. Hence, a necessary condition for the existence of other optimal solutions is that $z_j - c_j = 0$ for at least one nonbasis vector $\mathbf{v}_j$. If this condition is satisfied, then any nonbasis vector $\mathbf{v}_j$ for which $z_j - c_j = 0$ can be inserted into the basis without changing the value of z. In this way a (possibly) different optimal basic feasible solution will be obtained. (In case of degeneracy, as we have seen, a change of basis may fail to produce a different basic feasible solution. Thus, the condition stated above is *necessary*, but not *sufficient*, for the existence of more than one optimal solution.) By continuing this process of inserting vectors $\mathbf{v}_j$ for which $z_j - c_j = 0$, we may be able to obtain several different optimal basic feasible solutions. The following example illustrates the procedure:

			3	1	1	2	−1	4	2	1
Basis	*Obj*	$\mathbf{b}$	$\mathbf{v}_1$	$\mathbf{v}_2$	$\mathbf{v}_3$	$\mathbf{v}_4$	$\mathbf{v}_5$	$\mathbf{v}_6$	$\mathbf{v}_7$	$\mathbf{v}_8$
$\mathbf{v}_6$	4	6	2	0	1	0	1	1	1	−1
$\mathbf{v}_2$	1	3	1	1	1	0	2	0	2	3
$\mathbf{v}_4$	2	4	1	0	−2	1	3	0	−2	2
$z_j - c_j$		35	8	0	0	0	13	0	0	2

Example 21. Suppose the accompanying tableau is obtained in the solution of a standard maximizing problem involving eight variables. The corresponding basic feasible solution $\mathbf{x}^{(1)} = [0, 3, 0, 4, 0, 6, 0, 0]$ is optimal by Theorem 1. Since $z_3 - c_3 = z_7 - c_7 = 0$, we can obtain other optimal basic feasible solutions by inserting either $\mathbf{v}_3$ or $\mathbf{v}_7$ into the basis. If $\mathbf{v}_3$ is inserted, the following tableau is obtained:

			3	1	1	2	−1	4	2	1
Basis	*Obj*	$\mathbf{b}$	$\mathbf{v}_1$	$\mathbf{v}_2$	$\mathbf{v}_3$	$\mathbf{v}_4$	$\mathbf{v}_5$	$\mathbf{v}_6$	$\mathbf{v}_7$	$\mathbf{v}_8$
$\mathbf{v}_6$	4	3	1	−1	0	0	−1	1	−1	−4
$\mathbf{v}_3$	1	3	1	1	1	0	2	0	2	3
$\mathbf{v}_4$	2	10	3	2	0	1	7	0	2	8
$z_j - c_j$		35	8	0	0	0	13	0	0	2

Thus, $\mathbf{x}^{(2)} = [0, 0, 3, 10, 0, 3, 0, 0]$ is another optimal basic feasible solution. The only vector which can now be inserted into the basis to obtain an optimal basic feasible solution different from $\mathbf{x}^{(1)}$ and $\mathbf{x}^{(2)}$ is $\mathbf{v}_7$. Inserting $\mathbf{v}_7$ for $\mathbf{v}_3$, we obtain the following tableau:

			3	1	1	2	−1	4	2	1
Basis	*Obj*	$\mathbf{b}$	$\mathbf{v}_1$	$\mathbf{v}_2$	$\mathbf{v}_3$	$\mathbf{v}_4$	$\mathbf{v}_5$	$\mathbf{v}_6$	$\mathbf{v}_7$	$\mathbf{v}_8$
$\mathbf{v}_6$	4	$\frac{9}{2}$	$\frac{3}{2}$	$-\frac{1}{2}$	$\frac{1}{2}$	0	0	1	0	$-\frac{5}{2}$
$\mathbf{v}_7$	2	$\frac{3}{2}$	$\frac{1}{2}$	$\frac{1}{2}$	$\frac{1}{2}$	0	1	0	1	$\frac{3}{2}$
$\mathbf{v}_4$	2	7	2	1	−1	1	5	0	0	5
$z_j - c_j$		35	8	0	0	0	13	0	0	2

The optimal solution corresponding to this tableau is $\mathbf{x}^{(3)} = [0, 0, 0, 7, 0, \frac{9}{2}, \frac{3}{2}, 0]$. Having found these three optimal basic feasible solutions, we can conclude, using Theorem 9, that, if $t_1 + t_2 + t_3 = 1$ and each $t_i \geqq 0$, then the vector $t_1\mathbf{x}^{(1)} + t_2\mathbf{x}^{(2)} + t_3\mathbf{x}^{(3)} = [0, 3t_1, 3t_2, 4t_1 + 10t_2 + 7t_3, 0, 6t_1 + 3t_2 + \frac{9}{2}t_3, \frac{3}{2}t_3, 0]$ is an optimal feasible solution.

Returning now to our general discussion, suppose we have found a basic feasible solution $\mathbf{x}^{(1)}$ for which no $z_j - c_j$ has the proper sign for improvement of z. Then, of course, $\mathbf{x}^{(1)}$ is optimal. Let $z_0 = z(\mathbf{x}^{(1)})$. For convenience, assume that the basis associated with $\mathbf{x}^{(1)}$ consists of $\mathbf{v}_1, \mathbf{v}_2, \ldots, \mathbf{v}_m$, that $z_{m+1} - c_{m+1} = z_{m+2} - c_{m+2} = \cdots = z_{m+r} - c_{m+r} = 0$, and that $z_j - c_j \neq 0$ for $m + r + 1 \leqq j \leqq n$. Let $\bar{\mathbf{x}} = [\bar{x}_1, \bar{x}_2, \ldots, \bar{x}_n]$ be any feasible solution. By formula (36), Section 3–4, we have

$$z_0 - z(\bar{\mathbf{x}}) = \sum_{j=m+r+1}^{n} (z_j - c_j)\bar{x}_j.$$

Since each $z_j - c_j$ has the same sign and is nonzero, it follows that $\bar{\mathbf{x}}$ will be optimal if, and only if, $\bar{x}_j = 0$ for each $j = m + r + 1, \ldots, n$. Suppose $\bar{\mathbf{x}}$ is both optimal and basic. Then either its associated basis contains only vectors $\mathbf{v}_j$ with $1 \leqq j \leqq m + r$ or else, if other vectors are in the basis, the corresponding components are zero. But, in the latter case, it follows from Theorem 12, Chapter 2, that, if we retain those basis vectors $\mathbf{v}_j$ with $1 \leqq j \leqq m + r$, we can adjoin to this "partial basis" additional vectors $\mathbf{v}_i$ with $1 \leqq i \leqq m + r$ to make up a full basis. Hence, each optimal basic feasible solution has an associated basis (though it may not be unique) consisting of vectors $\mathbf{v}_j$ with $1 \leqq j \leqq m + r$. In other words, to determine all optimal basic feasible solutions, we need only find one basic feasible solution $\mathbf{x}^{(1)}$ which satisfies the conditions of Theorem 1 and then find all basic feasible solutions whose bases contain only vectors $\mathbf{v}_j$ for which $z_j - c_j = 0$ ($z_j - c_j$ associated with $\mathbf{x}^{(1)}$). Suppose these basic feasible solutions are $\mathbf{x}^{(1)}, \ldots, \mathbf{x}^{(r)}$. Then, by Theorem 9, the convex combinations of $\mathbf{x}^{(1)}, \ldots, \mathbf{x}^{(r)}$ form a family of optimal solutions of the problem. This family, however, need not be the totality of *all* optimal solutions (see Exercise 8 below).

EXERCISES

1. Each of the conditions below involving x and y describes a set of points in the plane, namely, the collection of all points (x, y) whose coordinates satisfy the condition. In each case, draw a sketch of the set and use it to classify the set as convex or nonconvex.

(a) $x^2 + y^2 < 2y$
(b) $x^2 + y^2 > 0$
(c) $y \geqq x^2$
(d) $y < x^2$
(e) $(1/x) + y \leqq 2, \quad x > 0$
(f) $|x + y| \leqq 2$

2. Let $\mathbf{v}_1 = [-2, 0, 3, 4]$, $\mathbf{v}_2 = [4, 2, -2, 0]$, $\mathbf{v}_3 = [10, 8, -1, 2]$, and $\mathbf{v}_4 = [6, 6, 0, 2]$.

(a) Is the point (vector) $\mathbf{v} = [1, 1, 1, 2]$ on the line determined by $\mathbf{v}_1$ and $\mathbf{v}_2$?
(b) Is $[-2, 2, 2, 2]$ on the line segment $L[\mathbf{v}_3, \mathbf{v}_4]$?
(c) Do the line segments $L[\mathbf{v}_1, \mathbf{v}_2]$ and $L[\mathbf{v}_3, \mathbf{v}_4]$ have a common point? If so, find it.

3. Let $\mathbf{v}_1, \mathbf{v}_2, \ldots, \mathbf{v}_n$ be vectors in a vector space $\mathscr{V}$, and let C be the set of all convex combinations of these vectors. Prove that C is a convex set.

4. Let C be a convex set in a vector space $\mathscr{V}$. Prove that no three extreme points of C can be collinear.

5. Let C be the set of all r-dimensional vectors $[x_1, \ldots, x_r]$ satisfying the following system of inequalities:

$$\begin{cases} a_{11}x_1 + a_{12}x_2 + \cdots + a_{1r}x_r \leqq b_1, \\ a_{21}x_1 + a_{22}x_2 + \cdots + a_{2r}x_r \leqq b_2, \\ \cdots \quad \cdots \quad \cdots, \\ a_{m1}x_1 + a_{m2}x_2 + \cdots + a_{mr}x_r \leqq b_m. \end{cases}$$

Let C' denote the set of all $(m + r)$-dimensional vectors $[x_1, \ldots, x_r, x_{r+1}, \ldots, x_{r+m}]$ satisfying the related system of equations in nonnegative variables:

$$\begin{cases} a_{11}x_1 + a_{12}x_2 + \cdots + a_{1r}x_r + x_{r+1} = b_1, \\ a_{21}x_1 + a_{22}x_2 + \cdots + a_{2r}x_r + x_{r+2} = b_2, \\ \cdots \quad \cdots \quad \cdots, \\ a_{m1}x_1 + a_{m2}x_2 + \cdots + a_{mr}x_r + x_{r+m} = b_m, \\ x_j \geqq 0 \quad (j = r+1, \ldots, r+m). \end{cases}$$

Let $\mathbf{x} = [x_1, \ldots, x_r]$ be any member of C, and let $\mathbf{x}' = [x_1, \ldots, x_r, x_{r+1}, \ldots, x_{r+m}]$ be the corresponding member of C'. Prove that $\mathbf{x}$ is an extreme point of C if, and only if, $\mathbf{x}'$ is an extreme point of C'.

6. The following tableau displays an optimal basic feasible solution $\mathbf{x}^{(1)} = [0, 6, 0, 12, 8, 5, 0, 0]$ of a standard maximizing problem involving eight variables:

			2	2	−1	3	2	4	0	0
Basis	*Obj*	**b**	$\mathbf{v}_1$	$\mathbf{v}_2$	$\mathbf{v}_3$	$\mathbf{v}_4$	$\mathbf{v}_5$	$\mathbf{v}_6$	$\mathbf{v}_7$	$\mathbf{v}_8$
$\mathbf{v}_4$	3	12	1	0	1	1	0	0	1	−1
$\mathbf{v}_2$	2	6	3	1	−2	0	0	0	−1	3
$\mathbf{v}_6$	4	5	0	0	−1	0	0	1	−1	−1
$\mathbf{v}_5$	2	8	2	0	2	0	1	0	2	4
$z_j - c_j$		84	11	0	0	0	0	0	1	7

(a) Find another optimal basic feasible solution $\mathbf{x}^{(2)}$, and prove that $\mathbf{x}^{(1)}$ and $\mathbf{x}^{(2)}$ are the *only* optimal basic feasible solutions.

(b) Prove that each optimal solution must be a convex combination of $\mathbf{x}^{(1)}$ and $\mathbf{x}^{(2)}$.

(c) Find an optimal solution for which $x_6 = 8$.

7. The following tableau displays an optimal basic feasible solution $\mathbf{x}^{(1)} = [0, 8, 0, 4, 0, 3, 0, 1, 0]$ of a standard maximizing problem involving nine variables:

			3	2	−1	1	4	4	1	0	0
Basis	*Obj*	**b**	$\mathbf{v}_1$	$\mathbf{v}_2$	$\mathbf{v}_3$	$\mathbf{v}_4$	$\mathbf{v}_5$	$\mathbf{v}_6$	$\mathbf{v}_7$	$\mathbf{v}_8$	$\mathbf{v}_9$
$\mathbf{v}_2$	2	8	2	1	3	0	3	0	−1	0	6
$\mathbf{v}_8$	0	1	1	0	2	0	1	0	3	1	−2
$\mathbf{v}_4$	1	4	−5	0	2	1	2	0	1	0	3
$\mathbf{v}_6$	4	3	1	0	1	0	−1	1	1	0	−3
$z_j - c_j$		32	0	0	13	0	0	0	2	0	3

(a) Find two other optimal basic feasible solutions, and prove that no more optimal basic feasible solutions exist.

(b) Find an optimal solution $\mathbf{x} = [x_1, x_2, \ldots, x_9]$ for which $x_1 = \frac{1}{2}$ and $x_2 = 7$.

8. Give a two-variable example in which not all optimal solutions are convex combinations of basic optimal solutions.

CHAPTER **FOUR**

NETWORKS AND FLOWS

In this chapter we will present a brief account of a few topics from the theory of networks, culminating in the treatment of the transportation problem by the method of Ford and Fulkerson. Most of the basic concepts of network theory are easily grasped intuitively and several of these ideas are presented informally in the first section, in which a *maximal flow* problem is considered from a purely intuitive point of view. This serves as an introduction to the more careful study of the mathematical model known as a *network with capacity* which occupies most of Section 4–2. In that section, also, the solution of the maximal flow problem is described in detail. A special problem known as the *transshipment problem* is discussed in Section 4–3, the main result of which is Gale's Feasibility Theorem. This theorem plays an important role in the solution of the transportation problem which is presented in Section 4–4.

4-1. *AN EXAMPLE.*

In Fig. 17, T denotes a transmitter of signals of some sort, R denotes a receiver, and N_1, N_2, N_3, and N_4 denote devices which can relay the signals. The numbers adjacent to the lines indicate the maximum number of signals per second which can travel along various routes. For example, a maximum of 12 signals per second can travel from T to N_1, a maximum of 5 signals per second from N_2 to N_1, and so on. Signals may be sent only along the routes shown. Thus, no signals may be transmitted *directly* from T to N_4, but only by way of one or more intermediate points, such as $T \rightarrow N_1 \rightarrow N_3 \rightarrow N_4$. We shall assume that the system operates under *steady-state* conditions, by which we mean that each of the relaying devices is transmitting signals at

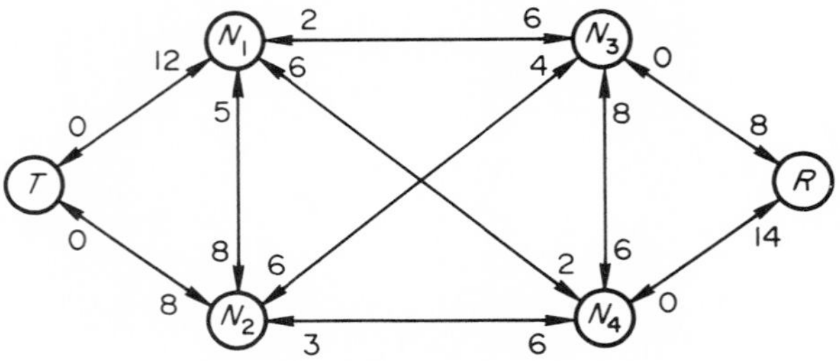

Figure 17

exactly the same rate as it receives them. Also, we assume that the devices can be set in advance so as to transmit signals along any desired route or combination of routes. For example, T might be set to transmit 12 signals per second to N_1 and none to N_2. N_1, which would be receiving 12 signals per second from T, might be set to transmit 6 signals per second to N_3, 2 signals per second to N_4, and 4 signals per second to N_2, and so on. The problem we wish to consider is that of determining how the devices should be set so that the maximum number of signals per second will be sent from T and received at R.

That this can be formulated as a linear programming problem may be seen as follows: Let x_{ij} be the number of signals to be sent per second from N_i to N_j ($i = 0, 1, \ldots, 5; j = 0, 1, \ldots, 5$), where for convenience we let $N_0 = T$ and $N_5 = R$. Then the number of signals per second transmitted from T is $x_{01} + x_{02}$, and we wish to maximize this number subject to the conditions that no more signals be sent along any path than the maximum indicated in the diagram and that the number of signals transmitted by each relaying device equals the number received. Thus we may state our problem as follows:

Maximize $z = x_{01} + x_{02}$ subject to

$$\left\{\begin{array}{l}
x_{01} + x_{21} + x_{31} + x_{41} = x_{12} + x_{13} + x_{14}, \\
x_{02} + x_{12} + x_{32} + x_{42} = x_{21} + x_{23} + x_{24}, \\
x_{13} + x_{23} + x_{43} = x_{31} + x_{32} + x_{34} + x_{35}, \\
x_{14} + x_{24} + x_{34} = x_{41} + x_{42} + x_{43} + x_{45}, \\
x_{01} \leqq 12, \quad x_{02} \leqq 8, \quad x_{12} \leqq 8, \quad x_{21} \leqq 5, \quad x_{13} \leqq 6, \\
x_{31} \leqq 2, \quad x_{23} \leqq 4, \quad x_{32} \leqq 6, \quad x_{14} \leqq 2, \quad x_{41} \leqq 6, \\
x_{34} \leqq 6, \quad x_{43} \leqq 8, \quad x_{35} \leqq 8, \quad x_{45} \leqq 14, \text{ and each } x_{ij} \geqq 0.
\end{array}\right.$$

(*Note*: Variables such as $x_{03}, x_{04}, \ldots$, corresponding to pairs of devices between which transmission is not permitted are not involved in this problem.)

We have omitted in this formulation the requirement that each x_{ij} be an *integer*, though the nature of the physical problem clearly indicates that this condition should be imposed. The reason for this omission is that, if the restriction to integral variables be added to the constraints of a linear programming problem, the resulting problem cannot properly be called a linear programming problem according to our definition and may not be solvable by the methods of Chapter 3. In the present case, however, it will follow from later developments that an optimal solution of the linear programming problem in which all variables are integers does exist and, hence, that the problem could have been solved by our previous methods. The solution by these methods would be quite cumbersome, to say the least, and so we wish to describe a different, more efficient approach to the problem. In the next section we shall describe a systematic procedure for solving any problem of the maximal-flow variety, of which the present example is a special case. Our purpose now is to try to make clear the intuitive notion behind the method.

Each signal transmitted from T and received by R traverses some *path*, such as $T \longrightarrow N_1 \longrightarrow N_3 \longrightarrow R$, $T \longrightarrow N_2 \longrightarrow N_4 \longrightarrow N_1 \longrightarrow N_3 \longrightarrow R$, etc. The procedure we are going to describe involves consideration of such paths and the determination of the *capacity* of each path, i.e., the maximum number of signals which can be transmitted per second along that path. The path $T \longrightarrow N_1 \longrightarrow N_3 \longrightarrow R$, for example, has a capacity of 6, which is the smallest of the capacities of the three segments $T \longrightarrow N_1$, $N_1 \longrightarrow N_3$, and $N_3 \longrightarrow R$ which make up this path. Similarly, the path $T \longrightarrow N_2 \longrightarrow N_1 \longrightarrow N_3 \longrightarrow R$ has a capacity of 5. Note carefully, however, that we cannot simultaneously send 6 signals per second along the first of these paths and 5 along the second, because this would require sending 11 signals per second from N_1 to N_3, thus exceeding the capacity of the segment $N_1 \longrightarrow N_3$.

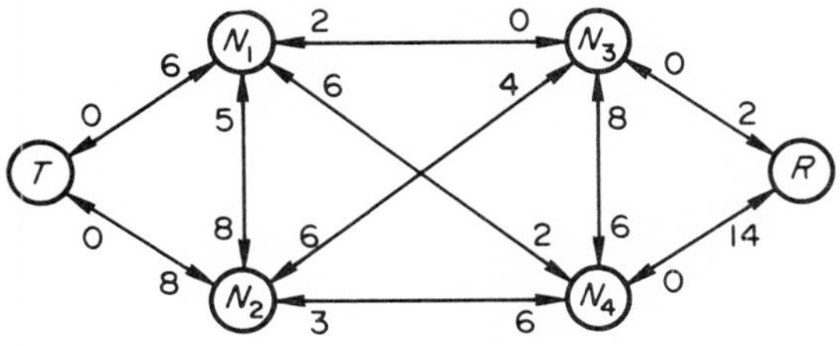

Figure 18

We first select a path from T to R and send as many signals along this path as possible. Suppose we select the path $T \longrightarrow N_1 \longrightarrow N_3 \longrightarrow R$. As we saw above, the capacity of this path is 6, so we tentatively agree to send 6 signals per second along this path. One way to keep track of this and avoid overloading the path at some later stage is to subtract 6 from the capacity of each segment of this path. The network with these new capacities is shown in Fig. 18. In this new network we again seek a path of positive capacity from T to R. One such path is $T \longrightarrow N_2 \longrightarrow N_4 \longrightarrow R$, whose capacity is also 6. We send 6 signals per second along this path and form new capacities by subtracting 6 from the capacity of each segment of this path. The result is shown in Fig. 19. We next select the path $T \longrightarrow N_1 \longrightarrow N_2 \longrightarrow N_3 \longrightarrow N_4 \longrightarrow R$

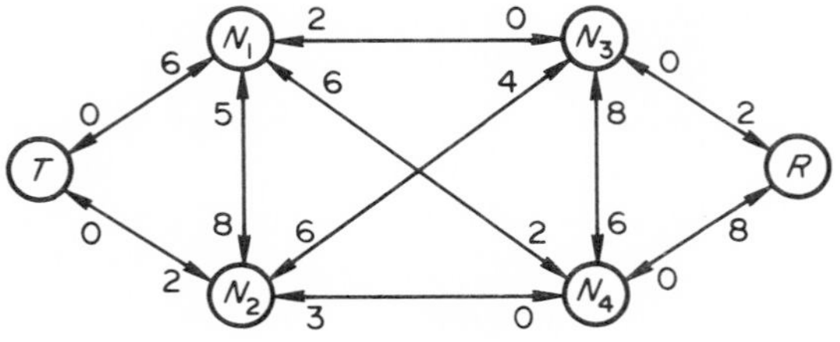

Figure 19

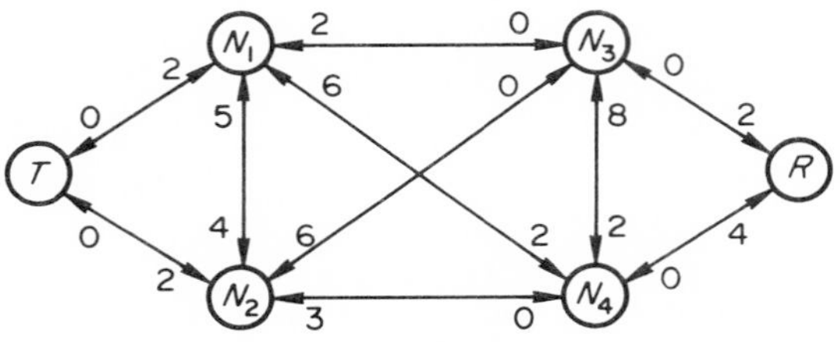

Figure 20

in this new network. Its capacity is 4, so we send 4 signals per second along this path and subtract 4 from the capacity of each of its segments to obtain the next network, shown in Fig. 20. In this network, we find the path $T \longrightarrow N_1 \longrightarrow N_4 \longrightarrow R$ of capacity 2. Assigning a flow of 2 signals per second to this path and subtracting gives the network of Fig. 21. In this network, it is easy to see that there is no path of positive capacity from T to R. Hence,

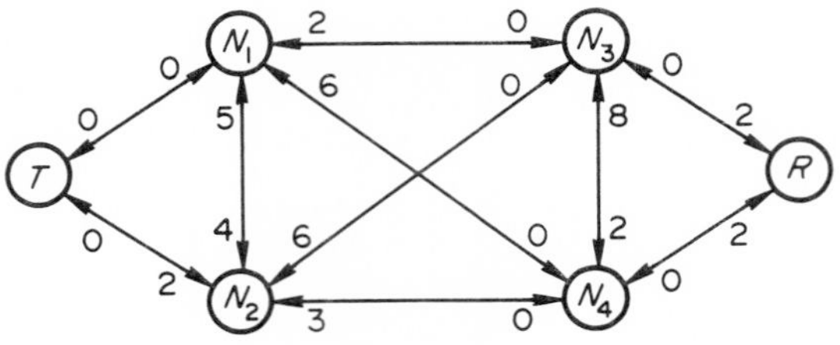

Figure 21

the process cannot be continued. At this point, the total number of signals per second being sent from T to R can be found by adding the capacities of the various paths considered so far. The result is $6 + 6 + 4 + 2 = 18$. In Fig. 22, we have labeled the branches of the network to show their original capacities, just how many signals are being sent along each branch, and the direction in which these signals are traveling. It seems evident that 18 is the maximum number of signals per second which can be sent through this network from T to R since every path from T to R is being used to its full

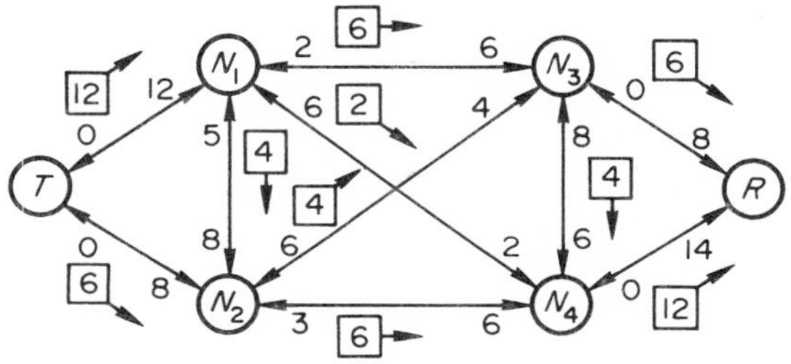

Figure 22

capacity. This conclusion will be justified rigorously by Theorem 2 of the next section. To conclude the present discussion, we point out that the solution shown in Fig. 22 is not unique. Another, giving the same total number of signals per second, is shown in Fig. 23.

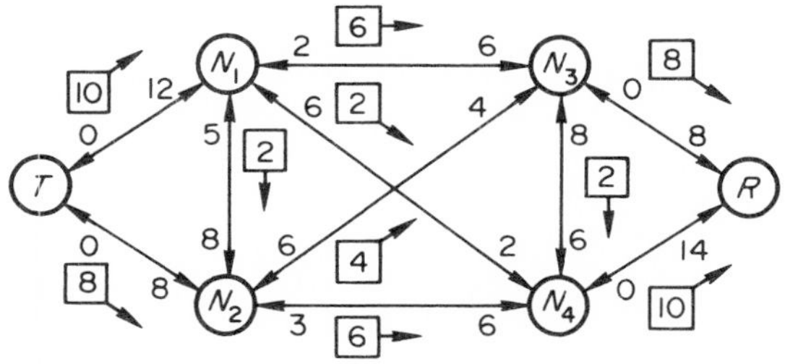

Figure 23

EXERCISES

1. If possible, find optimal solutions for the problem of this section other than the ones shown in Figs. 22 and 23.

2. Each of the diagrams below is to be interpreted as in the example. In each case determine the maximum number of signals per second which can be sent from T to R. In parts (c), (d), (e), and (f) assume that $0 < a < b < c$ and express your answer in terms of a, b, and c.

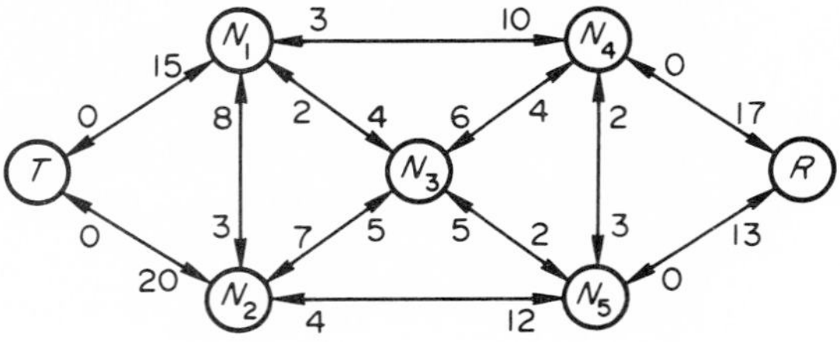

N1
N4
T
N3
R
N2
N5
3
10
15
0
8
2
4
6
4
2
17
0
3
7
5
5
2
3
13
0
20
4
12
0

(a)

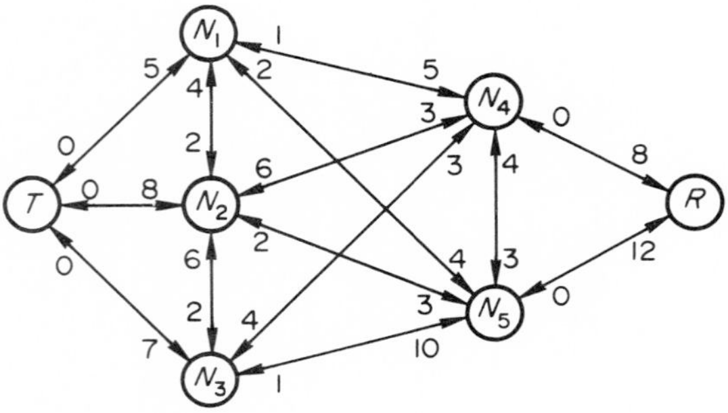

N1
N4
T
N2
R
N5
N3
1
2
5
5
4
3
0
0
2
6
3
4
8
0
8
2
4
3
12
0
6
3
0
2
4
7
10
1

(b)

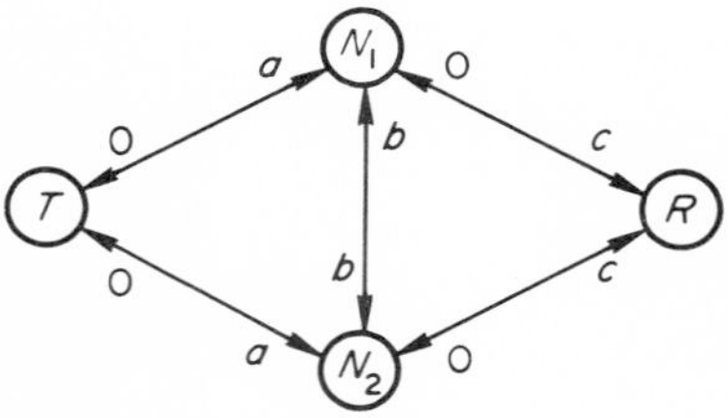

N1
T
R
N2
a
0
b
c
0
0
b
c
0
a
0

(c)

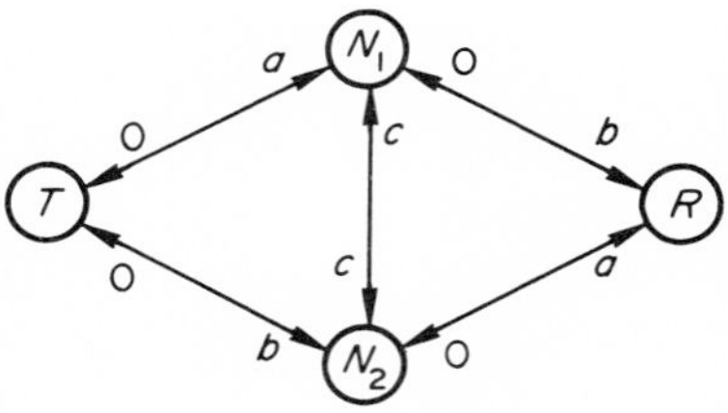

N1
T
R
N2
a
0
c
b
0
0
c
a
b
0

(d)

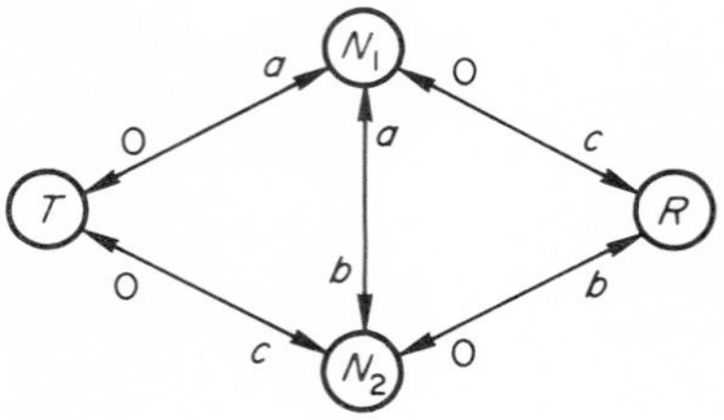

N1
T
R
N2
a
0
a
c
0
0
b
b
c
0

(e)

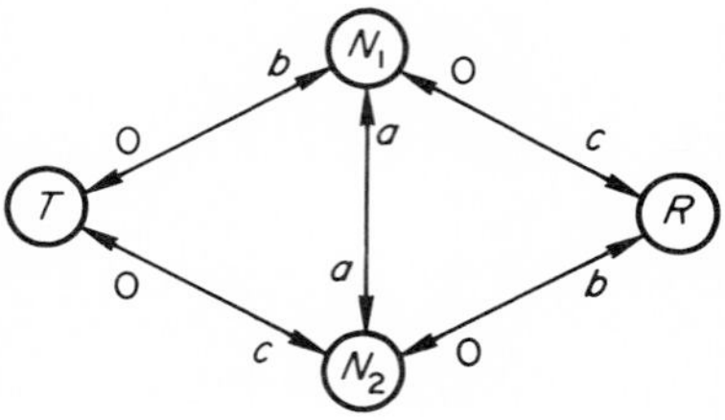

N1
T
R
N2
b
0
a
c
0
0
a
b
c
0

(f)

4-2. *NETWORKS, FLOWS, AND THE MAXIMAL FLOW PROBLEM.*

The example in the preceding section illustrates a type of problem, known as a maximal-flow problem, which is of fundamental importance in the theory of networks. In this section we shall discuss maximal-flow problems in détail. We must begin by making precise the meaning of terms such as *network*, *path*, *flow*, etc., which were used without formal definition in the previous section. In our discussions it will be very convenient to use a few concepts and notations from the theory of sets. For the benefit of the reader who has little or no acquaintance with elementary set theory, we digress for a paragraph to give a brief discussion of the necessary topics.

The notions of *set* and *belonging to a set* are usually taken to be primitive or undefined concepts. The notation used to express the fact that an object called x belongs to a set called $\mathscr{A}$ is "$x \in \mathscr{A}$," which may be read "x belongs to $\mathscr{A}$," or "x is a member of $\mathscr{A}$." If $\mathscr{A}$ and $\mathscr{B}$ are sets, we say that "$\mathscr{A}$ is contained in $\mathscr{B}$," or "$\mathscr{A}$ is a subset of $\mathscr{B}$," if, and only if, each member of $\mathscr{A}$ is also a member of $\mathscr{B}$. It is convenient to postulate the existence of an *empty set*, denoted by ϕ, which is a subset of each set and which has no members. The symbolism "$\mathscr{A} \subset \mathscr{B}$" is used to express the fact that $\mathscr{A}$ is contained in $\mathscr{B}$. Sets $\mathscr{A}$ and $\mathscr{B}$ are said to be *equal*, written "$\mathscr{A} = \mathscr{B}$," if, and only if, $\mathscr{A} \subset \mathscr{B}$ and $\mathscr{B} \subset \mathscr{A}$, i.e., if, and only if, each object which belongs to one of $\mathscr{A}$ and $\mathscr{B}$ belongs also to the other. Any two sets $\mathscr{A}$ and $\mathscr{B}$ may be combined in several ways to form other sets. The *union* of $\mathscr{A}$ and $\mathscr{B}$, denoted by $\mathscr{A} \cup \mathscr{B}$, is the collection of all objects x such that either $x \in \mathscr{A}$ or $x \in \mathscr{B}$ (or both). The *intersection* of $\mathscr{A}$ and $\mathscr{B}$, written $\mathscr{A} \cap \mathscr{B}$, is the collection of all objects x such that $x \in \mathscr{A}$ and $x \in \mathscr{B}$. The *complement of $\mathscr{B}$ relative to $\mathscr{A}$*, written $\mathscr{A} - \mathscr{B}$, is the collection of all objects belonging to $\mathscr{A}$, but not to $\mathscr{B}$. To illustrate the last three definitions, suppose $\mathscr{A}$ is the set of all positive integers and $\mathscr{B}$ is the set of all integers less than 5. Then $\mathscr{A} \cup \mathscr{B}$ is the set of all integers, $\mathscr{A} \cap \mathscr{B}$ contains only the integers 1, 2, 3, and 4, and $\mathscr{A} - \mathscr{B}$ consists of all integers greater than, or equal to, 5. If $\mathscr{A} \cap \mathscr{B} = \phi$, we say that $\mathscr{A}$ and $\mathscr{B}$ are *disjoint*. A *finite set* is one which is either empty or, for some positive integer n, has exactly n members. To indicate that $\mathscr{A}$ is a finite set whose members are the objects $x_1, x_2, \ldots, x_n$, we use the notation $\mathscr{A} = \{x_1, x_2, \ldots, x_n\}$. Given objects x and y, we can form what is called the *ordered pair with first element x and second element y*, denoted by (x, y). We omit the precise set-theoretic definition of ordered pair. It is made in such a way that $(x_1, y_1) = (x_2, y_2)$ if, and only if, $x_1 = x_2$ and $y_1 = y_2$. If $\mathscr{A}$ and $\mathscr{B}$ are sets, then the collection of all ordered pairs (x, y) in which $x \in \mathscr{A}$ and $y \in \mathscr{B}$ is called the *cartesian product of $\mathscr{A}$ and $\mathscr{B}$* and is denoted by $\mathscr{A} \times \mathscr{B}$. In particular, $\mathscr{A} \times \mathscr{A}$ is the set of all ordered pairs (x, y) in which both x and y belong to $\mathscr{A}$.

Returning now to the main subject, let us reconsider the example of the previous section. The transmitter, receiver, and relaying devices form a finite set, say $\mathcal{N}$, and the integers telling us how many signals per second may be sent between the various devices may be thought of as the values of a function, say c, defined on the cartesian product $\mathcal{N} \times \mathcal{N}$. This motivates the following definition:

DEFINITION 1. Let $\mathcal{N}$ be a finite set, and let c be an integer-valued function defined on $\mathcal{N} \times \mathcal{N}$ such that $c(x, y) \geqq 0$ and $c(x, x) = 0$ for each x and y in $\mathcal{N}$. The pair $(\mathcal{N}, c)$ is called a *network with capacity*. The objects in the set $\mathcal{N}$ are called *nodes*, the ordered pairs (x, y) in $\mathcal{N} \times \mathcal{N}$ are called *branches*, and the function c is called the *capacity function*.

Instead of *network with capacity*, we shall usually say simply *network*. As the definition indicates, the essential ingredients of a network are a finite set of nodes and an assignment of a nonnegative integer (capacity) to each ordered pair of nodes (branch). The concept of a network serves as a mathematical model for many physical situations other than the one described in the previous section. The nodes may represent warehouses, factories, airports, or even people, with correspondingly varied interpretations of capacities.

The nodes T and R in the example have special properties: Each branch terminating at T has zero capacity, and at least one (in fact, more than one) branch beginning at T has positive capacity; each branch beginning at R has zero capacity, and at least one branch terminating at R has positive capacity. Physically, we referred to T and R as transmitter and receiver, respectively. The names used for such nodes in the mathematical model, however, are *source* and *sink*, defined as follows:

DEFINITION 2. A node x in a network $(\mathcal{N}, c)$ is called a *source* if, and only if, $c(y, x) = 0$ for each y in $\mathcal{N}$ and $c(x, y) > 0$ for at least one y in $\mathcal{N}$. A node z is called a *sink* if, and only if, $c(z, y) = 0$ for each y in $\mathcal{N}$ and $c(y, z) > 0$ for at least one y in $\mathcal{N}$.

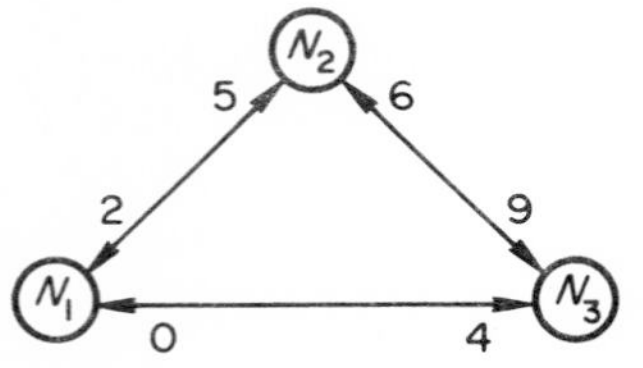

Figure 24

It is not logically necessary for a network to have either sources or sinks (see Fig. 24), but we shall be chiefly concerned with those which have both. For such networks, we adopt a special notation, as follows:

DEFINITION 3. We denote by the symbol $(\mathcal{N}, c; \mathcal{T}, \mathcal{R})$ a network $(\mathcal{N}, c)$ which has a nonempty set $\mathcal{T}$ of sources and a nonempty set $\mathcal{R}$ of sinks. Such a network is called a *network with sources and sinks*. In particular, if there is just one source T and one sink R, we write $(\mathcal{N}, c; T, R)$.

An example of a network with two sources and three sinks is shown in Fig. 25.

The problem we discussed in the preceding section was to determine the maximum number of signals which could be sent per second from the source to the sink. At each stage in the solution of the problem, we assigned an integer to each branch of the network, namely, the number of signals to be sent along that branch. This assignment of an integer to each of the branches,

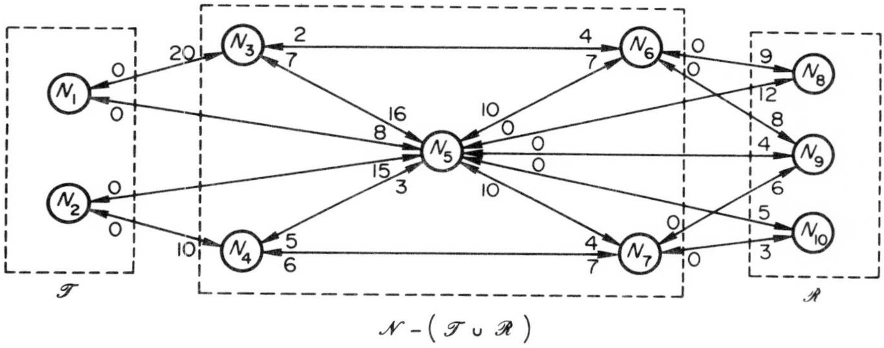

Figure 25

in accordance with certain restrictions to be made precise shortly, is what we are going to refer to as a *flow* in the network. Before we state the formal definition, however, let us consider in more detail the properties of a flow as they can be judged from the example in an attempt to see in advance how the definition should be formulated. The integer we assigned to a branch in the example had to be nonnegative and could not exceed the capacity of that branch. Also, for each node other than a source or sink, the number of signals per second coming into that node had to equal the number going out. In other words, in assigning these integers to the branches we defined an integer-valued function f on $\mathscr{N} \times \mathscr{N}$ with the properties that (i) $0 \leqq f(x, y) \leqq c(x, y)$ for each branch (x, y), and (ii) $\sum_{y \in \mathscr{N}} f(x, y) = \sum_{y \in \mathscr{N}} f(y, x)$ for each node x other than a source or sink, where the notation "$y \in \mathscr{N}$" accompanying the summations indicates that the sum is to be taken over all nodes y in $\mathscr{N}$, x being held fixed. Thus it might seem natural to define a flow in a network $(\mathscr{N}, c)$ as an integer-valued function f defined on $\mathscr{N} \times \mathscr{N}$ which satisfies requirements (i) and (ii). But consider Fig. 26, which shows an example of such a function for the network discussed in the previous section. This seems to be unnecessarily complicated. As far as the total number of signals per second transmitted from T and received at R is concerned, the simpler function defined in Fig. 27 gives the same result. Let f denote the function defined in Fig. 27, and let g be the function of Fig. 26.

Then the value of f on certain branches (x, y) is given by $f(x, y) = g(x, y) - g(y, x)$. For example, this is true if $x = N_1$ and $y = N_3$, but not if $x = N_3$ and $y = N_1$. If this equation held for all branches (x, y),

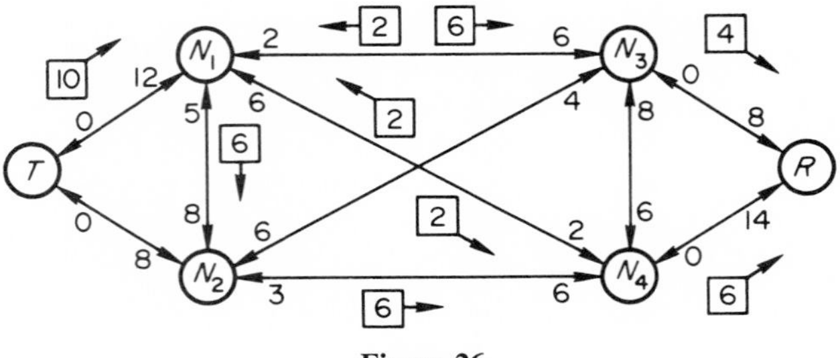

Figure 26

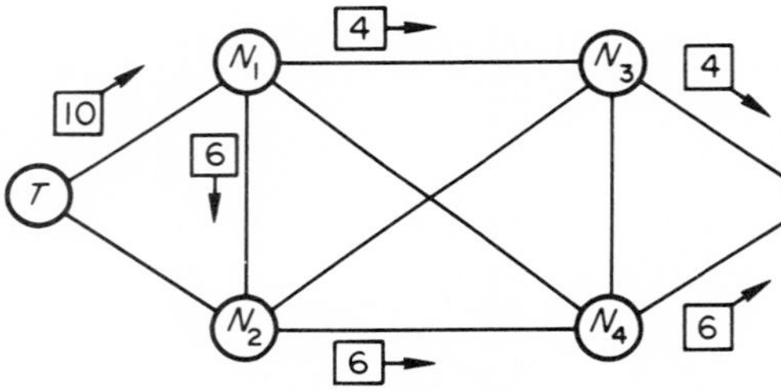

Figure 27

one easily verified consequence would be that $f(y, x) = -f(x, y)$ for each branch (x, y). Hence, some branches might be assigned positive integers, some negative, and others zero, but there would be no case in which both $f(x, y)$ and $f(y, x)$ were positive. Thus, the condition $f(y, x) = -f(x, y)$ would rule out situations such as the one shown in Fig. 26, but, on the other hand, it would raise the question of physical interpretation of negative flow in a branch. This is easily answered, however. If $f(x, y) = -5$, for example, this simply means that there is a *net* flow of five units from y to x. This intuitive idea of net flow is what we now formalize in the following definition:

DEFINITION 4. A *flow* in a network $(\mathcal{N}, c)$ is an integer-valued function f defined on $\mathcal{N} \times \mathcal{N}$ which has the following properties: (i) $f(x, y) \leqq c(x, y)$ for each branch (x, y); (ii) $f(y, x) = -f(x, y)$ for each branch (x, y); and (iii) $\sum_{y \in \mathcal{N}} f(x, y) = \sum_{y \in \mathcal{N}} f(y, x)$ for each node x other than a source or a sink.

Before proceeding further, we introduce some very convenient and useful notation due to D. Gale (see [1]), the use of which will permit us to eliminate cumbersome summation signs in much of the ensuing discussion. Suppose $\mathcal{N}$ is a finite set, h is a real-valued function defined on $\mathcal{N} \times \mathcal{N}$, and $\mathscr{A}$ and $\mathscr{B}$ are subsets of $\mathcal{N}$. Then we define the symbol $h(\mathscr{A}, \mathscr{B})$ as follows:

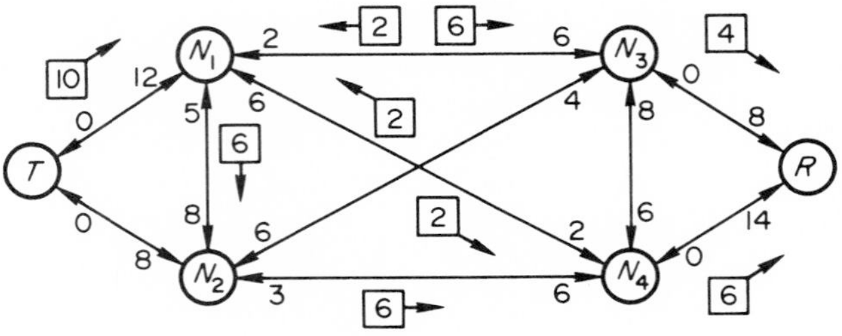

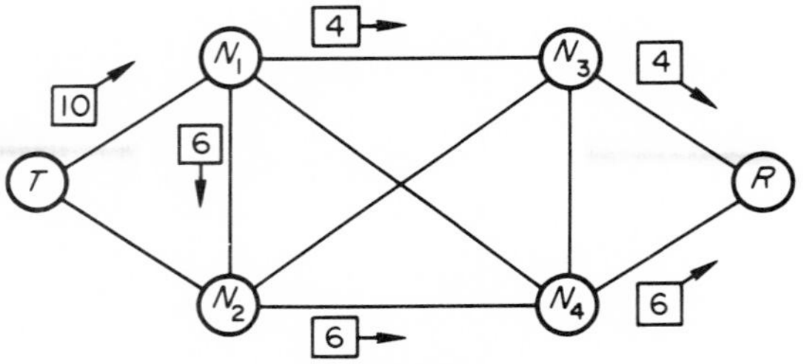

$$h(\mathscr{A}, \mathscr{B}) = \sum_{x \in \mathscr{A}} (\sum_{y \in \mathscr{B}} h(x, y)).$$

If either $\mathscr{A}$ or $\mathscr{B}$ is empty, we agree that $h(\mathscr{A}, \mathscr{B}) = 0$. In most of our discussions, h will be either a flow or a capacity function for a network. As an example, consider the network of the preceding section, and let c denote its capacity function. If $\mathscr{A} = \{T, N_1, N_2\}$ and $\mathscr{B} = \{N_3, N_4, R\}$, then $c(\mathscr{A}, \mathscr{B}) = c(N_1, N_3) + c(N_1, N_4) + c(N_2, N_3) + c(N_2, N_4) = 18$. If $\mathscr{A}$ contains a single node x, we write $h(x, \mathscr{B})$; a similar notation is used in case $\mathscr{B}$ contains only one node. Thus, property (iii) of Definition 4, stated in Gale's notation, says that $f(x, \mathscr{N}) = f(\mathscr{N}, x)$ for each node x other than a source or a sink.

Three basic properties of flows which will be needed later will now be stated. Each deals with the following situation: $(\mathscr{N}, c)$ is a network, f is a flow in $(\mathscr{N}, c)$, and $\mathscr{N}'$ is the set of all nodes which are neither sources nor sinks.

Property 1. If $\mathscr{A} \subset \mathscr{N}'$, then $f(\mathscr{A}, \mathscr{N}) = 0$.

Property 2. If $\mathscr{A} \subset \mathscr{N}$, then $f(\mathscr{A}, \mathscr{A}) = 0$.

Property 3. If $\mathscr{A} \subset \mathscr{N}$ and $\mathscr{B} \subset \mathscr{N}$, then $f(\mathscr{B}, \mathscr{A}) = -f(\mathscr{A}, \mathscr{B})$.

The proofs, which use parts (ii) and (iii) of Definition 4, are quite short and are left as exercises (Exercise 2 at the end of this section).

In the example of the previous section, we considered the *amount* of flow in the network, which meant the number of signals per second being sent from the transmitter to the receiver. We now wish to generalize this notion to arbitrary networks having sources and sinks. It seems clear that, in such networks, the amount of flow should be measured by the total flow out of the sources. Hence, we make the following definition:

DEFINITION 5. Let f be a flow in a network $(\mathscr{N}, c; \mathscr{T}, \mathscr{R})$. We define the *amount of the flow f*, denoted by $A(f)$, by the equation $A(f) = f(\mathscr{T}, \mathscr{N})$.

Intuitively, we feel that what goes into a network at the sources must come out at the sinks, so that the amount of a flow should be equal to the total flow into the sinks. That this is correct can be proved by use of property 1 (see Exercise 3 at the end of this section). As a particular example, consider the flow f corresponding to Fig. 22. We have $A(f) = f(T, \mathscr{N}) = f(T, N_1) + f(T, N_2) = 12 + 6 = 18$ and $f(\mathscr{N}, R) = f(N_3, R) + f(N_4, R) = 6 + 12 = 18$.

We should expect also that, if f is any flow in a network $(\mathscr{N}, c; \mathscr{T}, \mathscr{R})$, then $A(f) \geqq 0$. Let us check to see if this is a consequence of the definition. If $x \in \mathscr{T}$ and $y \in \mathscr{N}$, then $f(y, x) \leqq c(y, x) = 0$. Hence, $f(x, y) = -f(y, x) \geqq 0$. Thus $A(f)$, as the sum of nonnegative numbers, is itself nonnegative.

Having defined the amount of a flow, we can now define maximal flows and state exactly what we mean by the maximal-flow problem:

DEFINITION 6. A flow f in a network $(\mathcal{N}, c; \mathcal{T}, \mathcal{R})$ is said to be *maximal* provided that, if g is any other flow in $(\mathcal{N}, c; \mathcal{T}, \mathcal{R})$, then $A(f) \geqq A(g)$. The maximal-flow problem for a given network with sources and sinks is the problem of finding a maximal flow in that network.

The rest of this section is devoted to the description and justification of a general method for solving maximal-flow problems. It is essentially a matter of formalizing the procedure used in the preceding section, but using our revised concept of flow as given by Definition 4. We must first introduce some new terminology and discuss further properties of flows.

DEFINITION 7. A *path* in a network $(\mathcal{N}, c)$ is a finite sequence of branches $(x_1, x_2), (x_2, x_3), \ldots, (x_{k-1}, x_k)$ in which the nodes $x_1, x_2, \ldots, x_k$ are all different from each other, with the possible exception of x_1 and x_k. We denote this path by the symbol $(x_1, x_2, \ldots, x_k)$. The node x_1 is called the *initial point*, and x_k is called the *terminal point*. If $x_1 = x_k$, the path is called a *loop*, or *closed path*. If $x_1 \neq x_k$, the path is called a *simple path from x_1 to x_k*. The *capacity* of a path (simple or closed) is defined to be the smallest of the capacities of the branches of the path. If $\mathcal{A}$ and $\mathcal{B}$ are nonempty disjoint subsets of $\mathcal{N}$, a *path from $\mathcal{A}$ to $\mathcal{B}$* is a (necessarily simple) path whose initial point lies in $\mathcal{A}$, whose terminal point lies in $\mathcal{B}$, and whose intermediate points (if any) lie in neither $\mathcal{A}$ nor $\mathcal{B}$.

DEFINITION 8. A flow f in a network $(\mathcal{N}, c)$ is said to *saturate* a path $(x_1, x_2, \ldots, x_k)$ in the network if, and only if, there is at least one branch (x_{i-1}, x_i) of the path for which $f(x_{i-1}, x_i) = c(x_{i-1}, x_i)$.

Intuitively, a flow saturates a path when it is impossible to increase the flow along the path without overloading it. The procedure used in the example of the last section involved finding paths from the source to the sink and then saturating these paths. Our next objective is to prove that in a network $(\mathcal{N}, c; \mathcal{T}, \mathcal{R})$ a flow which saturates every path from $\mathcal{T}$ to $\mathcal{R}$ must actually be maximal. Toward that objective, we now introduce the terminology of *cuts*:

DEFINITION 9. A *cut* in a network $(\mathcal{N}, c; \mathcal{T}, \mathcal{R})$ is an ordered pair $(\mathcal{U}, \mathcal{V})$ of subsets of $\mathcal{N}$ with the properties that $\mathcal{T} \subset \mathcal{U}$, $\mathcal{R} \subset \mathcal{V}$, $\mathcal{U} \cap \mathcal{V} = \phi$, and $\mathcal{U} \cup \mathcal{V} = \mathcal{N}$. The *capacity* of a cut $(\mathcal{U}, \mathcal{V})$ is defined to be the number $c(\mathcal{U}, \mathcal{V})$. If f is a flow in $(\mathcal{N}, c; \mathcal{T}, \mathcal{R})$, we call $f(\mathcal{U}, \mathcal{V})$ the *amount of flow across the cut* $(\mathcal{U}, \mathcal{V})$.

Thus a cut is essentially a division of the nodes into two classes such that all sources belong to one class, all sinks belong to the other, and every node belongs to exactly one of the two classes. As an illustration, consider the network of the preceding section. Let $\mathcal{U} = \{T, N_1, N_3\}$ and $\mathcal{V} = \{N_2, N_4, R\}$. Then $(\mathcal{U}, \mathcal{V})$ is a cut whose capacity is $c(\mathcal{U}, \mathcal{V}) = c(T, N_2) + c(N_1, N_2) + c(N_1, N_4) + c(N_3, N_2) + c(N_3, N_4) + c(N_3, R) = 38$. If f denotes the flow of Fig. 22, then we find similarly that $f(\mathscr{U}, \mathscr{V}) = 18$. Thus, for this example, we have $A(f) = f(\mathscr{U}, \mathscr{V}) \leqq c(\mathscr{U}, \mathscr{V})$. The following theorem asserts that this result holds for cuts and flows in general:

THEOREM 1. Let f be a flow and $(\mathscr{U}, \mathscr{V})$, a cut in a network $(\mathscr{N}, c; \mathscr{T}, \mathscr{R})$. Then we have

(1) $$A(f) = f(\mathscr{U}, \mathscr{V}) \leqq c(\mathscr{U}, \mathscr{V}).$$

Proof: The schematic diagram below may help in following the argument:

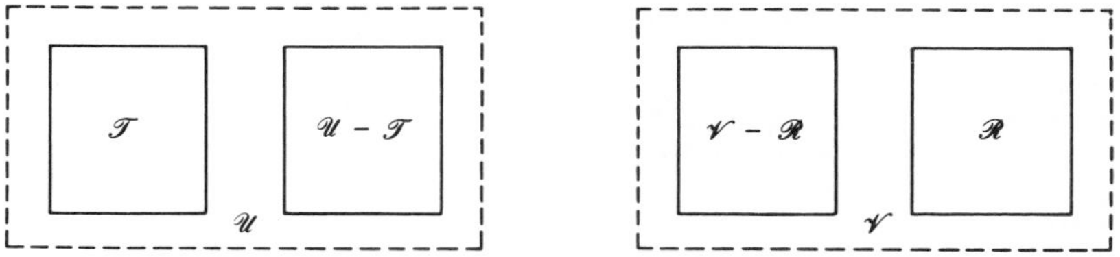

By definition, the amount of flow is given by $A(f) = f(\mathscr{T}, \mathscr{N})$. Since $\mathscr{N}$ is the union of the disjoint sets $\mathscr{U}$ and $\mathscr{V}$, we can write $f(\mathscr{T}, \mathscr{N}) = f(\mathscr{T}, \mathscr{U}) + f(\mathscr{T}, \mathscr{V})$. Using the same reasoning again, thinking of $\mathscr{U}$ as $\mathscr{T} \cup (\mathscr{U} - \mathscr{T})$, we can write $f(\mathscr{T}, \mathscr{U}) = f(\mathscr{T}, \mathscr{T}) + f(\mathscr{T}, \mathscr{U} - \mathscr{T})$. But $f(\mathscr{T}, \mathscr{T}) = 0$ by property 2. Thus, we have $A(f) = f(\mathscr{T}, \mathscr{U} - \mathscr{T}) + f(\mathscr{T}, \mathscr{V})$, from which it follows that $f(\mathscr{T}, \mathscr{V}) = A(f) - f(\mathscr{T}, \mathscr{U} - \mathscr{T})$. By similar reasoning, we have $f(\mathscr{U}, \mathscr{V}) = f(\mathscr{T}, \mathscr{V}) + f(\mathscr{U} - \mathscr{T}, \mathscr{V}) = A(f) - f(\mathscr{T}, \mathscr{U} - \mathscr{T}) + f(\mathscr{U} - \mathscr{T}, \mathscr{V})$. Using properties 2 and 3, we can write $f(\mathscr{U}, \mathscr{V}) = A(f) + f(\mathscr{U} - \mathscr{T}, \mathscr{T}) + f(\mathscr{U} - \mathscr{T}, \mathscr{V}) + f(\mathscr{U} - \mathscr{T}, \mathscr{U} - \mathscr{T}) = A(f) + f(\mathscr{U} - \mathscr{T}, \mathscr{N})$. By property 1, $f(\mathscr{U} - \mathscr{T}, \mathscr{N}) = 0$; hence, $f(\mathscr{U}, \mathscr{V}) = A(f)$. The inequality $f(\mathscr{U}, \mathscr{V}) \leqq c(\mathscr{U}, \mathscr{V})$ is a consequence of the fact that $f(x, y) \leqq c(x, y)$ for each branch (x, y).

We are now ready to prove the theorem which justifies the saturated-path approach to maximal-flow problems:

THEOREM 2. A flow f in a network $(\mathscr{N}, c; \mathscr{T}, \mathscr{R})$ which saturates every path from $\mathscr{T}$ to $\mathscr{R}$ is maximal.

Proof: Let $\mathscr{U}$ be the subset of $\mathscr{N}$ consisting of all sources and all nodes x in $\mathscr{N} - \mathscr{T}$ such that there is a path from $\mathscr{T}$ to x unsaturated by f. Let $\mathscr{V} = \mathscr{N} - \mathscr{U}$. Since f saturates every path from $\mathscr{T}$ to $\mathscr{R}$, it follows that $\mathscr{R} \subset \mathscr{V}$ and hence that $(\mathscr{U}, \mathscr{V})$ is a cut. Hence, Theorem 1 tells us that $A(g) = g(\mathscr{U}, \mathscr{V}) \leqq c(\mathscr{U}, \mathscr{V})$ for each flow g in $(\mathscr{N}, c; \mathscr{T}, \mathscr{R})$. If we can show that $f(\mathscr{U}, \mathscr{V}) = c(\mathscr{U}, \mathscr{V})$, then we shall have $A(f) \geqq A(g)$ for each flow g and, consequently, f will be maximal.

To this end, assume the contrary: $f(\mathscr{U}, \mathscr{V}) < c(\mathscr{U}, \mathscr{V})$. Then there must be a branch (x, y) with x in $\mathscr{U}$ and y in $\mathscr{V}$ for which $f(x, y) < c(x, y)$. If x is a source, then (x, y) is a path from $\mathscr{T}$ to y unsaturated by f. The existence of such a path implies $y \in \mathscr{U}$, in contradiction to $y \in \mathscr{V}$ and $\mathscr{U} \cap \mathscr{V} = \phi$. If x is not a source, then there is a path $(x_1, x_2, \ldots, x_{k-1}, x)$ from $\mathscr{T}$ to x which is unsaturated by f. Each of the nodes $x_1, \ldots, x_{k-1}$ obviously belongs to $\mathscr{U}$ and hence $x_i \neq y$ for each $i = 1, \ldots, k - 1$. Consequently, adjoining the branch (x, y) to this path produces a path from $\mathscr{T}$ to y unsaturated by f. Again, this implies $y \in \mathscr{U}$, and we have a contradiction. Thus, the inequality $f(\mathscr{U}, \mathscr{V}) < c(\mathscr{U}, \mathscr{V})$ cannot hold, and we must have $f(\mathscr{U}, \mathscr{V}) = c(\mathscr{U}, \mathscr{V})$.

As our intuition would lead us to suspect, the converse of Theorem 2 also holds:

THEOREM 3. A maximal flow f in a network $(\mathscr{N}, c; \mathscr{T}, \mathscr{R})$ saturates every path from $\mathscr{T}$ to $\mathscr{R}$.

Proof: It is sufficient to prove that a flow which fails to saturate every path from $\mathscr{T}$ to $\mathscr{R}$ is not maximal. Let f be such a flow. Then there is a path $(x_1, x_2, \ldots, x_k)$ with $x_1 \in \mathscr{T}$, $x_k \in \mathscr{R}$, and $x_i \in \mathscr{N} - (\mathscr{T} \cup \mathscr{R})$ for $1 < i < k$ which is not saturated by f. This means that $f(x_i, x_{i+1}) < c(x_i, x_{i+1})$ for each $i = 1, \ldots, k - 1$. Let d be the smallest of the positive integers $c(x_i, x_{i+1}) - f(x_i, x_{i+1})$ $(i = 1, \ldots, k - 1)$. We define a function f_1 on $\mathscr{N} \times \mathscr{N}$ by putting $f_1(x_i, x_{i+1}) = f(x_i, x_{i+1}) + d$ and $f_1(x_{i+1}, x_i) = f(x_{i+1}, x_i) - d$ for each $i = 1, \ldots, k - 1$, and letting $f_1(x, y) = f(x, y)$ for each other branch (x, y). It may easily be verified that f_1 satisfies the requirements of Definition 4 and hence is a flow. Now $f_1(x_1, x_2) = f(x_1, x_2) + d$ and $f_1(x, y) = f(x, y)$ for each branch (x, y) other than (x_1, x_2) for which $x \in \mathscr{T}$. Hence, $A(f_1) = A(f) + d > A(f)$, which shows that f is not maximal and completes the proof.

Combining the results of Theorems 2 and 3, we can say that a flow f in a network $(\mathscr{N}, c; \mathscr{T}, \mathscr{R})$ is maximal if, and only if, f saturates every path from $\mathscr{T}$ to $\mathscr{R}$. Using Theorem 1 and the construction employed in the proof of Theorem 2, we obtain a criterion for maximality in terms of cuts as follows:

THEOREM 4. A flow f in a network $(\mathscr{N}, c; \mathscr{T}, \mathscr{R})$ is maximal if, and only if, there is a cut $(\mathscr{U}, \mathscr{V})$ in the network such that $A(f) = c(\mathscr{U}, \mathscr{V})$.

We leave the details of the proof to the student (Exercise 5 at the end of this section).

A cut in a network $(\mathscr{N}, c; \mathscr{T}, \mathscr{R})$ whose capacity is less than, or equal to, the capacity of any other cut is said to be a *minimal* cut. The following theorem, known as the *max-flow min-cut* theorem, is an immediate consequence of the preceding results:

THEOREM 5. In a network $(\mathscr{N}, c; \mathscr{T}, \mathscr{R})$ the value of a maximal flow equals the capacity of a minimal cut.

Before proceeding to describe the solution of the maximal-flow problem based on the preceding results, we wish to show that it is sufficient to consider networks having exactly one source and one sink. Consider a network $(\mathscr{N}, c; \mathscr{T}, \mathscr{R})$ with sources and sinks. Adjoin to the set $\mathscr{N}$ of nodes two new nodes T and R, and let $\mathscr{N}^* = \mathscr{N} \cup \{T, R\}$ (see Fig. 28). We wish to define a capacity function c^* on $\mathscr{N}^* \times \mathscr{N}^*$ so that a network $(\mathscr{N}^*, c^*)$ is

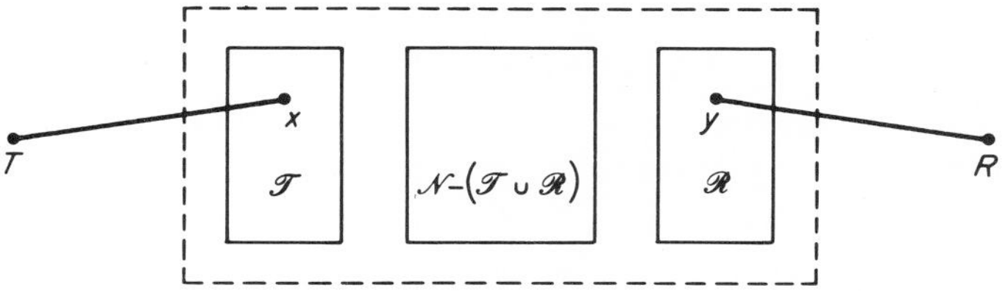

Figure 28

obtained in which T is the only source and R is the only sink. Also, we wish to be able to find a maximal flow in $(\mathscr{N}, c; \mathscr{T}, \mathscr{R})$ by finding a maximal flow in $(\mathscr{N}^*, c^*; T, R)$. In defining c^*, we think intuitively of T as being a sort of "master source" from which each of the original sources in $\mathscr{T}$ is supplied, and we think of R as an "ultimate sink" which is supplied from the original sinks in $\mathscr{R}$. For $x \in \mathscr{T}$, we define $c^*(T, x) = c(x, \mathscr{N})$, since we wish to be able to send as much into x as could possibly be sent out. Similarly, for $y \in \mathscr{R}$, we define $c^*(y, R) = c(\mathscr{N}, y)$, since we wish to be able to send as much out of y as could possibly be sent in. For nodes w and z, both in $\mathscr{N}$, we define $c^*(w, z) = c(w, z)$; i.e., we do not change capacities already defined. Finally, we define $c^*(w, z) = 0$ for each branch (w, z) of $\mathscr{N}^* \times \mathscr{N}^*$ which has not already been assigned a capacity by the above definitions. It is easily seen that T is the only source and R the only sink in the network thus defined.

Now we wish to show that a maximal flow in $(\mathscr{N}, c; \mathscr{T}, \mathscr{R})$ can be determined from a maximal flow in $(\mathscr{N}^*, c^*; T, R)$. Let f^* be a maximal flow in $(\mathscr{N}^*, c^*; T, R)$. Intuitively, we might expect that, if we consider only the values that f^* assigns to the branches of $(\mathscr{N}, c; \mathscr{T}, \mathscr{R})$, this would determine a maximal flow f in $(\mathscr{N}, c; \mathscr{T}, \mathscr{R})$. Thus, we are led to define f on $\mathscr{N} \times \mathscr{N}$ by the rule $f(w, z) = f^*(w, z)$ for each w and z in $\mathscr{N}$. This function f is called the *restriction of f^* to $\mathscr{N} \times \mathscr{N}$*. It is easy to verify that f satisfies the requirements of Definition 4 and hence is a flow.

In order to establish that f is maximal, we consider an arbitrary flow g in $(\mathscr{N}, c; \mathscr{T}, \mathscr{R})$ and prove that $A(f) \geqq A(g)$. We have, by definition, $A(f^*) = f^*(T, \mathscr{N}^*) = f^*(T, \mathscr{T}) + f^*(T, \mathscr{N}^* - \mathscr{T})$. Now $c^*(T, x) = c^*(x, T) = 0$ for each x in $\mathscr{N}^* - \mathscr{T}$, from which it follows that $f^*(T, x) = 0$ for each x in $\mathscr{N}^* - \mathscr{T}$. Hence, $f^*(T, \mathscr{N}^* - \mathscr{T}) = 0$, and we have

$A(f^*) = f^*(T, \mathscr{T})$. Using property 1, we have $0 = f^*(\mathscr{T}, \mathscr{N}^*) = f^*(\mathscr{T}, T) + f^*(\mathscr{T}, R) + f^*(\mathscr{T}, \mathscr{N})$. But $f^*(\mathscr{T}, R) = 0$ and $f^*(\mathscr{T}, \mathscr{N}) = f(\mathscr{T}, \mathscr{N}) = A(f)$. Hence, $0 = A(f) - f^*(T, \mathscr{T}) = A(f) - A(f^*)$, or $A(f) = A(f^*)$.

Next, we can obtain from g a flow g^* in $(\mathscr{N}^*, c^*; T, R)$ in much the same way that c^* was obtained from c. To be exact, we define g^* as follows: $g^*(T, x) = -g^*(x, T) = g(x, \mathscr{N})$ for each x in $\mathscr{T}$; $g^*(y, R) = -g^*(R, y) = g(\mathscr{N}, y)$ for each y in $\mathscr{R}$; $g^*(w, z) = g(w, z)$ for each w and z in $\mathscr{N}$; and $g^*(w, z) = 0$ for each other branch (w, z) in $\mathscr{N}^* \times \mathscr{N}^*$. It is easy to verify that g^* is actually a flow in $(\mathscr{N}^*, c^*; T, R)$ and that g is the restriction of g^* to $\mathscr{N} \times \mathscr{N}$. Hence, the argument in the preceding paragraph establishes that $A(g) = A(g^*)$. The maximality of f^* now implies that $A(f) = A(f^*) \geqq A(g^*) = A(g)$, which proves that f is a maximal flow in $(\mathscr{N}, c; \mathscr{T}, \mathscr{R})$.

Similarly, if we start with a maximal flow f in $(\mathscr{N}, c; \mathscr{T}, \mathscr{R})$, we can construct a flow f^* in $(\mathscr{N}^*, c^*; T, R)$ such that f is the restriction of f^* to $\mathscr{N} \times \mathscr{N}$ and f^* is maximal. Hence, the maximal flow problem in a given network $(\mathscr{N}, c; \mathscr{T}, \mathscr{R})$ is equivalent to the maximal-flow problem in the related network $(\mathscr{N}^*, c^*; T, R)$.

Without loss of generality, then, we can restrict our attention to networks having a single source and a single sink. We shall next describe a systematic procedure for solving maximal-flow problems in such networks. It is essentially the same as the method employed in the example, but with modifications imposed by our definition of flow and simplifications brought about by the use of matrix representations.

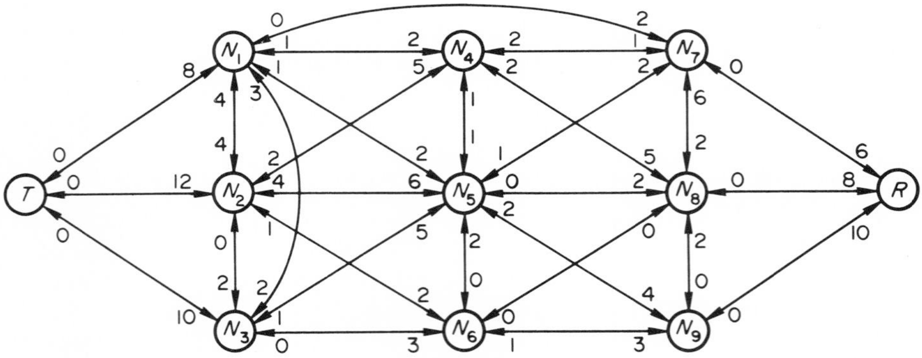

Figure 29

We start with a given network $(\mathscr{N}, c; T, R)$. This network uniquely determines, and is determined by, its *capacity tableau*. This is a square array whose rows and columns are labeled with the names of the nodes. In the *cell* occupying the intersection of the row labeled x and the column labeled y appears the number $c(x, y)$, the capacity of branch (x, y). As an illustration, consider the network $(\mathscr{N}, c; T, R)$ shown in Fig. 29. The capacity tableau for this network is shown in Fig. 30. Zeros are not entered, so that each empty cell corresponds to a branch of zero capacity. The first step in the process is to find a path of positive capacity from T to R. This can be done directly from the capacity tableau as follows: Look at row T. Select a column, say N_{i_1}, such that the entry in row T, column N_{i_1}, is positive. Look at row N_{i_1}. Select a column, say N_{i_2}, such that the entry in row N_{i_1}, column N_{i_2},

	T	N_1	N_2	N_3	N_4	N_5	N_6	N_7	N_8	N_9	R
T		8 ✓	12	10							
N_1			4 ✓	2	2	2		2			
N_2		4		2	5	6 ✓	2				
N_3		3				5	3				
N_4		1	2			1		1	5		
N_5		1	4	1	1			2	2	4 ✓	
N_6			1			2				3	
N_7					2	1			2		6
N_8					2			6			8
N_9						2	1		2		10 ✓
R											

Figure 30

is positive and $i_2 \neq i_1$. Look at row N_{i_2}. Select a column, say N_{i_3}, such that the entry in row N_{i_2}, column N_{i_3}, is positive, $i_3 \neq i_2$, and $i_3 \neq i_1$. Continue in this way, if possible, until a row N_{i_k} is reached which has the property that the entry in row N_{i_k}, column R, is positive. Then the path $(T, N_{i_1}, N_{i_2}, \ldots, N_{i_k}, R)$ has positive capacity. Of course, one may make several false starts before a path of positive capacity is found, but, unless the zero flow is maximal, there will have to be at least one such path from T to R and it will be discovered after a finite number of trials. In Fig. 30, for example, the cells which are checked correspond to the branches of the path $(T, N_1, N_2, N_5, N_9, R)$ which has capacity 4.

Suppose, in the general case, that a path $P_1 = (T, N_{i_1}, \ldots, N_{i_k}, R)$ of positive capacity q_1 has been found. Then a flow f_1 in $(\mathcal{N}, c; T, R)$ may be defined as follows: Let $f_1(T, N_{i_1}) = f_1(N_{i_1}, N_{i_2}) = \cdots = f_1(N_{i_k}, R) = q_1$,

$f_1(N_{i_1}, T) = f_1(N_{i_2}, N_{i_1}) = \cdots = f_1(R, N_{i_k}) = -q_1$, and $f_1(x, y) = 0$ for each other branch (x, y). (We leave to the reader the proof that f_1 is actually a flow.) The number q_1 is entered in each of the cells (T, N_{i_1}), (N_{i_1}, N_{i_2}), $\ldots$, (N_{i_k}, R) and $-q_1$ is placed in each of the cells (N_{i_1}, T), (N_{i_2}, N_{i_1}), $\ldots$, (R, N_{i_k}). No entry in a cell means zero flow in the corresponding branch. The resulting tableau is called a *flow-capacity tableau.* Figure 31 shows the flow-capacity tableau corresponding to the path $(T, N_1, N_2, N_5, N_9, R)$ in the example.

	T	N_1	N_2	N_3	N_4	N_5	N_6	N_7	N_8	N_9	R
T		[8] 4	[12]	[10]							
N_1	-4		[4] 4	[2]	[2]	[2]		[2]			
N_2		[4] -4		[2]	[5]	[6] 4	[2]				
N_3		[3]				[5]	[3]				
N_4		[1]	[2]			[1]		[1]	[5]		
N_5		[1]	[4] -4	[1]	[1]			[2]	[2]	[4] 4	
N_6			[1]			[2]				[3]	
N_7					[2]	[1]			[2]		[6]
N_8					[2]			[6]			[8]
N_9						[2] -4	[1]		[2]		[10] 4
R										-4	

Figure 31

The next step is to subtract the flow number in each cell from the capacity number and assign these differences to the branches as new capacities. In other words, we form the capacity tableau for a network $(\mathcal{N}, c_1; T, R)$, where $c_1(x, y) = c(x, y) - f_1(x, y)$ for each branch (x, y). Figure 32 shows this tableau for the example. The above steps are now repeated, starting with this new capacity tableau. That is, a path P_2 of positive capacity q_2 from T to R is found, and a flow f_2 is defined which assigns q_2 to each branch of P_2, $-q_2$ to each oppositely directed branch, and zero to each other branch. Then a new capacity function c_2 is defined by $c_2(x, y) = c_1(x, y) - f_2(x, y)$, and the corresponding capacity tableau for $(\mathcal{N}, c_2; T, R)$ is formed. The process continues in this way until a capacity tableau is obtained in which there is no path of positive capacity from T to R. (We shall soon see that this must eventually occur.)

	T	N_1	N_2	N_3	N_4	N_5	N_6	N_7	N_8	N_9	R
T		4	12	10							
N_1	4			2	2	2		2			
N_2		8		2	5	2		2			
N_3		3				5	3				
N_4		1	2			1		1	5		
N_5		1	8	1	1			2	2		
N_6			1			2				3	
N_7					2	1			2		6
N_8					2			6			8
N_9						6	1		2		6
R										9	

Figure 32

Let us consider the stage of the process at which we have just obtained, say, the kth capacity tableau. At this point we have defined k capacity functions $c_1, \ldots, c_k$ (in addition to the original capacity function c) and k flows $f_1, \ldots, f_k$, each f_i being a flow of positive amount q_i in $(\mathscr{N}, c; T, R)$. We wish now to show that the function $f = f_1 + f_2 + \cdots + f_k$ is a flow in the original network $(\mathscr{N}, c; T, R)$ and that $A(f) = A(f_1) + A(f_2) + \cdots + A(f_k)$. The flows and capacities are related by the following equations:

$$c_1 = c - f_1, \qquad c_2 = c_1 - f_2, \ldots, c_k = c_{k-1} - f_k.$$

Solving these equations for $f_1, f_2, \ldots, f_k$ and adding the results, we obtain

$$\begin{aligned} f &= f_1 + f_2 + \cdots + f_k \\ &= (c - c_1) + (c_1 - c_2) + \cdots + (c_{k-1} - c_k) = c - c_k. \end{aligned}$$

This means that $f(x, y) = c(x, y) - c_k(x, y) \leqq c(x, y)$ for each branch (x, y) and, hence, that f satisfies condition (i) of Definition 4. Condition (ii) is verified as follows, using the fact that each f_i satisfies it:

$$f(x, y) = \sum_{i=1}^{k} f_i(x, y) = \sum_{i=1}^{k} (-f_i(y, x)) = -\sum_{i=1}^{k} f_i(y, x) = -f(y, x).$$

To verify condition (iii), let x be any node other than T or R. Then

$$f(x, \mathcal{N}) = \sum_{i=1}^{k} f_i(x, \mathcal{N}) = \sum_{i=1}^{k} f_i(\mathcal{N}, x) = f(\mathcal{N}, x).$$

Since each f_i is integer valued, so is f, and hence we have completely verified that f is a flow in $(\mathcal{N}, c; T, R)$. The amount of f is given by

$$A(f) = f(T, \mathcal{N}) = \sum_{i=1}^{k} f_i(T, \mathcal{N}) = \sum_{i=1}^{k} A(f_i),$$

as we wished to show.

Since $A(f_i) > 0$ for each i and flows are integer-valued functions, it follows that $A(f_i) \geqq 1$ for each i and hence that $A(f) \geqq k$, where $f = f_1 + \cdots + f_k$, as above. If the process described above could continue indefinitely, then we could obtain flows in $(\mathcal{N}, c; T, R)$ of arbitrarily large amounts. But this is contrary to the fact that $A(f) \leqq c(T, \mathcal{N})$ for each flow f in $(\mathcal{N}, c; T, R)$. Thus the process must eventually terminate; i.e., we must eventually determine a capacity function c_k such that, in the network $(\mathcal{N}, c_k; T, R)$, there is no path of positive capacity from T to R. Let us now show that

	T	N_1	N_2	N_3	N_4	N_5	N_6	N_7	N_8	N_9	R
T		[8] 7	[12] 4	[10] 8							
N_1	-7		[4] 4	[2]	[2] 1	[2]		[2] 2			
N_2	-4	[4] -4		[2]	[5] 5	[6] 3	[2]				
N_3	-8	[3]				[5] 5	[3] 3				
N_4		[1] -1	[2] -5			[1]		[1] 1	[5] 5		
N_5		[1]	[4] -3	[1] -5	[1]			[2] 2	[2] 2	[4] 4	
N_6			[1]			[2]				[3] 3	
N_7		-2			[2] -1	[1] -2			[2]		[6] 5
N_8					[2] -5	-2		[6]			[8] 7
N_9						[2] -4	[1] -3		[2]		[10] 7
R								-5	-7	-7	

Figure 33

the combined flow $f = f_1 + \cdots + f_k$ at such a stage is a maximal flow in $(\mathcal{N}, c; T, R)$. Consider an arbitrary path from T to R. Since the path has zero capacity relative to the capacity function c_k, it contains at least one branch (x, y) for which $c_k(x, y) = 0$. But, as we deduced earlier, the functions f, c, and c_k are related by the equation $f = c - c_k$. Hence, $f(x, y) = c(x, y)$, which means that the path is saturated by f. Since f saturates each path from T to R, f is maximal.

We leave it to the student to complete the application of this process to the network of Fig. 29. For relatively small problems such as this which are to be done with pencil and paper, a slight variation on the procedure is suggested: Make a single capacity tableau with large enough cells so that several flow numbers may be entered in each cell. Each time a branch is used, the new flow in the branch is simply added to the previous ones. Instead of subtracting to form new capacities, simply make sure at each stage that the sum of the flow numbers in each cell does not exceed the capacity. One maximal flow in the network of Fig. 29 is shown in the flow-capacity tableau of Fig. 33. Call this flow f. It is instructive to form, for this example, the cut $(\mathcal{U}, \mathcal{V})$ used in the proof of Theorem 2. The set $\mathcal{U}$, consisting of T and all nodes which can be reached by a path unsaturated by f, is composed of T, N_1, N_2, N_3, N_4, N_5, and N_6. Hence, $\mathcal{V}$ contains the remaining nodes N_7, N_8, N_9, and R. Computing the capacity of this cut, we obtain $c(\mathcal{U}, \mathcal{V}) = c(N_1, N_7) + c(N_4, N_7) + c(N_4, N_8) + c(N_5, N_7) + c(N_5, N_8) + c(N_5, N_9) + c(N_6, N_9) = 19 = A(f)$. The equality $c(\mathcal{U}, \mathcal{V}) = A(f)$ implies, according to Theorem 4, that f is maximal. Also, of course, $(\mathcal{U}, \mathcal{V})$ is a minimal cut.

EXERCISES

1. Suppose x and y are either both sources or both sinks in a network $(\mathcal{N}, c; \mathcal{T}, \mathcal{R})$. Prove from Definition 2 that $c(x, y) = 0$.
2. Prove properties 1, 2, and 3 from Definition 4.
3. In Definition 5, the amount of a flow was defined as the total flow out of the sources. Prove that this is the same as the total flow into the sinks. That is, if f is a flow in $(\mathcal{N}, c; \mathcal{T}, \mathcal{R})$, prove that $A(f) = f(\mathcal{N}, \mathcal{R})$.
Suggestion: Let $\mathcal{N}' = \mathcal{N} - (\mathcal{T} \cup \mathcal{R})$. Use property 1 to show that $f(\mathcal{N}', \mathcal{N}) = 0$ and hence that $f(\mathcal{T}, \mathcal{N}) - f(\mathcal{N}, \mathcal{R}) = f(\mathcal{N}, \mathcal{N}) = 0$.
4. In the network of Fig. 25, let $\mathcal{U} = \{N_1, N_2, N_3, N_5\}$ and $\mathcal{V} = \{N_4, N_6, N_7, N_8, N_9, N_{10}\}$. Find the capacity of the cut $(\mathcal{U}, \mathcal{V})$.
5. Prove Theorem 4.
6. For each of the following networks, form the capacity tableau, find a maximal flow by the methods of this section, and find the cut $(\mathcal{U}, \mathcal{V})$ used in the proof of Theorem 2: (a) the network of the example of the preceding section;

(b) the network of Exercise 1 of the preceding section; (c) the network of Exercise 2 of the preceding section; (d) the network of Fig. 25.

7. Find a maximal flow and the associated minimal cut for the network whose capacity matrix appears here.

	T	N_1	N_2	N_3	N_4	N_5	R
T		7	5	14	2		
N_1			2	4	1		8
N_2		10			3	2	4
N_3		7	7			6	4
N_4		1	2	3		12	3
N_5		6	4		4		9
R							

8. Follow the directions of Exercise 7 for the capacity matrix given here.

	T	N_1	N_2	N_3	N_4	N_5	N_6	R
T		12	8	10	3			
N_1			3	5		8		
N_2		10		2		4	2	
N_3		5	2		7	3		
N_4				4		1	2	15
N_5		6		2			10	7
N_6					9			10
R								

4-3. *THE TRANSSHIPMENT PROBLEM.*

First we shall state a physical problem whose mathematical formulation leads to the transshipment problem. We start with the same basic situation as in the transportation problem. A fixed time interval is considered. Known quantities of some product are stored in m warehouses, and there are n retail outlets, each of which requires a certain known amount of the product during the given time interval. It is assumed that the supplies and demands are expressed in integral numbers of units of some sort. It is possible to transport the product along various routes from the warehouses to the retail outlets, some shipments possibly being made via intermediate warehouses and/or retail outlets. We are given the maximum number of units of the product which can be shipped from one point (warehouse or retail outlet) to another during the fixed period of time and seek to determine if it is possible to meet all demands without exceeding any supplies.

To describe a mathematical model which is rather naturally suggested by this problem, we begin with a network $(\mathscr{N}, c)$. The set of nodes, $\mathscr{N}$, is divided into two classes $\mathscr{O}$ and $\mathscr{D}$ (Fig. 34), called the *origins* and *destinations*, respectively, corresponding to the warehouses and retail outlets. For x and y in $\mathscr{N}$, $c(x, y)$ is a nonnegative integer representing the maximum number of units which can be shipped from the point corresponding to x to the point corresponding to y during the given time interval. Note that this network need not have either sources or sinks.

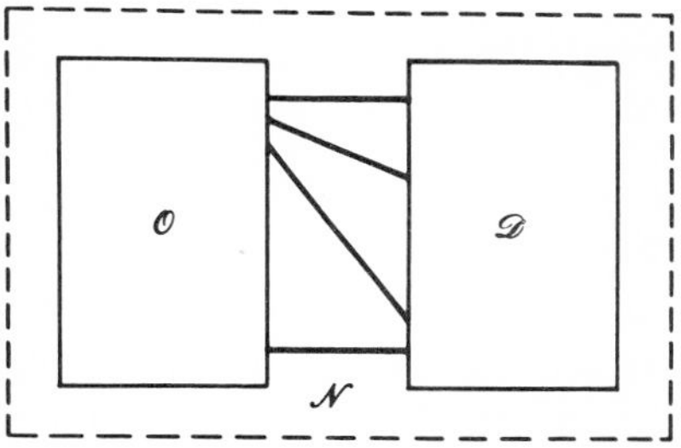

Figure 34

In order to account for the supplies and demands, we must incorporate into our model a feature not present in the networks we have considered so far. We assume the existence of positive integer-valued functions s and d defined on $\mathscr{O}$ and $\mathscr{D}$, respectively. For x in $\mathscr{O}$, $s(x)$ represents the number of units of the product stored at the warehouse corresponding to x. For y in $\mathscr{D}$, $d(y)$ represents the number of units of the product required during the given time period at the retail outlet corresponding to y.

At this point we introduce some further convenient notation due to Gale. If $\mathscr{N}$ is a finite set, $\mathscr{A}$ is a subset of $\mathscr{N}$, and h is a real-valued function defined on $\mathscr{A}$, we define

$$h(\mathscr{A}) = \sum_{x \in \mathscr{A}} h(x).$$

In case $\mathscr{A}$ is empty, we agree that $h(\mathscr{A}) = 0$. In our discussions, h will be either the supply function s or the demand function d. For example, $s(\mathscr{O})$ is the sum of all supplies, and $d(\mathscr{D})$ is the sum of all demands. For still more brevity, we shall write $S = s(\mathscr{O})$ and $D = d(\mathscr{D})$.

The objective in the physical problem is to find, if possible, a shipping schedule meeting all the demands without exceeding any supplies. In the mathematical problem, then, we seek an integer-valued function f defined on $\mathscr{N} \times \mathscr{N}$ such that (i) $0 \leqq f(x, \mathscr{N}) \leqq s(x)$ for each x in $\mathscr{O}$, (ii) $f(\mathscr{N}, y) = d(y)$ for each y in $\mathscr{D}$, (iii) $f(x, y) \leqq c(x, y)$ for each (x, y) in $\mathscr{N} \times \mathscr{N}$, and (iv)

$f(y, x) = -f(x, y)$ for each (x, y) in $\mathcal{N} \times \mathcal{N}$. Such a function f will be called a *feasible function* for the transshipment problem and the problem will be called *feasible* if, and only if, such a function exists. Notice that a feasible function need not be a flow in $(\mathcal{N}, c)$. For, if f satisfies (ii) and f is a flow, then we must have $d(y) = f(\mathcal{N}, y) = 0$ for each y in $\mathcal{D}$ which is not a sink.

Although the transshipment problem itself is not a maximal-flow problem, there is associated with each transshipment problem a maximal-flow problem and the two problems are equivalent in a certain sense. Suppose we start with a transshipment problem determined by a network $(\mathcal{N}, c)$, two disjoint sets $\mathcal{O}$ and $\mathcal{D}$ such that $\mathcal{N} = \mathcal{O} \cup \mathcal{D}$, and two positive integer-valued functions s and d defined on $\mathcal{O}$ and $\mathcal{D}$, respectively. In order to obtain the related maximal-flow problem, we adjoin to $\mathcal{N}$ two new nodes T and R (see Fig. 35), which will be the source and sink, respectively, in the new network. Let $\mathcal{N}^*$ denote the enlarged set of nodes, and define a capacity function c^* on $\mathcal{N}^* \times \mathcal{N}^*$ as follows: Let $c^*(T, x) = s(x)$ for each origin x, $c^*(y, R) = d(y)$ for each destination y, $c^*(w, z) = c(w, z)$ for each w and z in $\mathcal{N}$, and let c^* be zero on each other branch in $\mathcal{N}^* \times \mathcal{N}^*$. Since the supply and demand functions assume only positive values, it is clear that T is the only source, R is the only sink, and, hence, that we have defined a network $(\mathcal{N}^*, c^*; T, R)$. Physically, T might be considered a factory from which the warehouses are supplied, while R might be thought of as the totality of all consumers who obtain the product from the retail outlets.

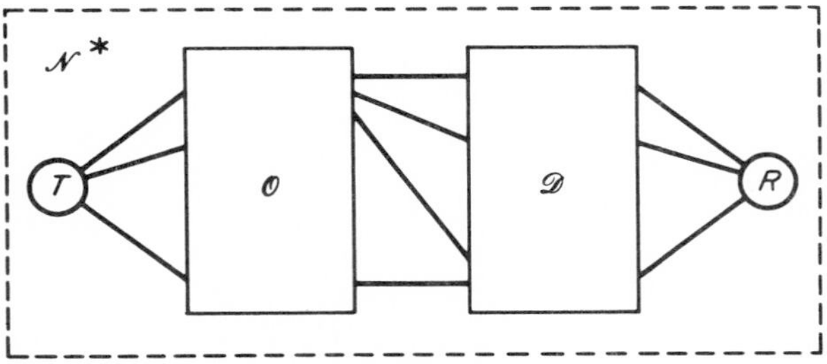

Figure 35

In order to investigate the sense in which the maximal-flow problem in $(\mathcal{N}^*, c^*; T, R)$ is equivalent to the transshipment problem, we start by assuming that a feasible function f for the transshipment problem is known. A related flow f^* in $(\mathcal{N}^*, c^*; T, R)$ may be defined as follows: Let $f^*(x, y) = f(x, y)$ for each x and y in $\mathcal{N}$, $f^*(T, x) = -f^*(x, T) = f(x, \mathcal{N})$ for each x in $\mathcal{O}$, $f^*(y, R) = -f^*(R, y) = f(\mathcal{N}, y)$ for each y in $\mathcal{D}$, and let f^* be zero on each other branch in $\mathcal{N}^* \times \mathcal{N}^*$. The proof that the function f^* so defined is actually a flow is left to the reader (see Exercise 5 at the end of this section). Assuming this result, we compute the amount $A(f^*)$ in two ways: By definition, $A(f^*) = f^*(T, \mathcal{N}^*)$, and by Exercise 2 of the preceding section, $A(f^*) = f^*(\mathcal{N}^*, R)$. The equalities and inequalities in the two lines below follow from the definition of f^* and from the feasibility of f:

$$(2) \qquad f^*(T, \mathcal{N}^*) = f^*(T, \mathcal{O}) = f(\mathcal{O}, \mathcal{N}) \leqq s(\mathcal{O}) = S,$$

$$(3) \qquad f^*(\mathcal{N}^*, R) = f^*(\mathcal{D}, R) = f(\mathcal{N}, \mathcal{D}) = d(\mathcal{D}) = D.$$

Hence, we have shown that, if the transshipment problem has a feasible function f, then there is a flow f^* in the related network $(\mathcal{N}^*, c^*; T, R)$ which satisfies

$$(4) \qquad D = A(f^*) \leqq S$$

and which has f as its restriction to $\mathcal{N} \times \mathcal{N}$. That f^* is a maximal flow in $(\mathcal{N}^*, c^*; T, R)$ follows from (4). For, if g^* is any flow in $(\mathcal{N}^*, c^*; T, R)$, we have $A(g^*) = g^*(\mathcal{D}, R) \leqq c^*(\mathcal{D}, R) = D = A(f^*)$. Also, it follows from (4), as well as being intuitively evident, that a *necessary* condition for feasibility of the transshipment problem is $D \leqq S$, i.e., the total demand does not exceed the total supply.

Now let us start over and assume that we have found a flow f^* in $(\mathcal{N}^*, c^*; T, R)$ satisfying (4). In particular, then, we are assuming $D \leqq S$. Can we now conclude that the transshipment problem is feasible? Let f be the restriction of f^* to $\mathcal{N} \times \mathcal{N}$. Then, for each x in $\mathcal{O}$ and each y in $\mathcal{D}$, we have

$$(5) \qquad f(x, \mathcal{N}) = f^*(x, \mathcal{N}^*) - f^*(x, T) - f^*(x, R) = f^*(T, x) \leqq s(x),$$

$$(6) \qquad f(\mathcal{N}, y) = f^*(\mathcal{N}^*, y) - f^*(T, y) - f^*(R, y) = f^*(y, R) = d(y).$$

Note that $f^*(T, x) \geqq 0$, since $f^*(T, x) = -f^*(x, T)$ and $f^*(x, T) \leqq c^*(x, T) = 0$. Hence, $f(x, \mathcal{N}) \geqq 0$. Thus, f satisfies requirements (i) and (ii) for a feasible function. That f also satisfies (iii) and (iv) follows from the fact that f^* is a flow. Hence the problem is feasible, and the restriction f of f^* to $\mathcal{N} \times \mathcal{N}$ is a feasible function.

Summarizing our results, then, we have shown that the transshipment problem determined by $(\mathcal{N}, c)$, $\mathcal{O}$, $\mathcal{D}$, s, and d is feasible if, and only if, there is a flow f^* in the related network $(\mathcal{N}^*, c^*; T, R)$ satisfying (4). Before proceeding to Gale's Feasibility Theorem, which is the main result of this section, let us consider some examples.

Example 1. Suppose we have a transshipment problem in which there are three origins with supplies of 30, 25, and 40 units and four destinations with demands of 35, 30, 20, and 15 units. Immediately we see that the problem is not feasible, since $S = 95 < 100 = D$.

Example 2. Fig. 36 shows the maximal-flow network determined by a transshipment problem with three origins O_1, O_2, and O_3 and three destinations D_1, D_2, and D_3. The supplies are 20, 12, and 8, while the demands are 15, 12, and 13, respectively. A maximal flow f^* in this network may be found by the methods of the previous section. The details of this solution are left to the student (see Exercise 1 at the end of this section), but the flow-capacity matrix for a maximal flow f^* is shown in Fig. 37. Since $A(f^*) = 40 = D = S$, this transshipment problem is feasible. The subtableau of Fig. 37 obtained by eliminating the rows and columns corresponding to T and R displays the feasible function f which is the restriction of f^* to $\mathcal{N} \times \mathcal{N}$.

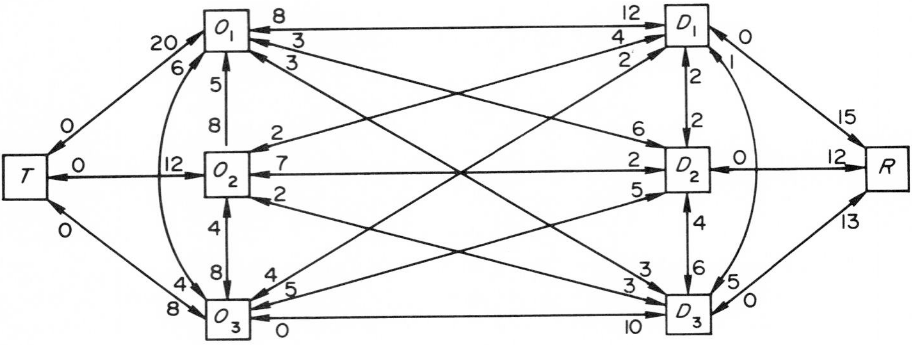

Figure 36

	T	O_1	O_2	O_3	D_1	D_2	D_3	R
T		[20] 20	[12] 12	[8] 8				
O_1	−20		[8]	[4]	[12] 12	[6] 6	[3] 2	
O_2	−12	[5]		[8] 5	[4] 3	[2] 1	[3] 3	
O_3	−8	[6]	[4] −5		[2]	[5] 5	[10] 8	
D_1		[8] −12	[2] −3	[4]		[2]	[5]	[15] 15
D_2		[3] −6	[7] −1	[5] −5	[2]		[6]	[12] 12
D_3		[3] −2	[2] −3	−8	[1]	[4]		[13] 13 .
R					−15	−12	−13	

Figure 37

This feasible function is not the only one possible, nor would we expect it to be, since maximal flows in general are not unique.

The transshipment problem which arises in connection with the transportation problem is of a special type which is illustrated in the next example:

Example 3. We consider here a transshipment problem in which no shipments are permitted from one origin to another or from one destination to another; i.e., $c(\mathcal{O}, \mathcal{O}) = c(\mathcal{D}, \mathcal{D}) = 0$. The following tableau displays all the necessary information:

	D_1		D_2		D_3		D_4		
O_1	10	8	42	36	5	7	4	11	50
O_2	9	3	8	2	9	14	18	10	32
O_3	5	2	30	40	6	6	38	7	18
	16		20		16		48		

In the cell occupying row i and column j, the number in the upper left-hand corner is $c(O_i, D_j)$ and the number in the upper right-hand corner is $c(D_j, O_i)$. The numbers at the extreme right of the tableau are the supplies, while those at the bottom are the demands. Thus $c(O_1, D_1) = 10$, $c(D_1, O_1) = 8$, $s(O_1) = 50$, and so on. To solve this problem, we find a maximal flow f in the related network, as in the preceding example. However, each path of positive capacity from T to R must proceed alternately from origin to destination to origin, and so on, and this fact makes possible certain computational conveniences. Instead of forming the 9 by 9 capacity matrix for the related maximal-flow problem, we can perform the necessary computations in the tableau above. Divide each cell into two parts by a vertical line. Determine a succession of flows $f_1, f_2, \ldots$, and, for each k, enter the number $f_k(O_i, D_j)$ in the left-hand portion of cell (i, j) and $f_k(D_j, O_i) = -f_k(O_i, D_j)$ in the right-hand portion. Note that the supplies are the initial capacities from T to the origins and the demands are the initial capacities from the destinations to R. Thus, for example, (T, O_1, D_1, R) is a path of capacity 10. Letting f_1 be the flow which sends 10 units along this path, we enter 10 in the left-hand side of cell (1, 1) and -10 in the right-hand side. The capacity of each branch involved in this path is now changed by subtracting the flow through that branch from its initial capacity, but these changes need not be written in. They are simply kept in mind as the computation proceeds. For instance, the total flow at any stage in the branch (T, O_1) is the sum of the entries in the left-hand sides of the cells in row 1. When this sum reaches 50, the branch (T, O_1) is saturated. We can easily determine many "3-branch" paths, such as (T, O_1, D_2, R), (T, O_2, D_1, R), and so on. Entering the numbers representing the flows corresponding to several such paths, we obtain the following tableau:

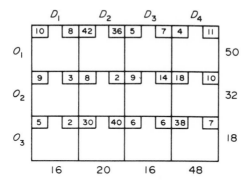

The check marks indicate that the branches (T, O_2), (T, O_3), (D_1, R), (D_2, R), and (D_3, R) are saturated. We have not yet satisfied the demand at D_4, nor used up the supply at O_1. Hence, either the transshipment problem is not feasible or else there is still at least one path of positive capacity from T to R. We seek such a path and find that $(T, O_1, D_2, O_3, D_4, R)$ has capacity 11.

	D_1		D_2		D_3		D_4		
O_1	[10] 10	[8] −10	[42] 20	[36] −20	[5] 5	[7] −5	[4] 4	[11] −4	50
O_2	[9] 6	[3] −6	[8]	[2]	[9] 9	[14] −9	[18] 17	[10] −17	32 ✓
O_3	[5]	[2]	[30]	[40]	[6] 2	[6] −2	[38] 16	[7] −16	18 ✓
	16 ✓		20 ✓		16 ✓		48		

	D_1		D_2		D_3		D_4		
O_1	[10] 10	[8] −10	[42] 20 11	[36] −20 −11	[5] 5	[7] −5	[4] 4	[11] −4	50 ✓
O_2	[9] 6	[3] −6	[8]	[2]	[9] 9	[14] −9	[18] 17	[10] −17	32 ✓
O_3	[5]	[2]	[30] −11	[40] 11	[6] 2	[6] −2	[38] 16 11	[7] −16 −11	18 ✓
	16 ✓		20 ✓		16 ✓		48 ✓		

Sending 11 units along this path and entering the corresponding numbers in the proper cells, we obtain the following tableau:
Since all demands are now satisfied, we have found a feasible function for the transshipment problem and the solution is complete.

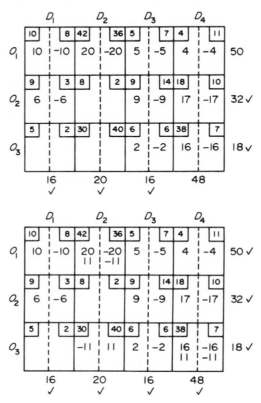

Example 4. In the network of Fig. 38, O_1, O_2, and O_3 are origins with supplies 6, 5, and 20, respectively, while D_1 and D_2 are destinations with demands 20 and 10. Although the sum of the supplies exceeds the sum of the demands, it is possible to see in another way, without actually finding a maximal flow in the related network, that this problem is not feasible. Let $\mathscr{M} = \{O_1, O_2, D_1\}$. In the set $\mathscr{M}$ there is an excess of demand over supply given by $20 - (6 + 5) = 9$. This excess demand can only be satisfied

by shipments originating outside of $\mathscr{M}$. But the sum $c(\mathscr{N} - \mathscr{M}, \mathscr{M})$ of the capacities of all branches leading into $\mathscr{M}$ from the outside is only 8, and, hence, it seems clear that the excess demand cannot possibly be satisfied.

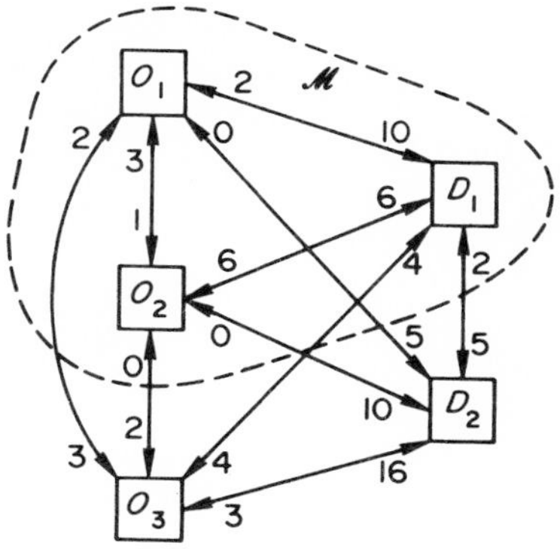

Figure 38

We conclude this section with the statement and proof of Gale's Feasibility Theorem for the transshipment problem, which justifies the reasoning used in Example 4 and which will be used in the next section in connection with the transportation problem.

THEOREM 6. Let $(\mathscr{N}, c)$ be a network with capacity. Let $\mathscr{O}$ and $\mathscr{D}$ be nonempty disjoint subsets of $\mathscr{N}$ such that $\mathscr{N} = \mathscr{O} \cup \mathscr{D}$. Let s and d be positive integer-valued functions defined on $\mathscr{O}$ and $\mathscr{D}$, respectively. Then the transshipment problem so determined, in which the nodes of $\mathscr{O}$ are the origins and those of $\mathscr{D}$, the destinations, is feasible if, and only if, for each subset $\mathscr{M}$ of $\mathscr{N}$ we have

$$d(\mathscr{M} \cap \mathscr{D}) - s(\mathscr{M} \cap \mathscr{O}) \leqq c(\mathscr{N} - \mathscr{M}, \mathscr{M}). \tag{7}$$

Proof: Suppose, first, that the problem is feasible, and let f be a feasible function. Let $\mathscr{M}$ be an arbitrary subset of $\mathscr{N}$. We must prove that (7) holds. Since f is a feasible function, we must have $d(y) = f(\mathscr{N}, y)$ for each y in $\mathscr{D}$ and hence $d(\mathscr{M} \cap \mathscr{D}) = f(\mathscr{N}, \mathscr{M} \cap \mathscr{D})$. Thinking of $\mathscr{N}$ as the union of the three disjoint sets $\mathscr{M} \cap \mathscr{O}$, $\mathscr{M} \cap \mathscr{D}$, and $\mathscr{N} - \mathscr{M}$ (Fig. 39), we can write $f(\mathscr{N}, \mathscr{M} \cap \mathscr{D}) = f(\mathscr{M} \cap \mathscr{O}, \mathscr{M} \cap \mathscr{D}) + f(\mathscr{M} \cap \mathscr{D}, \mathscr{M} \cap \mathscr{D}) + f(\mathscr{N} - \mathscr{M}, \mathscr{M} \cap \mathscr{D}) = f(\mathscr{M} \cap \mathscr{O}, \mathscr{M} \cap \mathscr{D}) + f(\mathscr{N} - \mathscr{M}, \mathscr{M} \cap \mathscr{D})$. Hence, we have

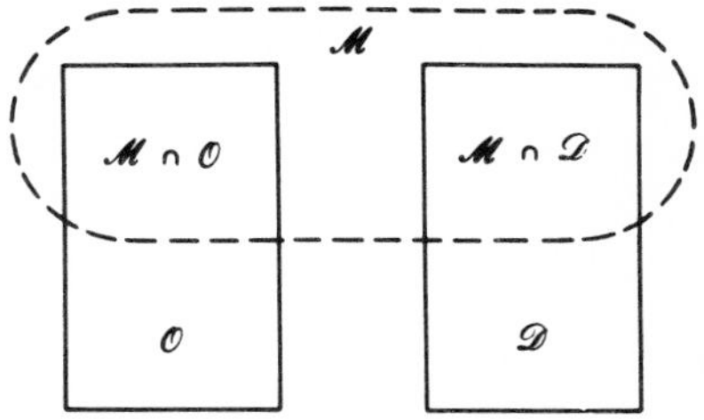

Figure 39

$$d(\mathscr{M} \cap \mathscr{D}) = f(\mathscr{M} \cap \mathscr{O}, \mathscr{M} \cap \mathscr{D}) + f(\mathscr{N} - \mathscr{M}, \mathscr{M} \cap \mathscr{D}). \tag{8}$$

Similarly, we have

$$s(\mathscr{M} \cap \mathscr{O}) \geqq f(\mathscr{M} \cap \mathscr{O}, \mathscr{N}) = f(\mathscr{M} \cap \mathscr{O}, \mathscr{M} \cap \mathscr{D}) + f(\mathscr{M} \cap \mathscr{O}, \mathscr{N} - \mathscr{M}),$$

from which it follows that

$$\begin{aligned} f(\mathscr{M} \cap \mathscr{O}, \mathscr{M} \cap \mathscr{D}) &\leqq s(\mathscr{M} \cap \mathscr{O}) - f(\mathscr{M} \cap \mathscr{O}, \mathscr{N} - \mathscr{M}) \\ &\leqq s(\mathscr{M} \cap \mathscr{O}) + f(\mathscr{N} - \mathscr{M}, \mathscr{M} \cap \mathscr{O}). \end{aligned} \tag{9}$$

Using (9) in (8), we obtain

$$d(\mathcal{M} \cap \mathcal{D}) \leqq s(\mathcal{M} \cap \mathcal{O}) + f(\mathcal{N} - \mathcal{M}, \mathcal{M} \cap \mathcal{O}) + f(\mathcal{N} - \mathcal{M}, \mathcal{M} \cap \mathcal{D})$$

or

$$d(\mathcal{M} \cap \mathcal{O}) - s(\mathcal{M} \cap \mathcal{O}) \leqq f(\mathcal{N} - \mathcal{M}, \mathcal{M}) \leqq c(\mathcal{N} - \mathcal{M}, \mathcal{M}),$$

which is the desired inequality (7).

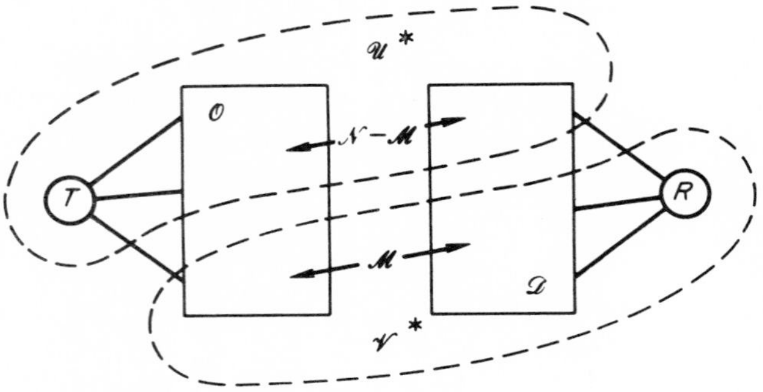

Figure 40

Now suppose that the transshipment problem is not feasible. We must show that a subset $\mathcal{M}$ of $\mathcal{N}$ exists for which (7) does not hold. Let f^* be a maximal flow in the related network $(\mathcal{N}^*, c^*; T, R)$. Then, from the results established earlier in this section, we know that $A(f^*) < D$. Hence, there is a cut $(\mathcal{U}^*, \mathcal{V}^*)$ in $(\mathcal{N}^*, c^*; T, R)$ such that $c^*(\mathcal{U}^*, \mathcal{V}^*) = A(f^*) < D$ (Fig. 40). Let $\mathcal{M} = \mathcal{V}^* \cap \mathcal{N} = \mathcal{V}^* - \{R\}$; then $\mathcal{N} - \mathcal{M} = \mathcal{U}^* \cap \mathcal{N} = \mathcal{U}^* - \{T\}$. We shall show that $\mathcal{M}$ is a set for which (7) fails to hold. From the definition of c^*, we have

$$\begin{aligned} c^*(\mathcal{U}^*, \mathcal{V}^*) &= c(\mathcal{N} - \mathcal{M}, \mathcal{M}) + c^*(T, \mathcal{M} \cap \mathcal{O}) + c^*[(\mathcal{N} - \mathcal{M}) \cap \mathcal{D}, R] \\ &= c(\mathcal{N} - \mathcal{M}, \mathcal{M}) + s(\mathcal{M} \cap \mathcal{O}) + d[(\mathcal{N} - \mathcal{M}) \cap \mathcal{D}] \\ &= c(\mathcal{N} - \mathcal{M}, \mathcal{M}) + s(\mathcal{M} \cap \mathcal{O}) + D - d(\mathcal{M} \cap \mathcal{D}). \end{aligned}$$

Hence,

$$c(\mathcal{N} - \mathcal{M}, \mathcal{M}) + s(\mathcal{M} \cap \mathcal{O}) + D - d(\mathcal{M} \cap \mathcal{D}) < D,$$

from which it follows that

$$c(\mathcal{N} - \mathcal{M}, \mathcal{M}) < d(\mathcal{M} \cap \mathcal{D}) - s(\mathcal{M} \cap \mathcal{O});$$

i.e., (7) does not hold for this set $\mathcal{M}$. This completes the proof of the Feasibility Theorem.

EXERCISES

1. Find a maximal flow in the network of Fig. 36, and thus obtain a feasible function for the transshipment problem of Example 2.
2. Find a maximal flow f^* in the network $(\mathcal{N}^*, c^*; T, R)$ associated with the transshipment problem of Example 4. Also find the minimal cut $(\mathcal{U}^*, \mathcal{V}^*)$ associated with f^*, and verify that the set $\mathcal{M} = \mathcal{V}^* \cap \mathcal{N}$ is indeed one which does not satisfy (7).

3. The tableau below shows the capacities in a transshipment problem. Find a feasible function or a set $\mathscr{M}$ for which (7) fails to hold if the supplies and demands are as follows:
(a) Supplies: 12, 30, 10, 8; demands: 28, 10, 7, 15.
(b) Supplies: 18, 19, 15, 8; demands: 28, 10, 12, 10.

	O_1	O_2	O_3	O_4	D_1	D_2	D_3	D_4
O_1					15			5
O_2	10			5	8	3	5	
O_3		8			5	2	15	7
O_4					5			4
D_1		10		5		3		
D_2							5	
D_3						7		3
D_4	8			5				

4. The tableaus below represent transshipment problems of the type illustrated in Example 3 in which no shipments are possible from origin to origin or from destination to destination. In each case, find either a feasible function or a set $\mathscr{M}$ for which (7) fails to hold.

	D_1	D_2	D_3	D_4	D_5	D_6	
O_1	6	4	2	8	3	5	22
O_2	3	2	4	2	4	4	17
O_3	3	7	3	5	1	6	13
O_4	5	8	2	3	6	1	18
	14	19	10	9	12	6	

(a)

	D_1		D_2		D_3		D_4		D_5		D_6		
O_1	8	10	3	7	4	4	2	3	1	1	2	6	12
O_2	2	3	1	4	1	4	3	1	5	2	3	5	15
O_3	4	2	2	6	2	3	1	3	8	4	5	1	20
O_4	5	6	4	1	8	3	1	2	1	5	3	3	13
	7		11		9		15		8		10		

(b)

	D_1		D_2		D_3		D_4		D_5		D_6		
O_1	2	3	4	4	3	2		6	10		4		15
O_2	3	2	4		7		8		4	6	2	2	20
O_3	8	2		2	3		6		2	4	4	3	18
O_4	1	2	3	6			7		1	5	5		17
	8		11		10		19		14		8		

(c)

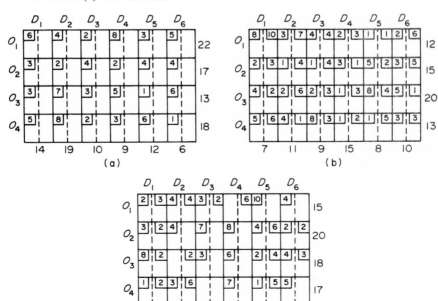

5. In proving the equivalence of a transshipment problem and its related maximal-flow problem, we began with a feasible function f for the transshipment problem and defined a function f^* on $\mathcal{N}^* \times \mathcal{N}^*$. Prove that the function f^* which we defined is actually a flow in the related network $(\mathcal{N}^*, c^*; T, R)$.

4-4. *THE TRANSPORTATION PROBLEM.*

The transportation problem was stated in Example 4, Section 1–2, but, for convenience of reference, we restate it here in slightly different form. We are given nonempty finite sets $\mathcal{O} = \{O_1, O_2, \ldots, O_m\}$ and $\mathcal{D} = \{D_1, D_2, \ldots, D_n\}$, the members of which are called *origins* and *destinations*, respectively. We are also given supply and demand functions s and d defined on $\mathcal{O}$ and $\mathcal{D}$, respectively, and a cost function c defined on $\mathcal{O} \times \mathcal{D}$. Each of these functions assumes only nonnegative integral values. We shall put $s_i = s(O_i)$, $d_j = d(D_j)$, and $c_{ij} = c(O_i, D_j)$ $(i = 1, \ldots, m; j = 1, \ldots, n)$. The problem is to find nonnegative integers x_{ij} which satisfy the inequalities

$$(10) \qquad \begin{cases} \sum_{j=1}^{n} x_{ij} \leqq s_i & (i = 1, \ldots, m) \\ \sum_{i=1}^{m} x_{ij} \geqq d_j & (j = 1, \ldots, n) \end{cases}$$

and which minimize the function

$$(11) \qquad z = \sum_{i=1}^{m} \sum_{j=1}^{n} c_{ij} x_{ij}.$$

A *feasible solution* of this problem is an mn-dimensional vector with nonnegative integral components x_{ij} satisfying (10).

As in the discussion of the transshipment problem, we put $S = s(\mathcal{O})$ and $D = d(\mathcal{D})$. If a feasible solution exists, then, from (10), we have

$$(12) \qquad S = \sum_{i=1}^{m} s_i \geqq \sum_{i=1}^{m} \left(\sum_{j=1}^{n} x_{ij}\right) = \sum_{j=1}^{n} \left(\sum_{i=1}^{m} x_{ij}\right) \geqq \sum_{j=1}^{n} d_j = D;$$

i.e., $S \geqq D$ is a *necessary* condition for the existence of feasible solutions. As we shall soon see, this condition is also sufficient.

In the special case $S = D$, it is easy to see from (12) that, for each feasible solution, equalities will hold throughout the set of constraints (10). Thus, in case $S = D$, we may state the problem as follows: Find nonnegative integers x_{ij} which minimize the function z given by (11) subject to

$$(13) \qquad \begin{cases} \sum_{j=1}^{n} x_{ij} = s_i & (i = 1, \ldots, m), \\ \sum_{i=1}^{m} x_{ij} = d_j & (j = 1, \ldots, n). \end{cases}$$

The case $S > D$ may be reduced to this by the introduction of a new destination with demand $S - D$ to which all shipping costs are zero (see Exercise 1 at the end of this section). Hence, from now on we shall assume $S = D$.

It is important to note that each transportation problem has at least one feasible solution. We shall now show this constructively by describing a method for finding a feasible solution. Consider an m by n tableau of empty cells in which the ith row of cells corresponds to O_i and the jth column, to D_j. Finding a feasible solution of the transportation problem is equivalent to filling in the tableau with nonnegative integers x_{ij} (x_{ij} occupying the cell in row i, column j) so that the sum of all the integers in the ith row is s_i and the jth column sum is d_j. (Figure 41 shows a special case with $m = 4$ and $n = 6$.) This can be done systematically in several ways, one of which, known as the *northwest corner rule*, we now describe. In the northwest corner cell (row 1, column 1), place the integer $x_{11} = \min(s_1, d_1)$ ($x_{11} = 20$ in the example of Fig. 41). This satisfies either the first row requirement or the first column requirement (or possibly both). If $x_{11} = s_1$, let $x_{1j} = 0$ for each $j = 2, \ldots, n$; if $x_{11} = d_1$, let $x_{i1} = 0$ for each $i = 2, \ldots, m$. In any case, having satisfied either the first row requirement or the first column requirement (or both), we eliminate that row or column (or both) from further consideration. Subtract x_{11} from the requirement of the first row or first column, whichever is *not* eliminated (no subtraction if both are eliminated), and follow the same procedure in the smaller tableau which remains. Note that, in the smaller tableau, the sum of the column requirements again equals the sum of the row requirements, since each equals the original common sum minus x_{11}. Continuing in this fashion, we satisfy either a row requirement or a column requirement at each stage. Hence, after a finite number of steps, we shall have satisfied either all row requirements or all column requirements. Suppose for definiteness that we have satisfied all column requirements. Then the sum of all the integers x_{ij} at that stage equals

	D_1	D_2	D_3	D_4	D_5	D_6	
O_1							40
O_2							25
O_3							30
O_4							25
	20	15	18	30	17	20	

Figure 41

	D_1	D_2	D_3	D_4	D_5	D_6	
O_1	20	15	5				40
O_2			13	12			25
O_3				18	12		30
O_4					5	20	25
	20	15	18	30	17	20	

Figure 42

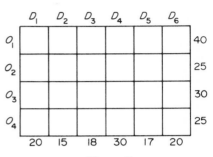

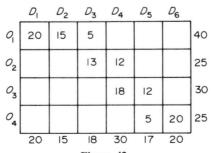

the sum D of all column requirements. But $D = S$, and the sum of the x_{ij}'s in any particular row cannot exceed the requirement for that row. Hence, each row requirement must be satisfied, and so we have found a feasible solution. A feasible solution found by the northwest corner rule in the above example is shown in Fig. 42.

Before we can describe the solution of the transportation problem, we must discuss briefly the concept of *duality* in linear programming. Consider a standard minimizing problem:

Minimize $z = \sum_{j=1}^{n} c_j x_j$ subject to

$$(14)\qquad \begin{cases} \sum_{j=1}^{n} a_{ij}x_j = b_i & (i = 1, \ldots, m), \\ x_j \geqq 0 & (j = 1, \ldots, n). \end{cases}$$

Corresponding to this problem, there is a related *maximizing* problem known as the *dual* of the given problem. The statement of this dual problem is as follows:

Maximize $w = \sum_{i=1}^{m} b_i y_i$ subject to

$$(15)\qquad \sum_{i=1}^{m} a_{ij}y_i \leqq c_j \qquad (j = 1, \ldots, n).$$

To distinguish between the two problems, the original problem is sometimes called the *primal*. As an example, suppose the primal calls for minimizing $z = 2x_1 + x_2 - 3x_3$ subject to

$$\begin{cases} x_1 + x_2 - 4x_3 + x_4 = 10, \\ 2x_1 - x_2 - x_3 - x_5 = 6, \\ 2x_1 + 2x_2 + x_3 + x_6 = 8, \\ x_j \geqq 0 \quad (j = 1, \ldots, 6). \end{cases}$$

Then the dual problem is the maximize $w = 10y_1 + 6y_2 + 8y_3$ subject to

$$\begin{cases} y_1 + 2y_2 + 2y_3 \leqq 2, \\ y_1 - y_2 + 2y_3 \leqq 1, \\ -4y_1 - y_2 + y_3 \leqq -3, \\ y_1 \leqq 0, \\ -y_2 \leqq 0, \\ y_3 \leqq 0. \end{cases}$$

A standard minimizing problem and its dual are closely related. For example, one easily proved relationship is the following: If $\mathbf{x}$ is a feasible solution of the primal and $\mathbf{y}$ is a feasible solution of the dual, then $w(\mathbf{y}) \leqq z(\mathbf{x})$. To see this, let $\mathbf{x} = [x_1, \ldots, x_n]$ and $\mathbf{y} = [y_1, \ldots, y_m]$ be vectors satisfying (14) and (15), respectively. Then we have

$$(16) \qquad w(\mathbf{y}) = \sum_{i=1}^{m} b_i y_i = \sum_{i=1}^{m} \left(\sum_{j=1}^{n} a_{ij} x_j \right) y_i$$
$$= \sum_{j=1}^{n} \left(\sum_{i=1}^{m} a_{ij} y_i \right) x_j \leqq \sum_{j=1}^{n} c_j x_j = z(\mathbf{x}).$$

An obvious consequence of this is that, if it should happen that $w(\mathbf{y}) = z(\mathbf{x})$, then $\mathbf{x}$ and $\mathbf{y}$ are optimal solutions of their respective problems. Necessary and sufficient conditions for this equality are given in the following important theorem:

THEOREM 7. If $\mathbf{x}$ and $\mathbf{y}$ are feasible solutions of the primal and dual problems, respectively, described above, then $z(\mathbf{x}) = w(\mathbf{y})$ if, and only if, for each j such that the strict inequality holds in the jth inequality of system (15), we have $x_j = 0$.

Proof: Suppose, first, that the equality $z(\mathbf{x}) = w(\mathbf{y})$ holds. If there were some j such that $x_j > 0$ while the strict inequality holds in the jth inequality of (15), then the strict inequality would hold in (16), giving $w(\mathbf{y}) < z(\mathbf{x})$. This contradicts our assumption that $z(\mathbf{x}) = w(\mathbf{y})$.

Now suppose that, for each j such that the strict inequality holds in the jth inequality of (15), we have $x_j = 0$. Then, for each j such that $x_j \neq 0$, we have

$$\sum_{i=1}^{m} a_{ij} y_i = c_j.$$

Consequently, it follows from (16) that

$$w(\mathbf{y}) = \sum_{j=1}^{n} \left(\sum_{i=1}^{m} a_{ij} y_i \right) x_j = \sum_{j=1}^{n} c_j x_j = z(\mathbf{x}).$$

completing the proof.

Of importance in the discussions to follow is the result stated in the next theorem:

THEOREM 8. If the primal and dual problems each have feasible solutions, then each has an optimal solution.

Proof: From the results of Chapter 3, we know that, for any minimizing problem, there are exactly three possibilities: (i) no feasible solutions exist, (ii) for each $M > 0$ there is a feasible solution $\mathbf{x}$ for which $z(\mathbf{x}) < -M$, and (iii) there is an optimal solution. In the case of the primal, possibility (i) is ruled out by the hypothesis of the theorem, and possibility (ii) is ruled out by the fact that, if $\mathbf{y}$ is any feasible solution of the dual, then $z(\mathbf{x}) \geqq w(\mathbf{y})$ for each feasible solution $\mathbf{x}$ of the primal. Therefore the primal must have an optimal solution. A similar argument proves that the dual must also have an optimal solution.

The above results on duality are sufficient for our purposes. For a more complete discussion of this subject, we refer the reader to a more advanced text such as [2, Chapter 5] or [3, Chapter 8].

Returning now to the transportation problem, let us consider for a moment the special case $m = 2$, $n = 4$, and ignore temporarily the requirement of integral variables. The problem may then be stated as follows:

Minimize $z = c_{11}x_{11} + c_{12}x_{12} + \cdots + c_{24}x_{24}$ subject to

$$
(17)\quad \begin{cases}
x_{11} + x_{12} + x_{13} + x_{14} & = s_1 \\
x_{21} + x_{22} + x_{23} + x_{24} & = s_2 \\
x_{11} + x_{21} & = d_1 \\
x_{12} + x_{22} & = d_2 \\
x_{13} + x_{23} & = d_3 \\
x_{14} + x_{24} & = d_4 \\
x_{ij} \geqq 0 \qquad (i = 1, 2; j = 1, 2, 3, 4). &
\end{cases}
$$

The dual of this problem is as follows:

Maximize $w = s_1y_1 + s_2y_2 + d_1y_3 + d_2y_4 + d_3y_5 + d_4y_6$ subject to

$$
(18)\quad \begin{cases}
y_1 + y_3 & \leqq c_{11}, \\
y_1 + y_4 & \leqq c_{12}, \\
y_1 + y_5 & \leqq c_{13}, \\
y_1 + y_6 & \leqq c_{14}, \\
y_2 + y_3 & \leqq c_{21}, \\
y_2 + y_4 & \leqq c_{22}, \\
y_2 + y_5 & \leqq c_{23}, \\
y_2 + y_6 & \leqq c_{24}.
\end{cases}
$$

It is convenient to change the notation slightly by replacing y_3, y_4, y_5, and y_6 with y'_1, y'_2, y'_3, and y'_4, respectively. The dual problem can then be written as follows:

Maximize $w = s_1y_1 + s_2y_2 + d_1y'_1 + d_2y'_2 + d_3y'_3 + d_4y'_4$ subject to

$$y_i + y'_j \leqq c_{ij} \qquad (i = 1, 2; j = 1, 2, 3, 4).$$

In the general case, if one imagines the constraints of the primal written out, as in (17), it is easily seen that the dual problem is as follows: Maximize

$$(19)\qquad w = \sum_{i=1}^{m} s_iy_i + \sum_{j=1}^{n} d_jy'_j$$

subject to

$$(20)\qquad y_i + y'_j \leqq c_{ij} \qquad (i = 1, \ldots, m; j = 1, \ldots, n).$$

Note that this dual problem has at least one feasible solution, namely, the one obtained by putting $y_i = y'_j = 0$ for each i and j. Since we have previously shown that the primal likewise has at least one feasible solution, it follows from Theorem 8 that, ignoring the requirement of integral variables, both the transportation problem and its dual have optimal solutions.

Now consider what Theorem 7 says about this situation: If x_{ij} ($i = 1, \ldots, m; j = 1, \ldots, n$) are nonnegative real numbers satisfying (13) and y_i and y'_j are real numbers satisfying (20) and if we write $\mathbf{x} = [x_{11}, \ldots, x_{mn}]$ and $\mathbf{y} = [y_1, \ldots, y_m, y'_1, \ldots, y'_n]$, then $w(\mathbf{y}) = z(\mathbf{x})$ if, and only if, for each i and j such that $y_i + y'_j < c_{ij}$, we have $x_{ij} = 0$. Since integers are real numbers, a true statement results if we replace "real numbers" by "integers" in the preceding sentence. Thus, to solve the transportation problem (with integral variables), it would be sufficient to find nonnegative integers x_{ij} and integers y_i and y'_j such that (13) and (20) hold and such that $x_{ij} = 0$ whenever $y_i + y'_j < c_{ij}$.

A method for doing this will now be described. It is an iterative process and begins with the selection of a set of integers y_i and y'_j satisfying (20). Having selected these integers, the next step is to investigate the existence of nonnegative integers x_{ij} satisfying (13) together with the condition that $x_{ij} = 0$ if $y_i + y'_j < c_{ij}$. The problem of determining whether or not such integers x_{ij} exist is equivalent to determining the feasibility or nonfeasibility of the transshipment problem with origin set $\mathscr{O}$, destination set $\mathscr{D}$, supply function s, demand function d, and capacity function γ defined as follows: $\gamma(O_i, D_j) = S$ if $y_i + y'_j = c_{ij}$ and $\gamma(x, y) = 0$ for each other branch (x, y) in $\mathscr{N} \times \mathscr{N}$ ($\mathscr{N} = \mathscr{O} \cup \mathscr{D}$).

To see the equivalence of these problems, suppose, first, that there exist nonnegative integers x_{ij} satisfying (13) and for which $x_{ij} = 0$ when $y_i + y'_j < c_{ij}$. Then we can define a feasible function f for the transshipment problem described above as follows: Let $f(O_i, D_j) = x_{ij}$, $f(D_j, O_i) = -x_{ij}$, and $f(x, y) = 0$ on each other branch (x, y) of $\mathscr{N} \times \mathscr{N}$. Then we have

$$f(O_i, \mathscr{N}) = \sum_{j=1}^{n} f(O_i, D_j) = \sum_{j=1}^{n} x_{ij} = s_i \qquad (i = 1, \ldots, m),$$

$$f(\mathscr{N}, D_j) = \sum_{i=1}^{m} f(O_i, D_j) = \sum_{i=1}^{m} x_{ij} = d_j \qquad (j = 1, \ldots, n).$$

These equations show that requirements (i) and (ii) for a feasible function, stated in the previous section, are satisfied. It is easy to verify that the other two requirements (iii) and (iv) are also satisfied and, hence, that f is actually a feasible function for the transshipment problem.

Now suppose that a feasible function f for the transshipment problem exists. Let $x_{ij} = f(O_i, D_j)$ for each $i = 1, \ldots, m$ and $j = 1, \ldots, n$. Then, because of the way the capacity function γ is defined and because f is feasible, we have $x_{ij} \geqq 0$ for each $i = 1, \ldots, m$ and $j = 1, \ldots, n$. Also, we have

$$f(O_i, \mathscr{N}) = \sum_{j=1}^{n} f(O_i, D_j) = \sum_{j=1}^{n} x_{ij} \leqq s_i \qquad (i = 1, \ldots, m),$$

$$f(\mathscr{N}, D_j) = \sum_{i=1}^{m} f(O_i, D_j) = \sum_{i=1}^{m} x_{ij} = d_j \qquad (j = 1, \ldots, n)$$

Hence, the integers x_{ij} satisfy (10), and, as we proved earlier, this together with the assumption $S = D$ implies that the x_{ij}'s satisfy (13). Finally, since $\gamma(O_i, D_j) = \gamma(D_j, O_i) = 0$ if $y_i + y'_j < c_{ij}$, we have $x_{ij} = f(O_i, D_j) = 0$ for all such i and j. The equivalence of the problems is therefore established.

Summarizing, the integers y_i and y'_j chosen at the first step determine a transshipment problem in which all capacities are zero except for those branches (O_i, D_j) for which $y_i + y'_j = c_{ij}$; such branches are assigned capacity S, which in effect allows unlimited flow through these branches, since S is the total supply. The second step in the process consists of determining the feasibility or nonfeasibility of this transshipment problem. This can be done by the use of the Feasibility Theorem (Theorem 6) and/or the method illustrated by Example 3 of the previous section. If the problem is feasible and a feasible function f is found, then an optimal solution of the transportation problem is obtained by putting $x_{ij} = f(O_i, D_j)$. In this case the process terminates after the second step.

Suppose, however, that the transshipment problem is not feasible. Then, according to the Feasibility Theorem, there must be a subset $\mathscr{M}$ of $\mathscr{N}$ such that

$$d(\mathscr{M} \cap \mathscr{D}) - s(\mathscr{M} \cap \mathscr{D}) > \mathscr{V}(\mathscr{N} - \mathscr{M}, \mathscr{M}). \tag{21}$$

Since the capacity of each branch of the network is either 0 or S, the number $\gamma(\mathscr{N} - \mathscr{M}, \mathscr{M})$ is either 0 or some positive integral multiple of S. But the number on the left side of (21) is at most S. Hence, since (21) holds, we must have $\gamma(\mathscr{N} - \mathscr{M}, \mathscr{M}) = 0$. This implies that for each origin O_i in $\mathscr{N} - \mathscr{M}$ and each destination D_j in $\mathscr{M}$, we have $y_i + y'_j < c_{ij}$. We can use this fact in attempting to find a set $\mathscr{M}$ satisfying (21). For each D_j included in $\mathscr{M}$, we must also include in $\mathscr{M}$ all origins O_i for which $y_i + y'_j = c_{ij}$.

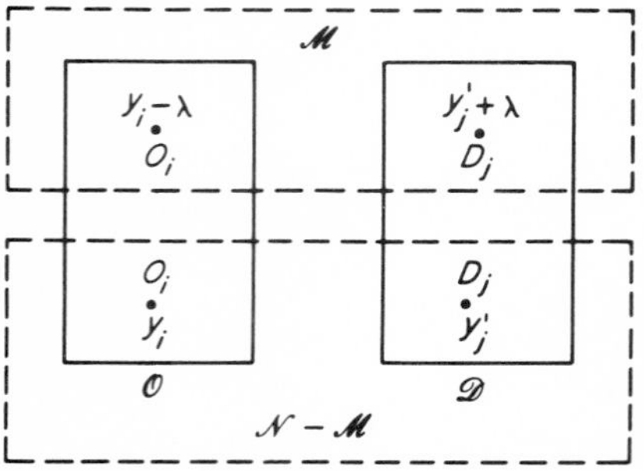

Figure 43

Having found a set $\mathscr{M}$ satisfying (21), we next determine new integers $\hat{y}_i$ and $\hat{y}'_j$ satisfying (20) as follows: Let λ denote the smallest of all the differences $c_{ij} - (y_i + y'_j)$ for O_i in $\mathscr{N} - \mathscr{M}$ and D_j in $\mathscr{M}$. Note that $\lambda \geqq 1$. Then define

$$\hat{y}_i = \begin{cases} y_i & \text{for each } i \text{ such that } O_i \in \mathscr{N} - \mathscr{M}, \\ y_i - \lambda & \text{for each } i \text{ such that } O_i \in \mathscr{M}, \end{cases} \tag{22}$$

and

$$\hat{y}'_j = \begin{cases} y'_j & \text{for each } j \text{ such that } D_j \in \mathscr{N} - \mathscr{M}, \\ y'_j + \lambda & \text{for each } j \text{ such that } D_j \in \mathscr{M}. \end{cases} \tag{23}$$

Schematically, we might picture the situation as in Fig. 43. By examining all cases, we see that $\hat{y}_i + \hat{y}'_j \leqq c_{ij}$ for each i and j, so that we have in fact determined a new feasible solution of the dual problem. Moreover, the value of the dual objective function w has been increased by at least the amount λ. To see this, call the original solution of the dual problem $\mathbf{y}$ and the new solution $\hat{\mathbf{y}}$. Then

$$\begin{aligned} w(\hat{\mathbf{y}}) &= \sum_{i=1}^{m} s_i \hat{y}_i + \sum_{j=1}^{n} d_j \hat{y}'_j \\ &= \sum_{i=1}^{m} s_i y_i - \lambda s(\mathscr{M} \cap \mathscr{O}) + \sum_{j=1}^{n} d_j y'_j + \lambda d(\mathscr{M} \cap \mathscr{D}) \\ &= w(\mathbf{y}) + \lambda[d(\mathscr{M} \cap \mathscr{D}) - s(\mathscr{M} \cap \mathscr{O})] \geqq w(\mathbf{y}) + \lambda. \end{aligned}$$

since $d(\mathscr{M} \cap \mathscr{D}) - s(\mathscr{M} \cap \mathscr{O}) \geqq 1$.

Having found a new solution of the dual problem, we now repeat the process. The integers $\hat{y}_i$ and $\hat{y}'_j$ determine a new transshipment problem. If a feasible function can be found for this problem, it will yield an optimal solution of the transportation problem and the process will terminate. If, on the other hand, the new transshipment problem is not feasible, then we must determine a new set $\mathscr{M}$ satisfying (21) (with γ replaced by the new capacity function). This new set $\mathscr{M}$ leads to still another solution of the dual problem, and so on. The value of w increases by at least 1 with each new solution of the dual problem, and each nonfeasible transshipment problem leads to a new solution of the dual problem. But, as we have previously observed, the dual problem has an optimal solution. Hence, after some finite number of steps, we must obtain a feasible transshipment problem and, hence, an optimal solution *with integral variables* of the transportation problem.

Let us now illustrate the process with a numerical example:

	D_1	D_2	D_3	D_4	D_5	D_6	
O_1	10	2	6	3	3	5	30
O_2	2	8	7	4	5	6	40
O_3	12	10	6	5	3	2	15
O_4	5	4	9	2	8	10	25
	20	15	25	28	10	12	

Figure 44

Example 5. The tableau of Fig. 44 determines a transportation problem with four origins and six destinations. The number in the northwest corner of cell (O_i, D_j) is c_{ij}, the cost of shipping one unit from O_i to D_j. Supplies are shown at the right and demands across the bottom of the tableau.

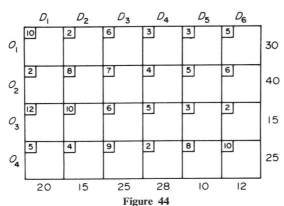

The steps in the solution are as follows:

Step 1. Determine a solution of the dual problem. One way of doing this, as we have observed earlier, is to let $y_i = y'_j = 0$ for each i and j. However, it seems clear that fewer steps will be required if we make a less trivial choice. One procedure is as follows: Let $y_i = \min\{c_{ij} | j = 1, \ldots, 6\}$ for each $i = 1, 2, 3, 4$. As it happens, each y_i is 2 in this example. Then let $y'_j = \min\{c_{ij} - y_i | i = 1, 2, 3, 4\}$ for each $j = 1, \ldots, 6$. Thus $y'_1 = 0$, $y'_2 = 0$, $y'_3 = 4$, $y'_4 = 0$, $y'_5 = 1$, and $y'_6 = 0$. These numbers are then entered in the tableau as shown in Fig. 45. (The asterisks and check marks in Fig. 45 will be explained shortly.)

	D_1	* D_2	* D_3	* D_4	* D_5	* D_6	
* O_1	[10] 2+0	[2] ✓ 2+0	[6] ✓ 2+4	[3] 2+0	[3] ✓ 2+1	[5] 2+0	30
O_2	[2] ✓ 2+0	[8] 2+0	[7] 2+4	[4] 2+0	[5] 2+1	[6] 2+0	40
* O_3	[12] 2+0	[10] 2+0	[6] ✓ 2+4	[5] 2+0	[3] ✓ 2+1	[2] ✓ 2+0	15
* O_4	[5] 2+0	[4] 2+0	[9] 2+4	[2] ✓ 2+0	[8] 2+1	[10] 2+0	25
	20	15	25	28	10	12	

Figure 45

Step 2. Solve the transshipment problem determined by the solution of the dual problem found in step 1. In Fig. 45, the check marks indicate those cells (O_i, D_j) for which $y_i + y'_j = c_{ij}$. These are the branches of $\mathscr{N} \times \mathscr{N}$ which have positive capacity. We first seek a set $\mathscr{M}$ for which (21) holds, using the fact that $\mathscr{M}$ will satisfy (21) if, and only if, $d(\mathscr{M} \cap \mathscr{D}) > s(\mathscr{M} \cap \mathscr{O})$ and, for each D_j in $\mathscr{M}$, each O_i such that cell (O_i, D_j) is checked also belongs to $\mathscr{M}$. For example, if we put D_3 in $\mathscr{M}$, we must also include O_1 and O_3. By trial, we find that the set $\mathscr{M} = \{D_2, D_3, D_4, D_5, D_6, O_1, O_3, O_4\}$ satisfies these conditions. For this set, we have $d(\mathscr{M} \cap \mathscr{D}) - s(\mathscr{M} \cap \mathscr{O}) = 90 - 70 = 20$. The asterisks in Fig. 45 denote the members of $\mathscr{M}$. Note that the set $\mathscr{M}$ is not uniquely determined. For example, the set $\{D_4, O_4\}$ also satisfies (21).

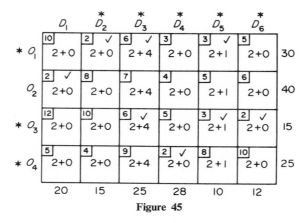

Step 3. Determine a new solution of the dual problem. This is done by use of formulas (22) and (23). The number λ is first determined as the smallest of the differences $c_{ij} - (y_i + y'_j)$ for O_i in $\mathscr{N} - \mathscr{M}$ and D_j in $\mathscr{M}$. In this case, O_2 is the only origin in $\mathscr{N} - \mathscr{M}$ and hence $\lambda = \min\{8 - 2, 7 - 6, 4 - 2, 5 - 3, 6 - 2\} = 1$. Thus, to obtain y_i and y'_j, we add 1 to each y'_j corresponding to a D_j in $\mathscr{M}$, subtract 1 from each y_i corresponding to O_i in $\mathscr{M}$, and leave the other integers y_i and y'_j unchanged. We enter this

new solution of the dual problem in the tableau in place of the old and again check the cells for which $y_i + y'_j = c_{ij}$. The result is the tableau of Fig. 46.

Step 4. Solve the transshipment problem determined by the solution of the dual problem found in step 3. The problem is again found to be non-feasible. This time we find that the set $\mathscr{M} = \{D_4, O_4\}$ satisfies (21), as indicated by the asterisks in Fig. 46.

Step 5. Determine a new solution of the dual problem. Again we find that $\lambda = 1$. The new solution of the dual problem is displayed in Fig. 47.

Step 6. Solve the transshipment problem determined by the solution of the dual problem found in step 5. In this case, we cannot find a set $\mathscr{M}$ satisfying (21), and so we seek a feasible function f by the method of Example 3 of the previous section. The first stage in this computation is shown in Fig. 48. Since a feasible function has not yet been obtained, we must seek a path of positive capacity from T to R. Such a path must begin $T \longrightarrow O_4$ and must end $D_6 \longrightarrow R$. By trial, we find that the path $T \longrightarrow O_4 \longrightarrow D_4 \longrightarrow O_2 \longrightarrow D_3 \longrightarrow O_1 \longrightarrow D_5 \longrightarrow O_3 \longrightarrow D_6 \longrightarrow R$ has capacity 7. Sending seven units

	D_1	D_2	D_3	* D_4	D_5	D_6	
O_1	10 1+0	2 ✓ 1+1	6 ✓ 1+5	3 1+1	3 ✓ 1+2	5 1+1	30
O_2	2 ✓ 2+0	8 2+1	7 ✓ 2+5	4 2+1	5 2+2	6 2+1	40
O_3	12 1+0	10 1+1	6 ✓ 1+5	5 1+1	3 ✓ 1+2	2 ✓ 1+1	15
* O_4	5 1+0	4 1+1	9 1+5	2 ✓ 1+1	8 1+2	10 1+1	25
	20	15	25	28	10	12	

Figure 46

	D_1	D_2	D_3	D_4	D_5	D_6	
O_1	10 1+0	2 ✓ 1+1	6 ✓ 1+5	3 ✓ 1+2	3 ✓ 1+2	5 1+1	30
O_2	2 ✓ 2+0	8 2+1	7 ✓ 2+5	4 ✓ 2+2	5 2+2	6 2+1	40
O_3	12 1+0	10 1+1	6 ✓ 1+5	5 1+2	3 ✓ 1+2	2 ✓ 1+1	15
O_4	5 0+0	4 0+1	9 0+5	2 ✓ 0+2	8 0+2	10 0+1	25
	20	15	25	28	10	12	

Figure 47

along this path, we obtain the tableau of Fig. 49. It is easy to check in Fig. 49 that we have found a feasible function f for the transshipment problem

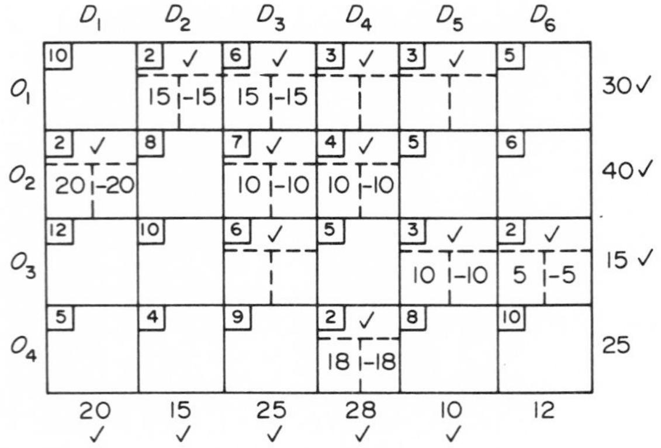

Figure 48

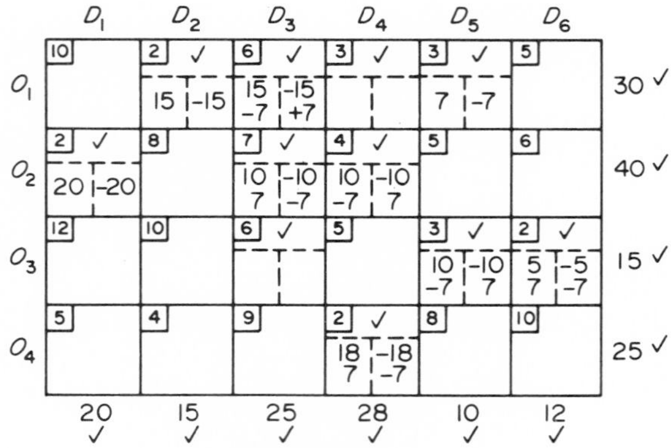

Figure 49

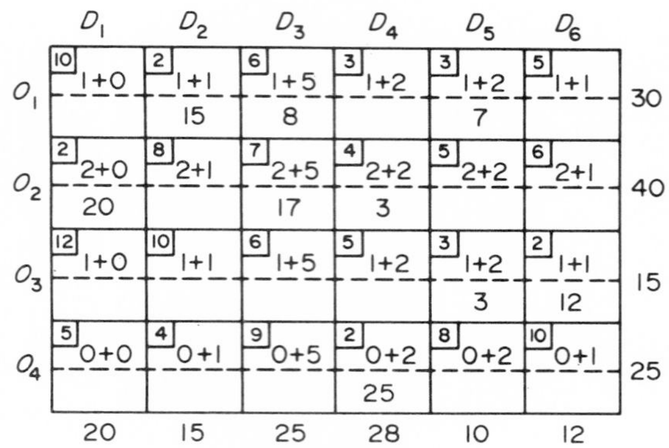

Figure 50

and, hence, that the numbers $x_{ij} = f(O_i, D_j)$ constitute an optimal solution of the transportation problem. In Fig. 50, we show both this solution of the transportation problem and the solution of the dual problem obtained at step 5. Verifying the equality $w = z = 353$ for these solutions, which is left to the student, is further proof that they are optimal solutions of their respective problems.

EXERCISES

1. Suppose we have a transportation problem (T) in which the total supply S exceeds the total demand D. (a) Explain why, given any feasible solution in which at least one of the demands is exceeded, there is another feasible solution with no larger total shipping cost, in which each demand is exactly met. (b) Assuming an optimal solution exists, use the result of (a) to explain why an optimal solution may be found among those feasible solutions for which the demands are exactly met. (c) Consider the related problem (T^*) obtained by introducing a new destination with demand $S - D$ to which all transportation costs are zero. Use the results of (a) and (b) to explain why an optimal solution of (T^*) yields an optimal solution of (T).

2. Explain, using a result proved in this section, why a transshipment problem in which each branch has capacity S and $S = D$ must necessarily be feasible.

3. Use the northwest corner rule to find a feasible solution for each of the following problems. Also determine the total shipping cost for each solution.

(a)

	D_1	D_2	D_3	D_4	D_5	D_6	
O_1	2	5	1	3	3	4	30
O_2	4	2	6	1	8	10	18
O_3	8	5	2	4	1	2	20
O_4	3	4	1	6	2	5	12
	10	17	7	15	13	18	

(b)

	D_1	D_2	D_3	D_4	D_5	D_6	D_7	
O_1	6	1	2	2	4	5	10	22
O_2	2	8	5	4	4	1	2	30
O_3	8	7	3	10	8	2	1	12
O_4	1	3	4	2	1	9	8	16
O_5	4	3	6	5	3	7	4	20
	13	15	28	19	10	6	9	

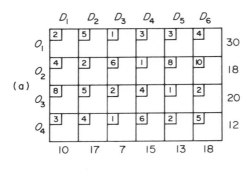

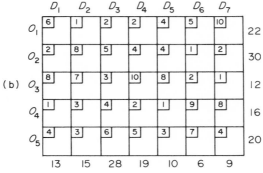

4. Consider the following linear programming problem:
Minimize $z = 2x_1 - x_2$ subject to

$$\begin{cases} x_1 - 2x_2 \geqq -4, \\ 2x_1 + x_2 \leqq 7, \\ x_1 - x_2 \leqq 2, \\ x_1 \geqq 0, \quad x_2 \geqq 0. \end{cases}$$

(a) Solve the problem graphically.
(b) Write the related standard problem.
(c) Formulate the dual of the related standard problem.
(d) Use the result of part (a) together with Theorems 7 and 8 to find an optimal solution of the dual problem.

5. Solve the transportation problems stated in Exercise 3.

6. Solve each of the following transportation problems by the method of this section. In each case, verify that your solution is optimal by showing that $z_{\min} = w_{\max}$, where z and w are the objective functions for the primal and dual problems, respectively.

	D_1	D_2	D_3	D_4	
O_1	8	10	7	6	50
O_2	12	9	4	7	40
O_3	9	11	10	8	30
	25	32	40	23	

(a)

	D_1	D_2	D_3	D_4	
O_1	9	4	12	2	36
O_2	3	6	5	5	40
O_3	4	2	3	6	26
O_4	10	9	9	11	28
	38	32	29	31	

(b)

	D_1	D_2	D_3	D_4	D_5	D_6	
O_1	12	8	9	7	4	5	40
O_2	8	15	4	12	9	6	35
O_3	10	10	5	4	10	11	20
O_4	7	6	10	9	8	10	25
	18	24	21	17	28	12	

(c)

	D_1	D_2	D_3	D_4	D_5	D_6	
O_1	5	10	7	4	6	3	28
O_2	8	4	5	2	3	4	13
O_3	7	5	8	6	5	6	15
O_4	10	7	10	8	3	5	24
	17	10	12	10	18	13	

(d)

7. A truck rental company has surplus trucks in Atlanta, Richmond, and Cincinnati and, at the same time, has a shortage of trucks in Memphis, Nashville, and Charlotte. The company wishes to move surplus trucks to fill the needs

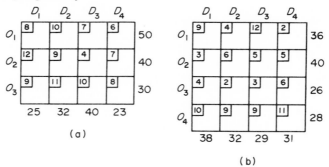

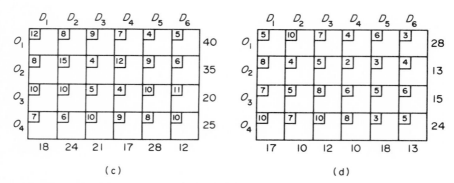

at minimum cost. The cost of moving a truck between cities and the numbers of trucks surplus and short are given in the accompanying table.

	Memphis	*Nashville*	*Charlotte*	*Trucks Surplus*
Atlanta	$68	$56	$39	12
Richmond	86	62	27	5
Cincinnati	51	29	50	13
Trucks Short	10	6	14	

Find the optimal truck relocation schedule.

8. If, in the previous problem, legal complications prevent trucks from Georgia being used in North Carolina, what is the minimum cost relocation plan?

9. A company has four manufacturing plants located at separate points in a city, while all finished goods are stored in a warehouse located near the center of the city. These goods must be transported by truck from the plants to the warehouse and, for this purpose, the company maintains its own trucks. However, they have insufficient capacity to meet next month's anticipated shipments and the services of trucking companies will have to be leased. Three trucking companies have bid on the amounts they can carry next month and the price per hundred pounds from the various plants. The pertinent data are shown in the accompanying table (units are hundreds of pounds and dollars per hundred pounds).

Source of Transportation	*Plant A*	*Plant B*	*Plant C*	*Plant D*	*Hauling Capacity*
Own Trucks	$6	$4	$8	$10	1000
Company 1	2	6	7	8	1000
Company 2	9	5	3	6	800
Company 3	8	1	5	4	500
To be moved	400	800	1200	600	

Determine the minimum cost shipping program.

CHAPTER FIVE

THE APPLICATION OF LINEAR PROGRAMMING

In the preceding chapters we have developed techniques for solving several forms of the linear programming problem. We gave little attention to the practical applications of these techniques in analysis of actual problems. In this chapter, we will discuss the role of linear programming methods in the solution of operational problems, will describe the necessary characteristics of a problem in order that it be solvable by linear programming, and will illustrate the application of linear programming through a number of examples pertaining to the industrial environment.

Our objective is to provide some insight into areas where application of linear programming has been fruitful and to describe problems and limitations to the use of programming methods. While there is a wide range of reported applications of linear programming, we chose those relating to the operation of an industrial organization. It is in this area that linear programming methods definitely have proved themselves to be valuable as decision making techniques.

5-1. *ROLE OF LINEAR PROGRAMMING IN THE ANALYSIS OF OPERATIONAL PROBLEMS.*

Many important problems involve determining the way in which certain operations should be carried out. For example, a production manager in a manufacturing organization may wish to determine the quantities of each of several products to be produced during the next month in the departments under his control, in order to meet given production goals at minimum cost. A shipping department supervisor may want to schedule his delivery trucks to meet given delivery commitments at the lowest possible cost. A company manager may wish to allocate a limited amount of capital to a number of competing investment opportunities, with the objective of maximizing the return on total investment. A chief engineer in a design department may wish to assign projects to his staff engineers in such a manner that he maximizes the probability of all projects being completed by a given date.

Operations are sometimes defined as *goal-oriented* activities of organizations. By goal-oriented, we mean that the organization is conducting these activities in order to achieve certain objectives, or goals. An operational problem involves a decision as to how these activities are best carried out in order to obtain the stated objectives. Thus, in the first example given above, the production manager may have considered that the objective of turning out the required production at minimum cost was in keeping with his company's profit objectives; his problem was, therefore, to plan his production activities to meet this goal. In reality, however, a production manager may have many other objectives, which are not easily measured in terms of costs; for example, stabilization of employment, balanced workload among departments, maintenance of employee morale. In general, the criteria for good solutions to operational problems are difficult to state and quantify.

Many operational problems are solved through an allocation process. Allocation involves the assignment of resources to specific activities in order to meet certain objectives. Usually there are constraints imposed upon the allocation process because of limited resources or restrictions on the levels of the various possible activities. All of the examples of operational problems given above are solved through an allocation process. The production manager must allocate the available machine time and labor hours in each department, along with raw materials, to the activities of producing the different products which have been scheduled. He is limited by the availability of machines and labor, the amount of raw materials on hand, and the number of units required to be produced for each type of product.

The shipping department supervisor must allocate the time and capacity of his trucks to deliver specific orders by a given time. He is constrained by the number of trucks and the capacities of each. Also he must consider the allowable delivery time associated with each order, and he must deliver the order within that interval.

In the capital budgeting example, the company manager's problem is allocating a limited supply of capital to activities represented by the available investment opportunities. Similarly, the chief engineer is allocating the time of his staff engineers to a given set of projects.

We may note that the output of the allocation process is a program by which specified activities are conducted. Since the criterion for an optimal allocation often is the maximization or minimization of some quantity which measures the effectiveness of the allocation, we should suspect that mathematical programming techniques would be useful in developing optimal solutions—provided that the allocation problem can be formulated into a meaningful mathematical model and that a procedure is available for derivation of a solution.

As we have seen in previous chapters, if an allocation problem can be formulated as a linear programming model, the machinery necessary for generating the optimal program is available to us. Fortunately, a great many practical allocation problems can be placed in a linear programming framework.

5-2. *FORMULATION OF LINEAR PROGRAMMING PROBLEMS.*

The process of formulating linear programming models involves the following essential activities, all of which require a comprehensive understanding of the problem environment:

1. Recognition of the problem.
2. Formulation of the mathematical model.
   a. Identification of the decision variables.
   b. Choice of a measure of effectiveness.
   c. Symbolic representation of the objective function.
   d. Identification of the constraints.
   e. Algebraic representation of the constraints.
3. Estimation of parameters in the model.

Perhaps the most difficult task of all is the recognition of the potential for the use of linear programming in a given problem situation. The ability to conclude, upon study of the problem environment, that a linear programming model would be a valid representation of the real world decision problem and to conceive of the exact nature of the model is primarily a function of the analytical capability, creativeness, and ingenuity of the researcher. However, this ability can be enhanced through the study of literature which either reports actual applications or suggests potential applications.

Linear programming methods find application in situations in which it is desired to find a program of action that is optimal for some measure of effectiveness and that is feasible in that it conforms to certain criteria, or constraints, imposed upon the decision maker. To model this situation, the researcher must initially determine what quantities define the program of action; i.e., he must first identify the *decision variables*. Specification of values for these variables will, in turn, dictate a program for carrying out the relevant operations of the organization. The objective of the decision maker is to determine optimal values for these variables.

The criterion of optimality is relative to a particular measure which defines the utility of the program to the decision maker. The problem of selecting an appropriate measure of effectiveness is not simple and should be given careful consideration, because the validity of the solution depends upon the degree to which the effectiveness measure truly reflects the objectives of the decision maker. Some measures commonly used in business and industry are profit, cost, return on investment, time, and probability.

The ability to express the chosen effectiveness measure as a linear function of the decision variables is required if a linear programming formulation is to be appropriate. Thus, the symbolic representation of the objective of the programming problem must have the following form:

$$c_1x_1 + c_2x_2 + \cdots + c_nx_n,$$

where $x_1, x_2, \ldots, x_n$ are the decision variables and $c_1, c_2, \ldots, c_n$ are parameters, such that c_i represents the contribution to effectiveness of one unit of variable x_i. This formulation implies that c_i is independent of the magnitude of x_i. For example, if c_1x_1 were to represent the "profit" associated with producing and selling x_1 units of a given product, then c_1 would be the difference between the unit variable revenue from selling and the unit variable cost of production and selling. (The difference is sometimes referred to as the "unit variable contribution to overhead and profit.") The requirement that c_1 be constant over all values of x_1 means that both the selling price and the unit variable cost must be constant over all x_1 (ignoring the remote possibility that price and cost vary jointly to yield a constant difference). If the appropriateness of this assumption is doubtful, then the validity of a linear programming model containing this profit component c_1x_1 would be suspect.

In all likelihood, considerable analysis will be required to determine the manner in which the effectiveness measure varies with each of the respective decision variables. It also may be that, through a redefinition of the decision variables, an appropriate linear objective function can be created from one which initially appears nonlinear. This latter possibility will be illustrated in several of the examples presented later in this chapter.

Unless there are constraints on the choice of values for the decision variables, solutions to the problem of maximizing or minimizing the objective function are trivial. However, almost without exception, practical problems will contain several constraints which must be identified and represented algebraically in terms of the decision variables. The constraints may relate to the level of activity of the operations being programmed; for example, a certain machine in a manufacturing plant must be scheduled for at least 36 hours during a week, or a wholesaler must ship at least 200 units to a given supplier within a month. The constraints that all x_i be nonnegative are of this type.

Other types of constraints represent limitations on the amount of resources available for allocation to the various activities called for by the program; for example, a manufacturer of fertilizer has only 350 tons of potash available for use during the next week, or only 380 hours of machine time are available in a stamping department during the next scheduling period.

A third type of constraint may describe the required technological relationships between the decision variables. For example, if x_1 is the percentage of Liquid A and x_2 is the percentage of Liquid B in a mixture of A and B, then obviously $x_1 + x_2 = 100$ is a constraint on the choice of x_1 and x_2.

It must be possible to express the constraints as linear inequalities or equalities in order to utilize the linear programming solution methods. It usually requires a detailed study to identify properly all relevant constraints and additional analysis to formulate them into linear algebraic expressions. Any simplification of the problem through elimination of irrelevant or marginal constraints will be rewarded in the solution process and any post-solution analysis.

A final problem to be overcome is the selection of numerical values for the parameters of the symbolic model. The $\{c_j\}$ in the objective function and the $\{a_{ij}\}$ and $\{b_i\}$ in the constraints must be determined. This may require methods such as theoretical calculation, statistical estimation, reference to accounting records, use of production standards, or estimation based upon judgment and experience. The sensitivity of the linear programming solution to errors in determination of these coefficients can be analyzed, if desired, through techniques of parametric programming (not discussed in this text).

5-3. *INDUSTRIAL APPLICATIONS OF LINEAR PROGRAMMING.*

Perhaps the most fruitful area for the application of linear programming methods is found in the allocation of available resources to the various possible activities which an industrial concern might have at its disposal. In this section, a number of general types of industrial allocation problems will be described, with specific examples to be presented in the next section.

1. *Production planning—the product mix problem.* An industrial concern has available a certain productive capacity on various manufacturing processes and has the opportunity to utilize this capacity to manufacture various products. Typically, the different products will have different selling prices,

will require different amounts of production capacity at the several processes, and therefore will have different unit profits. Additionally, there may be minimum or maximum production levels set for given products. The problem is to determine the optimum, i.e., maximum profit, mix of products to produce for the capacities available. The solution would state how many units of each product to manufacture during the planning period.

2. *Production planning—the production-smoothing problem.* An industrial concern has the problem of scheduling its production over a number of future time periods, with the total time span being considered called the "planning horizon." The information available to the planner consists of the following:

(1) The number of units of each product to be required in each of the future periods. This information might be obtained from a sales forecast or from customers' orders.
(2) The number of units of each product in inventory at the start of the first period.
(3) The available sources of production, together with a quantitative measure of the capacity of each source, in each of the future time periods. These sources might be production during the regular working shift, production on overtime, or production at a source external to the industrial concern (i.e., subcontracting).
(4) Additional constraints, such as minimum or maximum inventory levels at the end of any period or minimum levels of production or employment.
(5) Cost information on each product. This would include the unit cost of production by whatever production alternatives are available and the unit purchase price from any subcontract alternative under consideration. Because a production plan could involve producing items in a given period and storing them for consumption in a later period, it also is necessary to have some measure of the cost of carrying an inventory from one period to the next. This inventory carrying cost should reflect the opportunity loss associated with investing money in inventory rather than in other investment possibilities, the risk of obsolescence, the risk of spoilage or damage, the cost of storage, and the cost of inventory taxes and insurance.

The problem is to determine a plan for production and procurement in each of the time periods under consideration such that the product demand requirements are satisfied and other constraints are not violated and such that combined costs of production and carrying inventory are minimized. The solution should specify the number of units of each product to be obtained from each production or procurement source in each of the future time periods.

3. *Production scheduling—alternate routings.* In this type of problem the quantities of product to be manufactured during a given period are fixed; however, there may be several alternate sequences (routings) of production processes by which a product can be manufactured. Each routing would have a different cost associated with it. Each manufacturing process would have a certain capacity, and the various products would have to compete for this capacity according to the particular routings selected for each product. The problem is to produce the required quantity of each product at minimum cost, subject to the constraints on process capacity. For each product, the solution would state how much of the required quantity of that product was to be produced by each alternative production routing. The possibility of outside purchase, instead of manufacture, could also be included.

4. *Distribution.* A wide range of industrial problems fall in the category of distribution problems. There exist certain sources of supply (e.g., warehouses, factories, mines) geographically distributed and certain other locations (e.g., retail stores, warehouses) where a need exists for the materials available at the sources. Depending upon the relative geographical locations, freight rates, and possibly other considerations, there is a certain cost associated with transporting a unit of product from a given source to a given destination. Given these transportation costs, the resources at each source, and the requirements at each destination, the problem is to determine the minimum-cost shipping program. The solution would state what quantities are to be shipped from each source to each destination.

5. *Production-distribution problems.* These problems occur when the products needed by the various destinations in a distribution problem do not exist in finished from, but rather must be manufactured at the sources before shipment. The sources may have different production costs. Thus we have a combination of the problem types described above, and the solution would state what is to be produced at each source and where the goods are to be shipped.

6. *Blending problems.* These problems will occur when a product can be made from a variety of available raw materials of various composition and prices. The manufacturing process involves blending (mixing) some of all of these materials in varying quantities to make a product conforming to given specifications. The supply of raw materials and the specifications serve as constraints in obtaining the minimum-cost material blend. The solution would state the number of units of each raw material which are to be blended to make one unit of product.

The problem types described above constitute only a sampling of the areas where linear programming methods can prove beneficial. It should have been noted that, in each case, there is an optimization problem under constraint and that assumptions of linearity for the objective function and for the constraints might well be valid. In the next section, we shall present some specific examples.

5-4. *EXAMPLE LINEAR PROGRAMMING FORMULATIONS.*

The following are examples of linear programming models for problems similar to those described in the previous section.

Example 1. *A production planning model.* Consider a manufacturer faced with the problem of meeting the demand for a product over the next T periods. We shall denote the expected demands during this interval by $d_1, d_2, \ldots, d_T$, where d_j is the expected demand in the jth period. Suppose that the manufacturer can obtain this item from L different production or procurement sources. Let B_{ij} be the maximum number of units which can be obtained from source i in period j. Let X_{ij}, $i = 1, 2, \ldots, L, j = 1, \ldots, T$, be the number of units to be obtained from source i in period j. Thus the X_{ij} are the decision variables. Let c_{ij} be the cost of obtaining one unit of product from source i in period j, and use c_s to denote the cost of carrying one unit of product in inventory from one period to the next. Finally, we define I_o to be the initial inventory at the start of the planning period.

In formulating the model, it will be helpful to have an expression for the inventory at the end of any period t. Denoting this inventory by I_t, we have the following:

$$I_t = I_o + \sum_{j=1}^{t} \sum_{i=1}^{L} X_{ij} - \sum_{j=1}^{t} d_j. \tag{1}$$

At this point we might well note that, if we choose the X_{ij} such that $I_t \geqq 0$ for all t, we shall insure that the demand is met in each period.

The objective is stated as follows: Choose nonnegative X_{ij} such that the function

$$Z = \sum_{j=1}^{T} \sum_{i=1}^{L} c_{ij} X_{ij} + c_s \sum_{t=1}^{T} \left\{ I_o + \sum_{j=1}^{t} \sum_{i=1}^{L} X_{ij} - \sum_{j=1}^{t} d_j \right\} \tag{2}$$

is minimized. The first term in the objective function represents the cost of obtaining the product, and the last term denotes the inventory carrying costs $c_s \sum_{t=1}^{T} I_t$ which are incurred during the planning interval.

The constraints are of two types. The first type insures that the available capacities are not exceeded. Thus, we have LT constraints of the form

$$X_{ij} \leqq B_{ij}, \qquad \text{for } i = 1, 2, \ldots, L \text{ and } j = 1, 2, \ldots, T. \tag{3}$$

The second type of constraint insures that the demand in each period will be met. We have T constraints of the form

$$I_o + \sum_{j=1}^{t} \sum_{i=1}^{L} X_{ij} - \sum_{j=1}^{t} d_j \geqq 0, \qquad \text{for } t = 1, 2, \ldots, T. \tag{4}$$

ORIGINS		DESTINATIONS Demand Period						
Period	Source	1	2	3	• • •	T	Slack	Capacity
Initial Inventory		0	C_S	$2C_S$	• • •	$(T-1)C_S$		I_0
1	1	C_{11}	$C_{11}+C_S$	$C_{11}+2C_S$	• • •	$C_{11}+(T-1)C_S$	$C_{11}+TC_S$	B_{11}
	2	C_{21}	$C_{21}+C_S$	$C_{21}+2C_S$	• • •	$C_{21}+(T-1)C_S$	$C_{21}+TC_S$	B_{21}
	•	•	•	•	• • •	•	•	•
	L	C_{L1}	$C_{L1}+C_S$	$C_{L1}+2C_S$	• • •	$C_{L1}+(T-1)C_S$	$C_{L1}+TC_S$	B_{L1}
2	1		C_{12}	$C_{12}+C_S$	• • •	$C_{12}+(T-2)C_S$	$C_{12}+(T-1)C_S$	B_{12}
	2		C_{22}	$C_{22}+C_S$	• • •	$C_{22}+(T-2)C_S$	$C_{22}+(T-1)C_S$	B_{22}
	•		•	•	• • •	•	•	•
	L		C_{L2}	$C_{L2}+C_S$	• • •	$C_{L2}+(T-2)C_S$	$C_{L2}+(T-1)C_S$	B_{L2}
•	•			•	• • •	•	•	•
T	1				• • •	C_{1T}	$C_{1T}+C_S$	B_{1T}
	2				• • •	C_{2T}	$C_{2T}+C_S$	B_{2T}
	•				• • •	•	•	•
	L				• • •	C_{LT}	$C_{LT}+C_S$	B_{LT}
Demand		d_1	d_2	d_3	• • •	d_T	S	

$$S = I_0 + \sum_{j=1}^{T} \sum_{i=1}^{L} B_{ij} - \sum_{j=1}^{T} d_j$$

Figure 51

We can demonstrate the applicability of the transportation method of solution by displaying the model in tableau format. The result is contained in Fig. 51.

As a numerical illustration, suppose that three periods are under consideration and that two production alternatives, regular time and overtime, are available in each period. The following data are provided us:

Period	*Capacities in Units*		*Unit Production Cost*		*Anticipated Demand*
	Regular Time	*Overtime*	*Regular Time*	*Overtime*	
1	100	20	\$14	\$18	60
2	100	10	17	22	80
3	60	20	17	22	140

The cost of carrying one unit in inventory from one period to the next is \$1. The inventory level at the start of period 1 is 15 units.

The algebraic formulation of the problem is as follows:

Minimize $Z = 17X_{11} + 21X_{21} + 19X_{12} + 24X_{22} + 18X_{13} + 23X_{23} - 435$ subject to the constraints

$$X_{11} \leqq 100 \qquad X_{21} \leqq 20$$

$$X_{12} \leqq 100 \qquad X_{22} \leqq 10$$

$$X_{13} \leqq 60 \qquad X_{23} \leqq 20$$

$$X_{11} + X_{21} \geqq 45$$

$$X_{11} + X_{21} + X_{12} + X_{22} \geqq 125$$

$$X_{11} + X_{21} + X_{12} + X_{22} + X_{13} + X_{23} \geqq 265$$

(The student should verify that the use of Eqs. (1) through (4) yield the formulation given above.)

The transportation formulation of the problem is shown below.

ORIGINS		DEMAND IN PERIOD			Slack	Capacity
Period	Source	1	2	3		
Initial Inventory		0	1	2	X	15
1	1 R.T.	14	15	16	17	100
	2. O.T.	18	19	20	21	20
2	1 R.T.	X	17	18	19	100
	2. O.T.	X	22	23	24	10
3	1. R.T.	X	X	17	18	60
	2. O.T.	X	X	22	23	20
Demand		60	80	140	45	325

The framework of this type of problem can easily be expanded to include multiple plants, multiple products, minimum inventory levels, minimum production levels, and many other variations. A number of these are contained in the exercises at the end of this chapter.

Example 2. *A product mix problem.* A manufacturer can utilize his production facilities to manufacture any or all of n different products in a given period of time. The unit profit of product j is c_j. Constraints upon his production are imposed by limited capacity in each of his m production departments and by minimum and maximum production levels derived from contracts and sales forecasts. Let b_i, $i = 1, 2, \ldots, m$, be the available capacity in department i during the period, a_{ij} be the number of units of capacity in department i consumed in producing one unit of product j, and L_j and U_j be lower and upper limits, respectively, upon the production of product j. The problem is to determine the maximum-profit production program for the period.

Stated algebraically, the manufacturer wishes to choose nonnegative $x_1, x_2, \ldots, x_n$ to maximize

$$c_1x_1 + c_2x_2 + \cdots + c_nx_n$$

subject to constraints on departmental capacities

$$a_{i1}x_1 + a_{i2}x_2 + \cdots + a_{in}x_n \leqq b_i, \qquad i = 1, 2, \ldots, m$$

and production levels

$$\left.\begin{array}{l} x_j \geqq L_j \\ x_j \leqq U_j \end{array}\right\} \qquad j = 1, 2, \ldots, n.$$

We should observe that the size of this problem can be reduced by defining x'_j to be the production of product j in excess of L_j, the required minimum production level. Actually the manufacturer's decision problem involves the optimal use of the capacity which remains after he has satisfied his minimum requirements, and thus he is free only to specify the x'_j. The revised problem is to choose nonnegative $x'_1, x'_2, \ldots, x'_n$ to maximize

$$c_1x'_1 + c_2x'_2 + \cdots + c_nx'_n$$

subject to

$$a_{i1}x'_1 + a_{i2}x'_2 + \cdots + a_{in}x'_n \leqq b_i - \sum_{j=1}^{n} a_{ij}L_j, \qquad i = 1, 2, \ldots, m$$

$$x'_j \leqq U_j - L_j, \qquad j = 1, 2, \ldots, n.$$

To consider a numerical illustration, suppose there are three products and four manufacturing departments. The following data are available:

	Production Level		*Production Hours per Unit*				
Product	*Minimum*	*Maximum*	*Dept.* 1	*Dept.* 2	*Dept.* 3	*Dept.* 4	*Unit Profit*
A	20	200	0.10	0.06	0.18	0.13	\$10
B	0	100	0.12	0.05	—	0.10	12
C	70	180	0.15	0.09	0.07	0.08	15
Available Production Hours			36.0	30.0	37.0	38.0	

Let x_1, x_2, x_3 be the number of units of products A, B, and C, respectively, to be manufactured in this period.

The problem is to choose nonnegative x_1, x_2, x_3 to maximize

$$10x_1 + 12x_2 + 15x_3$$

subject to the constraints

$$\begin{aligned}
0.10x_1 + 0.12x_2 + 0.15x_3 &\leqq 36.0,\\
0.06x_1 + 0.05x_2 + 0.09x_3 &\leqq 30.0,\\
0.18x_1 \qquad\quad + 0.07x_3 &\leqq 37.0,\\
0.13x_1 + 0.10x_2 + 0.08x_3 &\leqq 38.0,\\
x_1 &\geqq 20.0,\\
x_1 &\leqq 200.0,\\
x_2 &\leqq 100.0,\\
x_3 &\geqq 70.0,\\
x_3 &\leqq 180.0.
\end{aligned}$$

An alternate way to state the problem results from defining x_1', x_2', x_3' to be the production of products A, B, and C in excess of the minimum production levels. The problem is to choose nonnegative x_1', x_2', x_3' to maximize

$$10x_1' + 12x_2' + 15x_3' + 1250$$

subject to the constraints

$$\begin{aligned}
0.10x_1' + 0.12x_2' + 0.15x_3' &\leqq 23.5,\\
0.06x_1' + 0.05x_2' + 0.09x_3' &\leqq 22.5,\\
0.18x_1' \qquad\quad + 0.07x_3' &\leqq 28.5,\\
0.13x_1' + 0.10x_2' + 0.08x_3' &\leqq 29.8,\\
x_1' &\leqq 180.0,\\
x_2' &\leqq 100.0,\\
x_3' &\leqq 110.0.
\end{aligned}$$

Example 3. *A cascaded production process.* Suppose that a manufacturer wishes to schedule a process consisting of two production operations in sequence and producing a single product. Because of the imbalance between productive capacity in given time periods, an in-process inventory of parts is maintained between the two operations. Also, a finished goods inventory is kept after the second operation. Assume T production periods are to be planned and that production in a given period can be used to satisfy demand in that period. There are two production alternatives available for each operation in each period: regular time and overtime. Let

d_j = expected demand for finished parts in period j,

x_{ij} = number of parts to be scheduled on regular time at operation i in period j,

y_{ij} = number of parts to be scheduled on overtime at operation i in period j,

a_{ij} = cost of producing one part on regular time at operation i in period j,
b_{ij} = cost of producing one part on overtime at operation i in period j,
A_{ij} = regular time production capacity (in parts) at operation i in period j,
B_{ij} = overtime production capacity (in parts) at operation i in period j,
I_{1j} = in-process inventory at the end of period j (I_{10} is the initial in-process inventory),
I_{2j} = finished parts inventory at the end of period j (I_{20} is the initial finished parts inventory),
c_1 = cost of carrying one part in in-process inventory from one period to the next, and
c_2 = cost of carrying one part in finished parts inventory from one period to the next.

The objective is to choose nonnegative x_{ij}, y_{ij}, $i = 1, 2, j = 1, 2, \ldots, T$, to minimize

$$\sum_{j=1}^{T} \sum_{i=1}^{2} (a_{ij}x_{ij} + b_{ij}y_{ij}) + c_1 \sum_{j=1}^{T} I_{1j} + c_2 \sum_{j=1}^{T} I_{2j}.$$

The first term represents the total production cost over the T periods, and the second and third terms represent the inventory carrying costs at the two inventory points. In working this problem to its conclusion, one should use the relationships

$$I_{1j} = I_{10} + \sum_{t=1}^{j} (x_{1t} + y_{1t}) - \sum_{t=1}^{j} (x_{2t} + y_{2t})$$

and

$$I_{2j} = I_{20} + \sum_{t=1}^{j} (x_{2t} + y_{2t}) - \sum_{t=1}^{j} d_t$$

to express the objective function (and the constraints which follow) entirely in terms of the $\{x_{ij}\}$ and the $\{y_{ij}\}$.

A constraint is the requirement that the production capacities not be exceeded:

$$x_{ij} \leqq A_{ij}, \qquad i = 1, 2, \qquad j = 1, 2, \ldots, T,$$
$$y_{ij} \leqq B_{ij}, \qquad i = 1, 2, \qquad j = 1, 2, \ldots, T.$$

A second constraint is that the demand for finished parts be met by operation 2. This means that the finished goods inventory will never be "negative":

$$I_{2j} \geqq 0, \qquad j = 1, 2, \ldots, T.$$

Finally, to insure that operation 2 is able to obtain semifinished parts from operation 1, we require that the in-process inventory never be "negative":

$$I_{1j} \geqq 0, \qquad j = 1, 2, \ldots, T.$$

A numerical example is given as Exercise 12 at the end of this chapter.

Example 4. *The caterer problem.* A classical example in the literature of linear programming is the "caterer problem." Its relevance to practical decision problems will be discussed after we have examined the structure of the version normally used to illustrate this type of model.

A caterer is faced with the problem of providing napkins for dinners on each of n consecutive days. The number of napkins required on the ith day will be denoted by d_i. These requirements may be met by purchasing new napkins at a cost of a cents per napkin or by laundering napkins soiled at an earlier dinner. Two types of laundry service are available: regular service, which requires r days and costs b cents per napkin, and special service, which requires $s < r$ days and costs $c > b$ cents per napkin. Thus a napkin soiled on the ith day could be used again on the $(i + r)$th day or the $(i + s)$th day depending upon whether or not special service was utilized. We suppose that $c < a$ and $r < n$. The napkins, which can be purchased in an unlimited supply, are of a special design appropriate only to this series of dinners; therefore, we may assume that they have no terminal value to the caterer. The problem is to meet the requirements for fresh napkins at minimum cost.

An algebraic definition of the caterer's decision problem requires the following variables:

$x_i =$ the number of napkins purchased for use on the ith day,
$y_i =$ the number of napkins sent to the laundry, regular service, on the ith day,
$z_i =$ the number of napkins sent to the laundry, special service, on the ith day, and
$I_i =$ the inventory of soiled napkins carried over to the $(i + 1)$st day.

The problem is to choose nonnegative $x_i, y_i, z_i, I_i, i = 1, 2, \ldots, n$, to minimize

$$\sum_{i=1}^{n} (ax_i + by_i + cz_i)$$

subject to the constraints

$$x_i + y_{i-r} + z_{i-s} = d_i, \qquad i = 1, 2, \ldots, n,$$

and

$$y_i + z_i + I_i - I_{i-1} = d_i, \qquad i = 1, 2, \ldots, n.$$

The first set of constraints insures that the requirements for each dinner are met (obviously $y_{i-r} = 0$ for $i \leq r$, and $z_{i-s} = 0$ for $i \leq s$), and the latter set of constraints defines the change in the inventory of soiled napkins (which is necessary since the $\{I_i\}$ are dependent upon the $\{d_i\}$, $\{y_i\}$, and $\{z_i\}$).

As a numerical example, suppose $n = 8$, $\{d_i\} = (100, 110, 145, 90, 150, 140, 120, 130)$, $a = 10$, $b = 4$, $c = 6$, $r = 4$, and $s = 2$. The problem is to choose nonnegative $x_i, y_i, z_i, I_i, i = 1, 2, \ldots, 8$, to minimize

$$\sum_{i=1}^{8} (10x_i + 4y_i + 6z_i)$$

subject to the constraints

$$
\begin{aligned}
x_1 \qquad\qquad\; &= 100,\\
x_2 \qquad\qquad\; &= 110,\\
x_3 \qquad + z_1 &= 145,\\
x_4 \qquad + z_2 &= 90,\\
x_5 + y_1 + z_3 &= 150,\\
x_6 + y_2 + z_4 &= 140,\\
x_7 + y_3 + z_5 &= 120,\\
x_8 + y_4 + z_6 &= 130,
\end{aligned}
$$

and

$$
\begin{aligned}
y_1 + z_1 + I_1 \qquad\; &= 100,\\
y_2 + z_2 + I_2 - I_1 &= 110,\\
y_3 + z_3 + I_3 - I_2 &= 145,\\
y_4 + z_4 + I_4 - I_3 &= 90,\\
y_5 + z_5 + I_5 - I_4 &= 150,\\
y_6 + z_6 + I_6 - I_5 &= 140,\\
y_7 + z_7 + I_7 - I_6 &= 120,\\
y_8 + z_8 + I_8 - I_7 &= 130,
\end{aligned}
$$

The caterer problem also may be formulated as a transportation problem. The method is illustrated in Fig. 52.

More practical and important applications of models of this type are related to maintenance problems, such as decisions to purchase and to overhaul aircraft engines.

Example 5. *A blending problem.* A product is formed by mixing together certain raw materials (ingredients). Some or all of n available ingredients may be used. The product must conform to m specifications on its properties, and these properties are linear functions of the quantity of each ingredient used. Let c_j be the unit cost of ingredient j, $j = 1, 2, \ldots, n$, and let a_{ij} be the contribution of a unit of ingredient j to property i of the product. Finally, let b_i be the specification on property i for a unit of product. This specification may be of the form "equal to b_i," "less than or equal to b_i," or "greater than or equal to b_i." The problem is to satisfy the specifications with a minimum-cost mix of the available ingredients.

The algebraic statement of this problem would be as follows: Let x_j be the fraction of a unit of ingredient j used for each unit of product. Choose nonnegative $x_1, x_2, \ldots, x_n$ to minimize

$$c_1x_1 + c_2x_2 + \cdots + c_nx_n$$

subject to

$$a_{i1}x_1 + a_{i2}x_2 + \cdots + a_{in}x_n \begin{Bmatrix} \leqq \\ = \\ \geqq \end{Bmatrix} b_i, \qquad \text{for } i = 1, 2, \ldots, m,$$

and

$$x_1 + x_2 + \cdots + x_n = 1.$$

As a numerical illustration, suppose a fertilizer manufacturer, who normally produces 5–10–5, 10–8–6, and 14–6–4, receives a special order for an 8–7–5 mix. ("10–8–6" means that the fertilizer is 10 per cent nitrates, 8 per cent phosphates, 6 per cent potash, and 76 per cent inert ingredients, by weight.) He wishes to fill this special order by blending quantities of the three standard fertilizers taken from his finished stock inventory. The value per pound is \$0.02 for 5–10–5, \$0.03 for 10–8–6, and \$0.04 for 14–6–4.

Demand / Source	Day 1	Day 2	Day 3	Day 4	Day 5	Day 6	Day 7	Day 8	Slack	Available
Purchased new	10	10	10	10	10	10	10	10	0	985*
Soiled on day 1	X	X	6	6	4	4	4	4	0	100
Soiled on day 2	X	X	X	6	6	4	4	4	0	110
Soiled on day 3	X	X	X	X	6	6	4	4	0	145
Soiled on day 4	X	X	X	X	X	6	6	4	0	90
Soiled on day 5	X	X	X	X	X	X	6	6	0	150
Soiled on day 6	X	X	X	X	X	X	X	6	0	140
Soiled on day 7	X	X	X	X	X	X	X	X	0	120
Soiled on day 8	X	X	X	X	X	X	X	X	0	130
Required	100	110	145	90	150	140	120	130	985	1970

* The supply of new napkins is unlimited, so using $\sum_{i=1}^{n} d_i$ as the "available quantity" is sufficient to permit the extreme solution of purchasing all napkins and sending none to the laundry.

Figure 52

Assume that he has a very large stock of the standard fertilizers in comparison with the size of the order for 8–7–5.

Let x_1, x_2, and x_3 represent the fraction of a pound of 5–10–5, 10–8–6, and 14–6–4, respectively, mixed to form a pound of 8–7–5. The problem is to choose nonnegative x_1, x_2, and x_3 to minimize

$$0.02x_1 + 0.03x_2 + 0.04x_3$$

subject to

$$\begin{aligned} 0.05x_1 + 0.10x_2 + 0.14x_3 &= 0.08, \\ 0.10x_1 + 0.08x_2 + 0.06x_3 &= 0.07, \\ 0.05x_1 + 0.06x_2 + 0.04x_3 &= 0.05, \\ x_1 + \quad x_2 + \quad x_3 &= 1.00. \end{aligned}$$

[This formulation describes the problem, but there is no solution meeting the constraints.]

Example 6. *A paper trim problem.* A certain paper machine produces paper in reels of a standard width, 180 inches. A set of customer orders for reels of a fixed length (diameter), but varying widths, is summarized below:

Width (inches)	*Number of Reels Ordered*
80	200
45	120
27	130

These narrower reels must be cut from 180-inch reels of the required length. A program for cutting the wide reels is required to minimize the total waste at the ends. A number of possibilities exist for cutting a 180-inch reel, and the logical alternatives are listed in the table below:

	Alternative								
	1	2	3	4	5	6	7	8	9
80-in. Widths	2	1	1	1	0	0	0	0	0
45-in. Widths	0	2	1	0	4	3	2	1	0
27-in. Widths	0	0	2	3	0	1	3	5	6
Waste	20	10	1	19	0	18	9	0	18

Let x_j be the number of 180-inch reels cut according to alternative j, $j = 1, 2, \ldots, 9$. The problem is to choose nonnegative $x_1, x_2, \ldots, x_9$ to minimize the waste function

$$20x_1 + 10x_2 + x_3 + 19x_4 + 18x_6 + 9x_7 + 18x_9$$

subject to

$$\begin{aligned} 2x_1 + x_2 + x_3 + x_4 &\geq 200, \\ 2x_2 + x_3 + 4x_5 + 3x_6 + 2x_7 + x_8 &\geq 120, \\ 2x_3 + 3x_4 + x_6 + 3x_7 + 5x_8 + 6x_9 &\geq 130. \end{aligned}$$

[This formulation of the objective function assumes that the few extra 80-, 45-, or 27-inch rolls to result from cutting an integral number of 180-inch reels can be utilized. If not, a more appropriate form of the objective function would be $x_1 + x_2 + \cdots + x_9$.]

EXERCISES

1. Solve the following production planning problem by specifying how many units of product should be manufactured each period in order to minimize the sum of inventory holding costs and production costs:

	Period 1	*Period* 2	*Period* 3	*Period* 4	*Period* 5
Regular Time Capacity, Units	120	100	90	140	90
Overtime Capacity, Units	30	40	20	40	60
Production Requirements, Units	110	160	100	100	150
Regular Time Cost per Unit	\$12	\$12	\$16	\$10	\$11
Overtime Cost per Unit	15	16	18	14	14

There are 20 units of product in inventory at the start of period 1. Assume the cost of carrying a unit in inventory from one period to the next is \$1.

2. A plant makes three products, *A*, *B*, and *C*. The following data describe the production planning problem:

Product	*Profit per Piece*	*Minimum Weekly Requirements*	*Processing Time in Hours per Piece*				
			Lathe Dept.	*Milling Dept.*	*Grinding Dept.*	*Inspection*	*Packing*
A	\$20	100 pieces	0.2	0.5	0.1	0.02	0.05
B	18	180	0.1	....	0.3	0.02	0.06
C	21	75	0.3	0.07	0.1	0.02	0.05
Department Capacity in Hours per Week			160	80	80	40	40

For example, product *A* would have to be processed through all five departments, while product *B* would not have to be processed through the milling department.

The problem is to find the weekly production rate for each product. Set this up as a linear programming problem.

3. A machine shop manufactures two products, *A* and *B*. The shop has four machines. There are several possibilities for the manufacture of each product, and the unit profit varies depending upon the particular combination of ma-

chines used. The following table gives the different possible routings and the associated time and profit values.

Product	*Routing*	*Unit Production Time in Hours*				*Unit Profit*
		Machine 1	*Machine* 2	*Machine* 3	*Machine* 4	
A	1	0.5	...	0.2	...	$2.00
	2	...	0.4	0.2	...	2.50
B	1	0.4	...	0.3	...	5.00
	2	0.4	...	...	0.4	4.00
	3	...	0.6	0.3	...	4.00
	4	...	0.6	...	0.4	3.00
Available Hours per Week		38	31	34	23	

The company has contracts which require that it make at least 100 units of product A and 85 units of product B each week. The problem is to determine the most profitable production program for the shop. Formulate this as a linear programming problem.

4. An agency which leases trucks for local hauling has the problem of a shortage of trucks in some locations and a surplus of trucks in other locations. Two types of trucks are involved. The following situation exists:

Location	*Trucks Short*		*Trucks Surplus*	
	Type I	*Type* II	*Type* I	*Type* II
Jacksonville	...	2	7	
Atlanta	10	...	...	1
Richmond	...	...	6	2
New Orleans	4	...	...	10
Nashville	...	4	5	
Charlotte	8	2		
Memphis	...	1		
Birmingham	...	...	2	3

The cost of moving a truck from one location to another is proportional to the mileage. The truck rental rates are sufficiently high to justify any relocation of a truck.

(a) Find the optimal relocation program, assuming that the truck types are not interchangeable.

(b) Find the optimal relocation program, assuming that type II trucks can be substituted for type I, but type I cannot substitute for type II. Further, assume that the cost to relocate a type II truck is 20 per cent more than the cost of the same move of a type I truck. For simplicity, assume that the two types of trucks have the same rental rate.

(*Note*: The analyst will have to consult mileage tables, thereby making this a research problem!)

5. A manufacturer of fertilizer markets four mixes of lawn fertilizer: 6–8–6,

10–6–4, 12–5–8, 14–5–10. The numbers refer to the percentage by weight of nitrates, phosphates, and potash, respectively, in the product.
Manufacturing is a mixing process whereby the active ingredients are mixed in the proper proportions with inert ingredients, and the mix is then packaged and sold.
For the period being planned, the manufacturer has available 2300 tons of nitrates, 1400 tons of phosphates, and 1800 tons of potash. He has access to a very large supply of the inert ingredients, so that they will not constrain his choice of a production program.
Demand data for the period are shown in the following table:

Product	*Selling Price per Ton*	*Sales Forecast*	
		Minimum	*Maximum*
6–8–6	$ 60	600 tons	8,000 tons
10–6–4	80	3,000 tons	no limit
12–5–8	100	none	10,000 tons
14–5–10	120	4,000 tons	no limit

The company must produce at least the minimum quantity forecast and will not produce an amount greater than the maximum forecast.
The costs per ton of the fertilizer components are the following: nitrates, $200; phosphates, $60; potash, $90; other ingredients, $15. Costs of packaging materials, mixing, bagging, and selling are estimated to be $20 per ton, regardless of the mix.
The problem is to determine how much of each product to produce. Formulate this problem for solution as a linear programming problem.

6. The following table contains production requirements and capacities for the next five production periods:

Period	*Regular Time Capacity*	*Overtime Capacity*	*Demand*
1	600	100	400
2	600	100	500
3	400	100	600
4	600	50	800
5	600	100	300

The initial inventory at the beginning of period 1 is 150 units.
The minimum inventory to be allowed is 100 units.
The minimum production level is to be 80 per cent of regular time capacity.
The unit production cost is $10 if produced on regular time and $14 if produced on overtime.
The cost of storing a unit from one period to the next is $2.
The final inventory is to be as small as possible consistent with the requirements for minimum inventory and minimum production levels.
(a) Formulate the problem algebraically as a linear programming problem.
(b) Place the problem in a tableau for solution as a transportation problem. (This is not easily done, because of the constraints on minimum production levels and minimum inventories. One can think of production capacity available

in a period as being made up of two parts, one whose use is required and one whose use is optional. Further, one can consider that a certain amount of inventory must be on hand at all times as a matter of policy.)

7. A company has three plants, all of which make the same product. This product is made to order and the decision problem is to determine at which plant an order should be made. The following orders are to be scheduled into production.

Customer	*Order Size*	*Shipping Costs per Unit*		
		From Plant 1	*From Plant* 2	*From Plant* 3
W	700 units	$ 8.00	$ 4.00	$ 6.00
X	1500	11.00	10.00	8.00
Y	400	6.00	12.00	7.00
Z	500	9.00	5.00	14.00

The production costs vary from plant to plant and so does the available capacity:

Plant	*Unit Production Cost*	*Available Capacity*
A	$45	1000 units
B	40	800
C	50	1500

Find the minimum-cost production-distribution schedule, assuming that orders can be split among the plants.

8. A small steel company makes special alloys to meet customer specifications. One customer requires an alloy involving four metals, and he has specified the following composition:

Metal	*Requirements**
A	No more than 18%
B	At least 30%
C	Between 40% and 60%
D	No more than 2%

*No impurities are permitted in the alloy.

Several ores are available from which the different metals may be obtained. These ores also contain impurities which would be separated and discarded. Pertinent data are contained in the following table:

Ore	*Metal A*	*Metal B*	*Metal C*	*Metal D*	*Impurities*	*Cost per Ton*
1	20%	20%	40%	0%	20%	$25
2	15	0	20	5	60	$10
3	0	40	30	0	30	$20
4	10	20	30	0	40	$18
5	10	25	25	10	30	$22
6	5	8	17	10	60	$12

The problem is to determine how much of each ore to use in producing 1 ton of alloy. Formulate this problem for solution by linear programming.

9. Suppose that the customer order referred to in Exercise 8 had been for 3000 tons, and the steel company had the following amounts of ore available:

Ore	*Tons*
1	1000
2	3000
3	2000
4	800
5	2600
6	1700

The problem is to find the minimum-cost program to fill the customer's order. Formulate this problem for solution by linear programming.

10. A department in a manufacturing plant produces two parts, *A* and *B*, made according to the following sequence of operations:

Product	*Operation*	*On Machine*	*Unit Processing Time in Hours*	*Fraction Scrap*
A	1	M1	0.03	0.01
	2	M2	0.07	0.05
	3	M3	0.05	0.02
B	1	M1	0.12	0.03
	2	M3	0.08	0.10
	3	M4	0.17	0.02
	4	M1	0.04	0.07

Machine operating data are as follows:

Machine	*Cost per Hour*	*Available Hours*
M1	$20	400
M2	30	340
M3	40	410
M4	50	160

Product data are as follows:

Product	*Unit Selling Price*	*Unit Raw-Material Cost*	*Demand Constraints*	
			Minimum	*Maximum*
A	$ 60	$20	100 units	none
B	100	25	150 units	250 units

The problem is to schedule production for this department in the next period. Set this problem up as a linear programming problem. Assume that all defective parts are detected and removed immediately upon their manufacture. (*Hint*: Let variables A and B represent the amount of each product *started* into production in the next period.)

11. A department processes three products, A, B, and C. Production for the next four periods is to be planned. The following data are available:

Product	*Hours per Piece*	*Initial Inventory*	*Requirements in Period*			
			1	2	3	4
A	0.2	20 pieces	400 pieces	100 pieces	80 pieces	200 pieces
B	0.1	50	30	120	200	400
C	0.4	30	200	200	600	1000

Period	*Available Capacity in Hours*	
	Regular Time	*Overtime*
1	250	50
2	250	40
3	230	40
4	230	40

The cost of an hour of production time is \$100 if regular time and \$150 if overtime. Costs to store one piece for one period are \$1, \$2, and \$2, for products A, B, and C, respectively.

(a) The problem is to meet the requirements with the lowest cost program. Formulate this algebraically as a linear programming problem. Solve for the optimal solution, using the transportation method.

(b) How would the formulation and solution of this problem be affected by a requirement that, at the completion of period 4, the inventory levels should be 10 units of product A, 15 units of product B, and 8 units of product C?

12. A product is processed through two operations sequentially, as illustrated below:

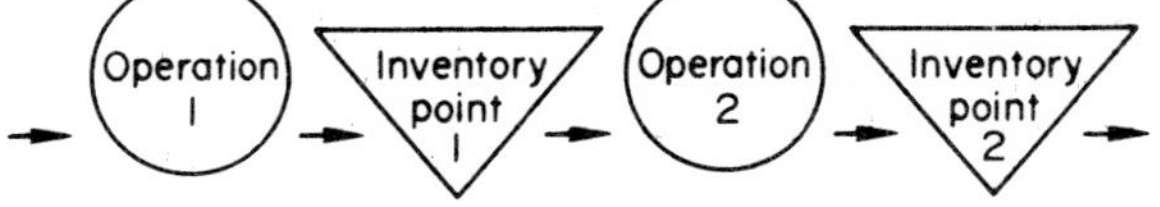

Production is to be planned for the next three time periods. The following data are available:

Period	*Demand Units*	*Available Production Capacity in Hours*			
		Operation 1		*Operation* 2	
		Regular Time	*Overtime*	*Regular Time*	*Overtime*
1	80	35	8	38	7
2	80	30	6	32	6
3	90	30	6	34	7

Operation	*Processing Time per Unit*	*Processing Cost per Unit*	
		Regular Time	*Overtime*
1	20 minutes	$10	$13
2	30	12	16

Inventory Point	*Initial Inventory*	*Unit Storage Cost per Period*
1	6	$2
2	5	1

The problem is to develop a production program which specifies how many units will be produced at each operation, regular time and overtime, in each period. The objective is to minimize the total cost of production and carrying inventory.

Formulate this problem as a linear programming problem.

13. Two plants *A* and *B* can each make three products *X*, *Y*, and *Z*. These plants work a regular five-day, three-shift work week, but can schedule overtime on the weekends if necessary. Three weeks' production is to be scheduled. The following data are available:

Production requirements in units:

Product	*Period* 1	*Period* 2	*Period* 3
X	120	100	50
Y	200	200	160
Z	70	100	140

Cost per unit:

Source	*Product X*	*Product Y*	*Product Z*
Plant *A*—regular time	$2.60	$4.20	$3.10
Plant *A*—overtime	2.90	4.70	3.30
Plant *B*—regular time	2.80	4.30	3.20
Plant *B*—overtime	3.20	4.80	3.40

Production capacities in hours:

	Period 1	*Period* 2	*Period* 3
Plant *A*—regular time	120	120	100
Plant *A*—overtime	40	40	20
Plant *B*—regular time	210	200	230
Plant *B*—overtime	80	60	80

Cost of storage per unit of inventory per period:

	Product X	*Product Y*	*Product Z*
Plant *A*	$0.15	$0.25	$0.18
Plant *B*	0.16	0.28	0.20

Unit production time in hours:

	Product X	*Product Y*	*Product Z*
Plant *A*	0.80	1.20	1.00
Plant *B*	0.80	1.30	1.10

The problem is to find the minimum-cost program to satisfy the production requirements. There is no inventory at the start of the first period. Formulate this problem for solution by linear programming.

REFERENCES

1. Gale, D., A Theorem on Flows in Networks, *Pacific Journal of Math.*, vol. 7, 1957, pp. 1073–82.

2. Gass, Saul I., *Linear Programming*, 2d ed. New York: McGraw-Hill Book Company, 1964.

3. Hadley, G., *Linear Programming*. Reading, Mass.: Addison-Wesley Publishing Company, Inc., 1962.

ANSWERS TO SELECTED EXERCISES

Chapter 1

1. (a) Maximum value is 12 and occurs only at (4, 0); minimum value is -9 and occurs only at $(-3, 0)$.

(b) Maximum value is 32 and occurs at each point of the segment joining $(3, -4)$ and (4, 0); minimum value is -24 and occurs only at $(-3, 0)$.

2. Maximum value is 12 and occurs only at (0, 3); there is no minimum value.

3. (a) $k > \frac{1}{3}$; maximum value is 1 for each $k > \frac{1}{3}$.

(b) $k \leqq \frac{1}{3}$; yes; for each $k < \frac{1}{3}$ the maximum value is -4 and, for $k = \frac{1}{3}$, the maximum value is 1.

(c) No. There is a discontinuity at $k = \frac{1}{3}$.

4. (a) No tables and 30 chairs (maximum profit is $90).

(b) Either 6 tables and 15 chairs or 7 tables and 12 chairs (maximum profit is $66).

5. (a) Maximum value is 21 and occurs only at (3, 9).

(b) Maximum value is $\frac{9}{4}$ and occurs only at $(\frac{3}{2}, \frac{27}{4})$.

(c) Maximum value is 90 and occurs only at (3, 9).

(d) Maximum value is $\frac{5}{2^{6/5}}$ and occurs only at $\left(\frac{3}{2^{1/5}}, \frac{9}{2^{3/5}}\right)$.

Chapter 2

Section **2–1***:*

1. (a) $\begin{pmatrix} 4 & 16 & 9 \\ 10 & 3 & 0 \end{pmatrix}$ (b) $\begin{pmatrix} 8 & 4 \\ 6 & 7 \\ -25 & 11 \end{pmatrix}$ (c) Undefined

(d) $\begin{pmatrix} 3 & 22 \\ 8 & 11 \end{pmatrix}$ (e) $\begin{pmatrix} 27 & 13 \\ -4 & 3 \end{pmatrix}$ (f) $\begin{pmatrix} 5 \\ 5 \end{pmatrix}$ (g) $\begin{pmatrix} -5 & 6 & 3 \\ 1 & 2 & 9 \\ 8 & 6 & 7 \end{pmatrix}$

(h) $\begin{pmatrix} 12 & 0 & 15 \\ 8 & 0 & 10 \\ -4 & 0 & -5 \end{pmatrix}$ (i) (7) (j) $\begin{pmatrix} -47 & 38 \\ -29 & 68 \\ -31 & 64 \end{pmatrix}$

2. n by m; $m = n$

7. (a) n by p

Section **2–2***:*

1. (a) Unique solution: $[-2, 3, 5]$

(b) No solutions

(c) All vectors of form $[4 + 2a, 4, 2 - 3a - 4b, a, b]$

(d) All vectors of form $[a, 0, -5 - \frac{5}{2}a + 3b, b, 3 + 4a - 3b, 4]$

(e) All vectors of form $[a - 1, a, 2]$

(f) No solutions

(g) All vectors of form $[a, -2a, a]$

Note: The expressions which appear in (c), (d), (e), and (g) are not the only correct ones.

3. (e) The smallest number in T is -17.

4. (a) All matrices $\mathbf{X}$ of the form $\mathbf{X} = \begin{pmatrix} 8 & -8a & -6 & -8b \\ 13 & -12a & -7 & -12b \\ & a & & b \end{pmatrix}$

(b) No solutions

(c) $\mathbf{X} = \begin{pmatrix} 8 & 10 & -1 \\ -2 & -2 & 1 \\ 2 & 1 & 1 \end{pmatrix}$ (d) $\mathbf{X} = \frac{1}{7}\begin{pmatrix} 2 & -3 \\ 1 & 2 \end{pmatrix}$

5. (a) $\begin{pmatrix} -14 & 11 & 4 \\ 4 & -3 & -1 \\ -3 & 2 & 1 \end{pmatrix}$ (b) $\frac{1}{2}\begin{pmatrix} -1 & 1 & 1 \\ 1 & 1 & -1 \\ 1 & -1 & 1 \end{pmatrix}$

(c) None exists. (d) $\begin{pmatrix} \frac{1}{2} & 0 & 0 & 0 \\ 0 & \frac{1}{3} & 0 & 0 \\ 0 & 0 & -\frac{1}{4} & 0 \\ 0 & 0 & 0 & \frac{1}{5} \end{pmatrix}$

7. Statement (c) is true.

8. (a) $\mathbf{X} = \mathbf{A}^{-1}\mathbf{B}$

10. Impossible changes: $U \longrightarrow I, I \longrightarrow U$

Section **2–3***:*

$\mathscr{V}$ is a vector space in Exercises 1, 3, 4, 5, 6, 7, 8, and 9(a). In Exercise 2, V_5 does not hold (and hence, V_6 is meaningless); in 9(b), $V_1, \ldots, V_6$ each fails to hold.

Section **2–4***:*

1. $\mathbf{b}_1 = 8\mathbf{a}_1 + 0\mathbf{a}_2 + 7\mathbf{a}_3 + 0\mathbf{a}_4$; $\mathbf{b}_2$ is not a linear combination of $\mathbf{a}_1, \mathbf{a}_2, \mathbf{a}_3$, and $\mathbf{a}_4$; $\mathbf{b}_3 = 6\mathbf{a}_1 + 0\mathbf{a}_2 - \mathbf{a}_3 + 0\mathbf{a}_4$.

2. $\mathbf{a}_1 = -9\mathbf{a}_2 + 4\mathbf{a}_4 + 5\mathbf{a}_7$, $\mathbf{a}_2 = \mathbf{a}_2 + 0\mathbf{a}_4 + 0\mathbf{a}_7$, $\mathbf{a}_3 = \mathbf{a}_2 - \mathbf{a}_4 + 2\mathbf{a}_7$, $\mathbf{a}_4 = 0\mathbf{a}_2 + \mathbf{a}_4 + 0\mathbf{a}_7$, $\mathbf{a}_5 = -6\mathbf{a}_2 + 4\mathbf{a}_4 + 5\mathbf{a}_7$, $\mathbf{a}_6 = \mathbf{a}_2 + 2\mathbf{a}_4 - 3\mathbf{a}_7$, $\mathbf{a}_7 = 0\mathbf{a}_2 + 0\mathbf{a}_4 + \mathbf{a}_7$.

3. (a) Independent

(b) Independent

(c) Dependent; $7k\mathbf{v}_1 - 23k\mathbf{v}_2 + 3k\mathbf{v}_3 + k\mathbf{v}_4 = \mathbf{0}$ for each real number k.

(d) Dependent; $0\mathbf{v}_1 + 0\mathbf{v}_2 + k\mathbf{v}_3 = \mathbf{0}$ for each k.

(e) Dependent; $(-4a - 2b + \frac{381}{2}c)\mathbf{v}_1 + (3a + b - 29c)\mathbf{v}_2 + a\mathbf{v}_3 + (-b + \frac{61}{2}c)\mathbf{v}_4 + b\mathbf{v}_5 - 7c\mathbf{v}_6 - \frac{9}{2}c\mathbf{v}_7 + c\mathbf{v}_8 = \mathbf{0}$ for any three numbers a, b, and c.

(f) Independent

10. (b) $ab_2c_3 \neq 0$

Section **2–5**:

1. (a) (i); (b) (iii); (c) (iii); (d) (iii); (e) (ii)

2. The numbers 1 and i form a basis. The vector space is 2-dimensional.

3. The matrices $\begin{pmatrix} 1 & 0 \\ 0 & 0 \end{pmatrix}$, $\begin{pmatrix} 0 & 1 \\ 0 & 0 \end{pmatrix}$, and $\begin{pmatrix} 0 & 0 \\ 1 & 0 \end{pmatrix}$ form a basis. The space is 3-dimensional.

4. (b) Corollary 1 to Theorem 10.

Section **2–6**:

1. $\mathbf{A} = \begin{pmatrix} 2 & 68 & 0 & -2 & 6 & 50 \\ -5 & -22 & 1 & -22 & 0 & -14 \\ 1 & -8 & 1 & 10 & -1 & 3 \\ 4 & 32 & 2 & 22 & 2 & 42 \end{pmatrix}$

2. (a) 3; (b) 1; (c) 4; (d) 2

3.

Basis	$\mathbf{a}_1$	$\mathbf{a}_2$	$\mathbf{a}_3$	$\mathbf{a}_4$	$\mathbf{a}_5$	$\mathbf{a}_6$
$\mathbf{a}_3$	0	0	1	$\frac{1}{8}$	$\frac{1}{4}$	$\frac{7}{4}$
$\mathbf{a}_2$	0	1	0	$-\frac{23}{8}$	$-\frac{3}{4}$	$-\frac{41}{4}$
$\mathbf{a}_1$	1	0	0	$\frac{1}{2}$	0	1

4. There are two others, obtained by inserting $\mathbf{a}_6$ and $\mathbf{a}_3$ into the basis.

5. There are two others, obtained by inserting $\mathbf{a}_4$ and $\mathbf{a}_6$ into the basis.

6. (a) $y_{1r} \neq 0$; (b) $\mathbf{a}_1 = (-1/y_{1r})\mathbf{a}_r - (y_{2r}/y_{1r})\mathbf{a}_2 - \cdots - (y_{mr}/y_{1r})\mathbf{a}_m$.

7. Besides those shown in (45), we have $[0, 0, 2, -8, 2]$, $[0, \frac{8}{3}, \frac{10}{9}, 0, \frac{26}{9}]$, $[5, 1, 0, 0, 9]$, and $[8, 0, -\frac{2}{3}, 0, \frac{38}{3}]$.

8. $[0, 2, 3, 0, -8]$; $[0, 26, -5, -4, 0]$.

9. $[4, -1, 2, 0]$, $[-6, 4, 0, -1]$, $[2, 0, \frac{8}{5}, -\frac{1}{5}]$, and $[0, 1, \frac{6}{5}, -\frac{2}{5}]$.

10. $[0, 2, 1, 0, 1]$ and $[0, 3, \frac{4}{3}, \frac{1}{3}, 0]$.

11. $v_3 = 6e_1 - 5v_1 + 3v_2$

Chapter 3

Section **3–1**:

2. Maximize $z = 2x_1 + 6x_2 + 0x_3 + 0x_4 + 0x_5$ subject to

$$\begin{cases} -x_1 + 4x_2 + x_3 + = 16 \\ x_1 + x_2 + x_4 = 9 \\ x_1 - x_2 + x_5 = 3 \\ x_j \geqq 0 \ (j = 1, 2, 3, 4, 5). \end{cases}$$

5. The feasible solutions of the related standard problem corresponding to corner points of the polygon are $[0, 0, 16, 9, 3]$, $[3, 0, 19, 6, 0]$, $[6, 3, 10, 0, 0]$, $[4, 5, 0, 0, 4]$, and $[0, 4, 0, 5, 7]$. The unique optimal solution is $[4, 5, 0, 0, 4]$.

8. There is no such solution.

Section 3–2:

1. $[0, 0, \frac{1}{2}, \frac{1}{2}, \frac{3}{2}, 0]$

2. $[0, 9, 1, 0, 0, 1]$

3. $[2, 0, 7, 0, 0, 0]$

5. Only the insertion of $\mathbf{v}_7$ will yield a non-degenerate solution. This solution is $[2, 0, 0, 1, 0, 3, 1, 4, 0]$.

6. Suppose $\mathbf{v}_k$ is the vector chosen to enter the basis. Then the resulting basic feasible solution is non-degenerate if and only if $y_{ik} < 0$ for each i corresponding to a basic variable which is zero and there is no tie for smallest among the ratios x_i/y_{ik} with $y_{ik} > 0$.

Section 3–3:

1. (a) Insert $\mathbf{v}_2$ for $\mathbf{v}_7$. New solution: $[0, 3, 0, 0, 3, 2, 0]$
(b) Insert $\mathbf{v}_3$ for $\mathbf{v}_5$. New solution: $[0, 0, 1, 0, 0, 1, 2]$
(c) Insert $\mathbf{v}_4$ for $\mathbf{v}_8$. New solution: $[0, 0, 1, 2, 0, 8, 0, 0, 2]$
(d) Insert $\mathbf{v}_1$ for $\mathbf{v}_2$. New solution: $[1, 0, 0, 0, 0, 0, 9, 2]$

2. (a) $\mathbf{v}_2$; (b) $\mathbf{v}_3$; (c) $\mathbf{v}_1$; (d) $\mathbf{v}_3$

3. To obtain maximum improvement of z in (a) replace $\mathbf{v}_6$ by $\mathbf{v}_3$ and in (b) replace $\mathbf{v}_7$ by $\mathbf{v}_4$. The constraints in the original problem are

$$\begin{cases} 2x_1 + 3x_2 + x_3 - x_4 + 6x_5 \leqq 2 \\ 2x_1 + x_2 - x_3 + x_4 + 2x_5 \leqq 1 \\ 5x_1 + 2x_2 + x_3 + 2x_4 - x_5 \leqq 3 \\ x_j \geqq 0 \; (j = 1, \ldots, 5). \end{cases}$$

The objective function is $z = 4x_1 - 2x_2 + 3x_3 - 3x_4 + x_5$.

4. The original problem is as follows: Maximize $z = x_1 + 4x_2 - 2x_3 + 3x_4 - x_5$ subject to

$$\begin{cases} x_1 - 3x_2 + x_3 + 2x_4 + 6x_5 \leqq 3 \\ 2x_1 + x_2 \qquad + 3x_4 + 2x_5 \leqq 6 \\ 4x_1 + x_2 \qquad - x_4 + x_5 \leqq 2 \\ x_j \geqq 0 \; (j = 1, \ldots, 5). \end{cases}$$

Section 3–4:

1. (a) $z_{\max} = \frac{53}{3}$ for $\mathbf{x} = [\frac{17}{3}, \frac{2}{3}, 0]$
(b) No optimal solution
(c) No optimal solution
(d) $z_{\min} = -4$ for $\mathbf{x} = [0, 2, 0]$
(e) No optimal solution

2. For each $\theta > 0$, $\mathbf{x}(\theta) = [\frac{13}{2} + \theta, \frac{7}{2} + 2\theta, 0, \theta, 9 + 5\theta, 0, 0]$ is a feasible solution and we have $z[\mathbf{x}(\theta)] = \frac{53}{2} + 8\theta$.

3. (a) $z_{\max} = 22$ for $\mathbf{x} = [0, 4, 0, 3]$
(b) $z_{\min} = 4$ for $\mathbf{x} = [0, 1, 0, 1, 0]$

7. Maximum weekly profit = \$1200 for 6000 units of *A* only.

8. Maximum weekly profit = \$1600 for 8000 units of *A* only.

9. Maximum weekly profit = \$196,000 for weekly production of 10,000 lbs. each of *A* and *B*, blended as follows:

	1	2	3
A	1000	4000	5000
B	3000	2000	5000

10. Maximum weekly profit = \$2,182,000/7 ≈ \$311,714.28 for weekly production of 120,000/7 lbs. of A and 20,000/7 lbs. of B, blended as follows:

	1	2	3
A	$\frac{12{,}000}{7}$	$\frac{38{,}000}{7}$	10,000
B	$\frac{16{,}000}{7}$	$\frac{4000}{7}$	0

11. Same as Exercise 9.

Section **3–6***:*

1. (a) $z_{\max} = 6$ for $\mathbf{x} = [4, 0, 0, 1]$
(b) $z_{\min} = 4$ for $\mathbf{x} = [2, 0, 2, 4]$
(c) No optimal solution
(d) $z_{\min} = \frac{38}{5}$ for $\mathbf{x} = [0, 1/5, 0, 7/5, 0]$

2. The optimal solution is shown in the accompanying table. The minimum cost is 120.

	R_1	R_2
W_1	3	15
W_2	11	0
W_3	6	0

3. $z_{\max} = 40$ for $\mathbf{x} = [20, 0, 0]$

4. (a) $z_{\max} = 336$ for $\mathbf{x} = [66, 0, 0, 30, 6, 12]$
(b) $z_{\max} = \frac{107}{4}$ for $\mathbf{x} = [\frac{59}{4}, 0, 0, \frac{5}{2}, 0, 0, \frac{1}{4}]$
(c) $z_{\max} = 33$ for $\mathbf{x} = [9, 3, 2, 0, 0, 1, 1]$
(d) $z_{\max} = 66$ for $\mathbf{x} = [0, 1, 0, 14, 2, 0, 0, 0]$
(e) No optimal solution

5. Maximum weekly profit = \$1100 for 4000 units of A, no units of B, and 3000 units of C.

Section **3–8***:*

1. $z_{\max} = \frac{11}{2}$ for $\mathbf{x} = [\frac{3}{2}, \frac{4}{3}, \frac{7}{6}]$
2. $z_{\max} = 17$ for $\mathbf{x} = [2, -1, 3]$
3. $z_{\min} = -13$ for $\mathbf{x} = [21, 16, -25]$
4. $z_{\min} = -12$ for $\mathbf{x} = [\frac{5}{2}, \frac{9}{2}, -5, 0]$

Section **3–9***:*

1. (a) Convex; (b) Non-convex; (c) Convex; (d) Non-convex; (e) Convex; (f) Convex.

2. (a) No; (b) No; (c) No common point.
6. (a) $\mathbf{x}^{(2)} = [0, 14, 4, 8, 0, 9, 0, 0]$
(c) $\mathbf{x} = [0, 12, 3, 9, \frac{5}{4}, 8, 0, 0]$
7. (a) $\mathbf{x}^{(2)} = [1, 6, 0, 9, 0, 2, 0, 0, 0]$, $\mathbf{x}^{(3)} = [0, 5, 0, 2, 1, 4, 0, 0, 0]$

Chapter 4

Section **4–1**:

1. There is another optimal solution with 11 signals per second being sent from T to N_1 and 7 signals per second from T to N_2.

2. (a) 28; (b) 20; (c) $2a$; (d) $a + b$; (e) smaller of $a + c$ and $2a + b$; (f) smaller of $b + c$ and $2b + a$.

Section **4–2**:

4. 51
6. (d) $A(f_{\max}) = 41$
7. $A(f_{\max}) = 28$
8. $A(f_{\max}) = 27$

Section **4–3**:

3. (a) Non-feasible; (b) Feasible
4. (a) Feasible; (b) Non-feasible; (c) Feasible

Section **4–4**:

3. (a) Cost $= 235$; (b) Cost $= 467$
4. (a) $z_{\min} = -2$ for $\mathbf{x} = [0, 2]$; (d) $w_{\max} = -2$ for $\mathbf{y} = [-\frac{1}{2}, 0, 0]$
5. (a) $z_{\min} = 164$; (b) $z_{\min} = 225$
6. (a) $z_{\min} = 848$; (b) $z_{\min} = 510$; (c) $z_{\min} = 614$; (d) $z_{\min} = 343$
7. Minimum cost = \$1221
8. Minimum cost = \$1493
9. Minimum Cost = \$12,000

INDEX